THE BIOLOGY OF MAN

an introduction to
Anatomy, Physiology and Hygiene

G. B. B. THOMAS, B.Sc., A.R.C.S., F.L.S., F.Z.S.
Deputy Headmaster, Peckham Manor School

and

M. F. S. THOMAS, B.Sc.

HULTON EDUCATIONAL PUBLICATIONS, LTD.

First published 1967 by Hulton Educational Publications Ltd., Raans Road, Amersham, Bucks.
Reprinted 1971
Reprinted 1973
Reprinted 1977
Reproduced and printed by photolithography and bound in Great Britain at
The Pitman Press, Bath

THE BIOLOGY OF MAN
an introduction to Anatomy, Physiology and Hygiene

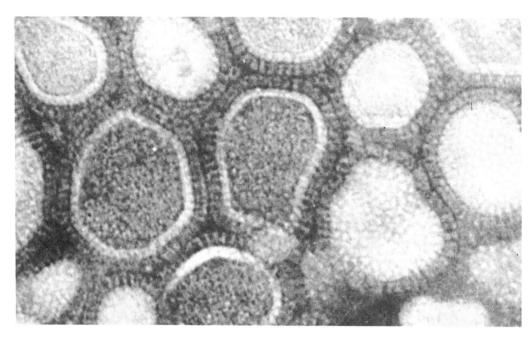

Influenza Virus Particles × 500,000

Polio Virus Particles in cytoplasmic fragments × 250,000

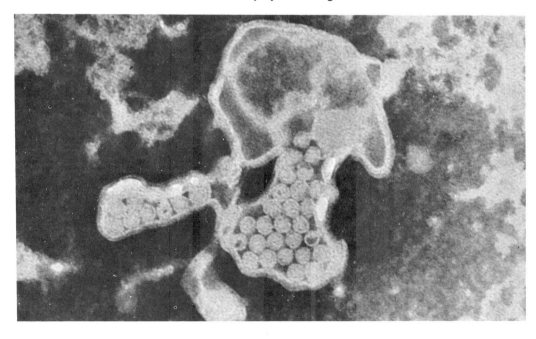

Preface

No apology need be offered for writing a book on human biology. There is a growing interest in all aspects of the subject and an increasing demand for an up-to-date book which presents the material in a visual and easily comprehended way.

We have tried to cover the syllabuses of all the major examining boards for the General Certificate of Education examinations at Ordinary Level. Many of the diagrams and plates as well as much of the text will be found to be within the range of pupils taking other examinations of the Beloe standard and pattern.

Many pupils now stay at school beyond the statutory school-leaving age to follow a general educational course without necessarily taking any Advanced Level examinations: such pupils may find the book useful especially if they are entering the nursing profession or one of the other ancillary medical services.

It is hoped, also, that the book may help to bridge the gulf between Arts and Science courses. It is now increasingly recognised that all Arts pupils should have some 'science' in their curriculum and this book may provide a suitable interest.

There is currently a moral and religious ferment which we see expressed in the press, upon the stage and on our television screens. It is the authors' experience that the problems posed are of great interest to many of our young people—contrary to what some would have us believe. For this reason there has been no attempt in this book to evade moral issues and small sections on such topics as science and religion, lung cancer, alcoholism, venereal disease and sex relations have been deemed to come within the scope of human biology in its wider sense. It is hoped that the paragraphs headed 'Thinking Points' will stimulate interest and discussion between young people on the vital issues of our day.

In a subject as integrated as human biology it has not been found possible to divide the book into parts, but Chapters 1–5 are introductory, Chapters 6–24 are mainly concerned with anatomy and physiology and Chapters 25–34 are chiefly about hygiene. Each chapter forms a little unit in itself so that should a teacher not wish to follow the sequence in the book he may readily select topics in an order of his own choosing.

The approach is biological and we have not hesitated to mention other animals and, indeed, plants, where relevant.

The numerous diagrams are intended to make the text more readily understood. Photographs have been included both to stimulate interest and to counteract the simplification which is an important feature of all diagrams. In some cases a drawing is used to help pupils interpret a photograph.

Any training in science must of necessity include practice in observation and experiment: it is hoped that the sections on practical work will help towards this end. Similarly a number of questions from the various examining boards are included for use at the teacher's discretion.

The authors wish to express their thanks to all those people who have helped to produce this book. We are indebted in particular to B. Campbell Thomas for his encouragement and for the drafts of figures 30.1, 30.3, 30.4 and 30.5, and to Dr. J. G. Cooper and Mr. L. S. Moss for their valuable suggestions and criticisms. Thanks are also due to Collings Design Group who prepared the diagrams. A full list of acknowledgements appears at the end of the book, but we must here record our thanks to our two typists, Mrs. A. P. Barns and Mrs. J. R. Hunt.

G. B. B. T.
M. F. S. T.

Contents

List of Tables

List of Plates

9

List of Diagrams

NOTE: The practical work suggested in this book should be carried out under the supervision of an adult.

What is Anatomy?

From the earliest times Man has shown an interest in the study of injury and disease. We know this from ancient records in many countries. There are, for example, descriptions of operations performed in Egypt and Crete as long ago as 3500 B.C.

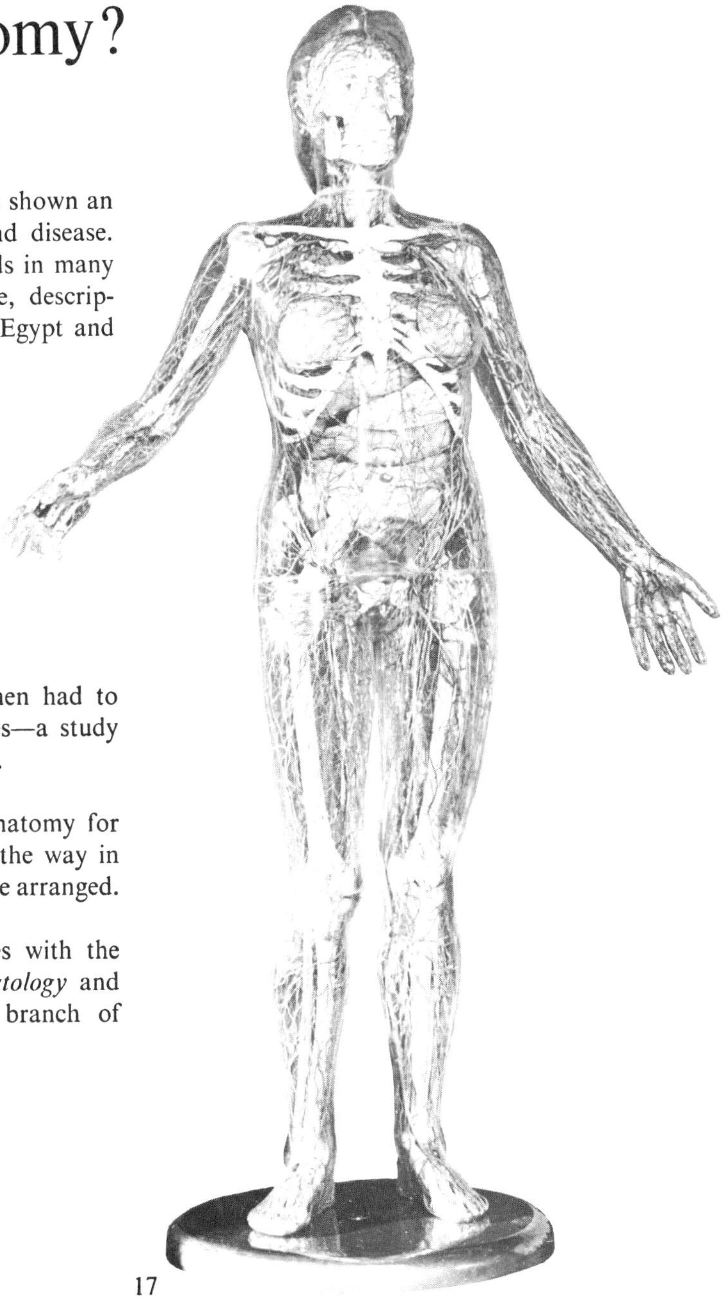

To perform such operations men had to study the *structure* of their bodies—a study which today is known as *anatomy*.

Plate 1 is a typical study in anatomy for it shows a transparent model of the way in which the structures of the body are arranged.

The study of minute structures with the aid of a microscope is called *histology* and may be regarded as a special branch of anatomy.

PLATE 1.
Juno: a study in anatomy.

What is Physiology?

Important as is the study of anatomy it is not alone sufficient to give us a true understanding of the human body. Once a structure is recognised and studied, the question of what it does soon arises in our minds. The study of how our bodies and their structures *function* is called *physiology*.

A great deal of our knowledge of physiology comes from observations made in hospitals and medical schools upon patients. Much physiological work is, however, carried out on animals and this work has been of tremendous benefit to mankind.

Plate 2 shows an experiment on the absorption of drugs through the intestine of a rat. Such an experiment is intended to find out whether a drug is absorbed through the intestine wall and, if so, how much is taken in during different intervals of time. Such physiological experiments are essential to our understanding of the functioning of our body.

PLATE 2. Drug absorption: a study in physiology.

What is Hygiene?

FIG. 1.1 A FLEA.

Hygiene is concerned with keeping our bodies healthy. Broadly it is of two kinds. *Personal hygiene* includes the care of our skin, teeth and eyes and the formation of good habits. *Social hygiene* deals with the wider issues of keeping whole communities—villages, towns, refugee camps—free from disease. It covers, for example, water supplies, sewage disposal, mass X-ray units and in Britain, the National Health Service.

Plate 3 shows *un*hygienic conditions in 1810. The lavatories in the picture drain directly into the river which provides the only water supply to the houses. Figure 1.1 shows a flea—an animal which thrives in dirty places. The following quotation is from the book called *Bleak House* written in 1852 by Charles Dickens: it describes perfectly the unhygienic conditions which were then prevalent.

'Jo lives—that is to say, Jo has not yet died—in a ruinous place, known to the like of him as Tom-all-Alones. It is a black, dilapidated street, avoided by all decent people; where the crazy houses were seized upon, when their decay was far advanced, by some bold vagrants, who, after establishing their own possession, took to letting them out in lodgings. Now, these tumbling tenements contain, by night, a swarm of misery. As, on the ruined human wretch, vermin parasites appear, so, these ruined shelters have bred a crowd of foul existence that crawls in and out of gaps in walls and boards; and coils itself to sleep, in maggot numbers, where the rain drips in; and comes and goes fetching and carrying fever.'

PLATE 3. Privies draining into the river—a lack of hygiene.

1. Living or Non-Living?

Characteristics of Living Things

Man, like all living organisms, is distinguished from dead material by his vital activities. These inter-related activities will be considered under the headings of *movement, nutrition, growth, excretion, reproduction* and *sensitivity*. As you read, apply the points mentioned to a living and to a non-living object, e.g. the baby and the crystals in Plates 4 and 5.

Movement. The ability to move is present in all living things. Most animals can move from place to place and some different kinds of movement—flying, jumping, swimming and climbing—are shown in Fig. 1.2. Some animals do not move the whole body much but remain in one place for a long time waiting for food to come to them instead of hunting it. *Hydra*, Fig. 17.2, is one such animal. Plants do not show movement to

PLATE 4. Calcite crystals.

PLATE 5. A baby.

Fig. 1.2. Some Kinds of Movement.

21

FIG. 1.3 MIMOSA.

a. Normal.
b. After leaves have been touched.

such a degree as do animals although the living material inside them is constantly moving. *Mimosa*, the sensitive plant, moves its leaves when they are touched—Fig. 1.3.

Nutrition. This process takes place in several stages in animals including Man. Firstly, there is *ingestion*—taking food into the body. Secondly, the food undergoes *digestion* to make it soluble, so that *absorption* can take place to enable the food to be distributed all over the body. *Assimilation* is the building up of new tissues and substances of high energy content. Finally, not all the food taken into the body is useful: *egestion* is the removal of solid waste.

Growth. This is more than an increase in size and weight. Crystals can 'grow' in this limited sense of the word. Growth in living things is the gradual wedging of new material *within* that already in existence. Notice, however, that the new substances are not permanently added. There is a continuous *breakdown* and *renewal* of living substance. This has been demonstrated by the use of radioactive isotopes, e.g. ^{15}N and ^{14}C. The radioactivity enables movements of atoms to be followed as long as they are in the body.

Some atoms disappear from the body in a few hours.

Growth occurs when the rate of manufacture of living material is greater than the speed of breakdown.

Fig. 1.4 shows the growth rate in human beings.

Respiration. This is the process by which energy is liberated in living things. *Breathing* or *External Respiration* is the taking in of oxygen and the giving out of carbon dioxide. *Tissue* or *Internal Respiration* is the complex series of chemical changes which occur in the living substance resulting in the release of energy. (See also under 'Metabolism' on page 24.)

Excretion. This word, like the words 'growth' and 'respiration', has a rather different meaning in physiology from its meaning in non-technical language. Here it means the removal from the body of unwanted materials produced as a result of the vital activities taking place in the living substance. The substances excreted are mainly *water* and *carbon dioxide* (formed during respiration) and *nitrogenous* substances which have resulted from the breakdown of proteins.

22

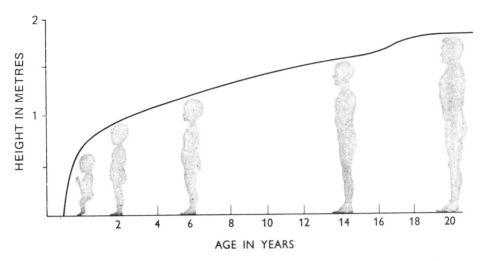

FIG. 1.4. The Human Growth Curve: size increases with age up to a limit.

Excretion should not be confused with egestion.

Reproduction. The ability to produce new individuals resembling the original organism is one of the unique features of living things. The type of reproduction varies from a splitting into two of the whole animal, e.g. as in *Amoeba*, to the complex reproduction of man himself. Reproduction ensures the continuity of the race.

Sensitivity. The ability to react to changes in the world outside the organism and to changes *within* the organism—as when we react to a stomach pain by being sick—is characteristic of all living things. The change in the external or internal environment is called a *stimulus*; the resulting action is the *response*. A good example of this is the watering of the mouth when we smell an appetising meal.

Borderline Cases

The case of the baby and the quartz crystals is a clear-cut example of the difference between a living and a non-living thing.

In some cases it is not so easy to decide whether something is alive or not. *Viruses* can be crystallised from solutions but the crystals when re-dissolved can infect living tissues and can multiply and carry out other life-like processes (Fig. 1.5).

Viruses are responsible for many diseases in both plants and animals (see page 287).

FIG. 1.5. VIRUS CRYSTALS.

a. Tobacco mosaic

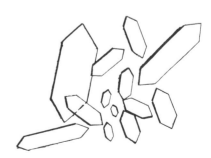

b. Poliomyelitis

23

Metabolism

The activities already described which distinguish living from non-living objects involve chemical changes taking place in the living material itself. The sum total of these processes is called *metabolism*.

As the living substance grows it takes in materials from outside itself and builds them up into new living material. This building up process is called *anabolism* or *biosynthesis*; it is a process which uses up energy.

The energy for biosynthesis is supplied by a second type of metabolism—a breaking down process during which energy is released. Breaking down processes are known as *katabolism* or *energy metabolism*.

Those reactions which provide energy are not entirely separate from those which use it. There is an important compound—*adenosine triphosphate* (A.T.P.)—which captures the energy released during katabolic processes and enables it to be used for biosynthesis. This is shown in a very simplified and diagrammatic form in Fig. 1.6.

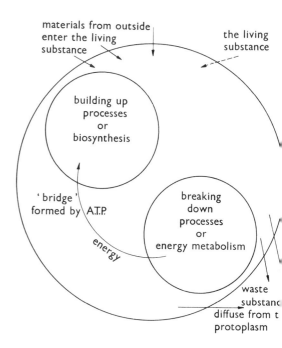

FIG. 1.6. The relationship between protoplasm and its environment. Substances spread into the protoplasm from the surrounding liquid. Some of these are broken down to release energy for biosynthesis. Waste substances diffuse out of the protoplasm.

Protoplasm

Protoplasm is the name given to the living substance of both plants and animals. It is this complex living material which exhibits all the activities already described.

The actual living activities of protoplasm are more easily studied in a simple animal like *Amoeba* (Fig. 1.7) than in a complex one such as Man, for in *Amoeba* under a microscope we have a portion of naked protoplasm. It is seen to consist of a transparent jelly-like substance containing a number of structures and darker granules of varying size.

If we watch *Amoeba* closely we see that it is only firm at the edge (the *ectoplasm*): the central part (*endoplasm*) is liquid and the other constituents can be seen rolling about in it. The ectoplasm and the endoplasm together make up the *cytoplasm*. The cytoplasm together with the *nucleus* constitutes the whole protoplasm. Under the microscope the protoplasm seems very much *alive*.

The *Amoeba* moves by the flowing of its protoplasm over the mud at the bottom of the pond in which it lives. The surface of the *Amoeba* at one end becomes softer allowing the protoplasm to flow forward as one or more *pseudopodia*. Amoeba also engulfs its food by means of the pseudopodia, subsequently digesting it in *food vacuoles* and egesting the useless remains from the surface

24

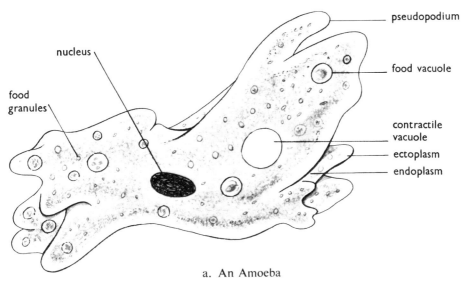

a. An Amoeba

b. Reproduction of Amoeba

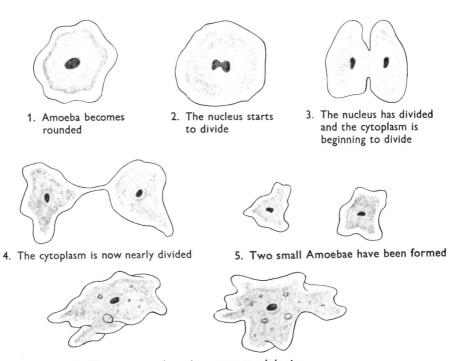

1. Amoeba becomes
   rounded

2. The nucleus starts
   to divide

3. The nucleus has divided
   and the cytoplasm is
   beginning to divide

4. The cytoplasm is now nearly divided

5. Two small Amoebae have been formed

6. The two new Amoebae grow to adult size

FIG. 1.7. AMOEBA.

of the protoplasm. The *contractile vacuole* excretes excess water and some carbon dioxide and nitrogenous waste. Most of its excretory substances, however, diffuse from the surface of the animal. Oxygen for respiration diffuses through the ectoplasm. *Amoeba* reproduces by splitting to form *two* individuals which then grow to 'adult' size. This reproduction is called *binary fission*.

Amoeba shows response to touch and to chemicals in the water. Its activities are largely controlled by the nucleus. This structure is essential for continued life, for it has been shown that an *Amoeba* from which the nucleus has been removed soon dies. It is also incapable of reproduction without the nucleus.

The Chemical and Physical Properties of Protoplasm. Protoplasm is a very complex material consisting of many substances in water. Water makes up 80% of the weight of protoplasm. Proteins are the main *building* constituents of protoplasm, while fats and carbohydrates, which also occur in the living material, are the chief *energy* producers.

The basic elements of protoplasm are *hydrogen, oxygen, nitrogen* and *carbon*, and together they make up most of the body weight. There are in addition other elements essential to protoplasm and Table 1 gives an indication of their importance to Man.

There are also present a large number of *trace elements*—so named because they are found in protoplasm in minute quantities only, e.g. copper, iodine, arsenic and fluorine.

Protoplasm can exist in either a liquid state (sol) or in an almost solid state (gel)—as in the endoplasm and ectoplasm respectively of *Amoeba*—a characteristic it shares with a number of non-living substances called *colloids*. A colloidal solution is a permanent suspension of sub-microscopic particles. Protoplasm can be killed by heat, severe dehydration and by many chemicals.

The nucleus consists of proteins called *nucleo-proteins*.

Element	Chemical symbol	Approximate number of grams in an average-sized man	Use in the protoplasm of Man
Calcium	Ca	1,700	Found in the blood, bones and teeth
Phosphorus	P	680	Found in the blood, bones and teeth
Chlorine	Cl	115	Important in body fluids
Sulphur	S	100	Important in protein formation
Potassium	K	70	Important in protein formation
Sodium	Na	70	Important in body fluids
Magnesium	Mg	40	Important in muscles and nerves
Iron	Fe	7	Used in making red blood cells

TABLE 1. SOME ELEMENTS FOUND IN PROTOPLASM.

2. Cells, Tissues, Organs and Systems

Introduction

In contrast to *Amoeba* the human body does not consist of one piece of protoplasm only. Our protoplasm, like that of all but the simplest animals, is divided into millions of units called cells. A cell may be defined as a unit of cytoplasm controlled by a nucleus, although there are exceptions to this rule: for example, red blood cells do not have a nucleus for part of their life.

Cells are of different kinds and have specific functions. Similar cells are grouped together to form *tissues*. Tissues are used to form *organs*—compact structures serving a definite purpose or purposes. Organs may be considered to form *systems*. These systems —e.g. blood system, nervous system, muscle system—all work together for the healthy functioning of the whole body. It is important to realise that tissues, organs and systems are all inter-related and function in harmony. It is disruption of one or more of these harmoniously functioning systems which leads to *disease* and finally to *death* itself.

Some Tools Used by Scientists

Plates 6 and 7 show two of the most important instruments in the hands of scientists today. They are both used in the study of cells and tissues. The modern electron microscope enables structures to be seen which are far beyond the range of the ordinary microscope.

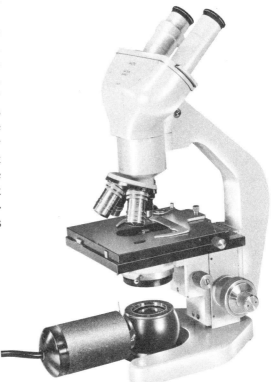

PLATE 6. A binocular light microscope.

PLATE 7. An electron microscope.

It was until recently thought that, apart from the larger structures in it, cytoplasm was a structureless substance, but work with the electron microscope has shown that this is far from true (Plates 8 and 9). This is a good example of how the invention of an instrument can open up whole fields of new and exciting work in science. Viruses are not visible with the ordinary light microscope and little was known about them until the invention of the electron microscope.

The camera is another very important tool of the research scientist—it is more accurate than either drawing or diagram—and it is widely used in the study of anatomy, physiology and hygiene as will become apparent during the reading of this book.

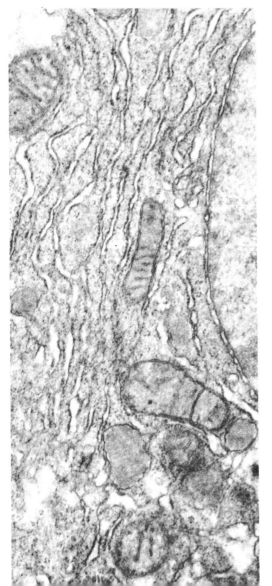

PLATE 8. An electronmicrophotograph of cell from the liver of a rat
(approximately × 60,000).

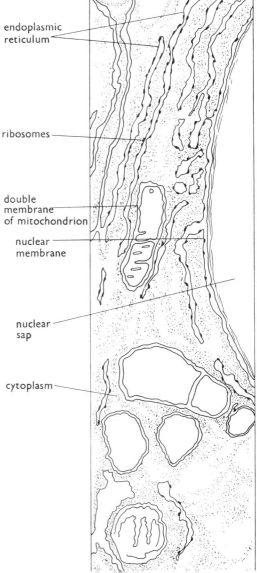

FIG. 2.1. Part of a rat liver cell to show the complex nature of the cytoplasm which, before the invention of the electron microscope was thought to be more or less 'structureless'.

endoplasmic reticulum

ribosomes

double membrane of mitochondrion

nuclear membrane

nuclear sap

cytoplasm

The Structure of the Cell

Plate 9 shows cells from the human intestine photographed through the electron microscope. Fig. 2.2 will help you to interpret the photograph. The unit, 'the cell', is clearly shown by the *cell membrane* which gives to this cell its characteristic shape. It should be remembered when looking at the photograph that a section through the cell is shown: in life the cells have a three-dimensional shape—rather like a cube. It is through this cell membrane that all the substances required by

PLATE 9. An electronmicrophotograph of cells from human intestine (approximately × 16,000).

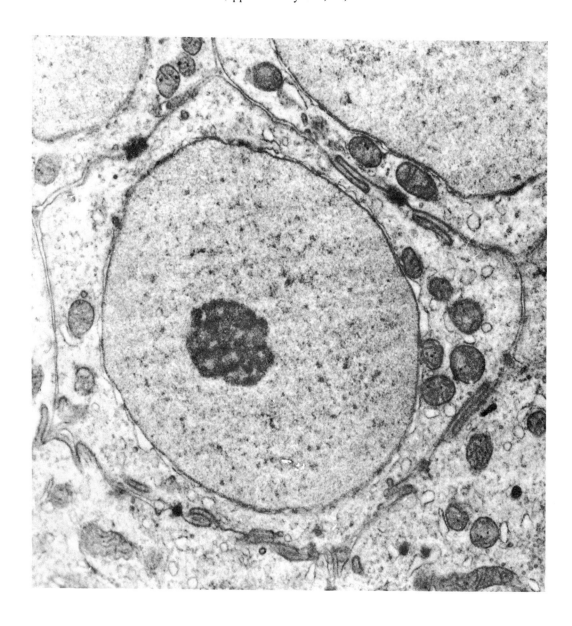

the cell for its life processes must enter. The *nucleus* is seen to occupy a large part of the cell and to be bounded by a clear *nuclear membrane*. Nuclear 'sap' is contained within the membrane and this consists largely of substances called *nucleo-proteins* which are of particular importance in connection with the handing on of characteristics from one generation to the next. The cytoplasm itself contains many *mitochondria*—structures thought to be closely connected with energy production within the cell.

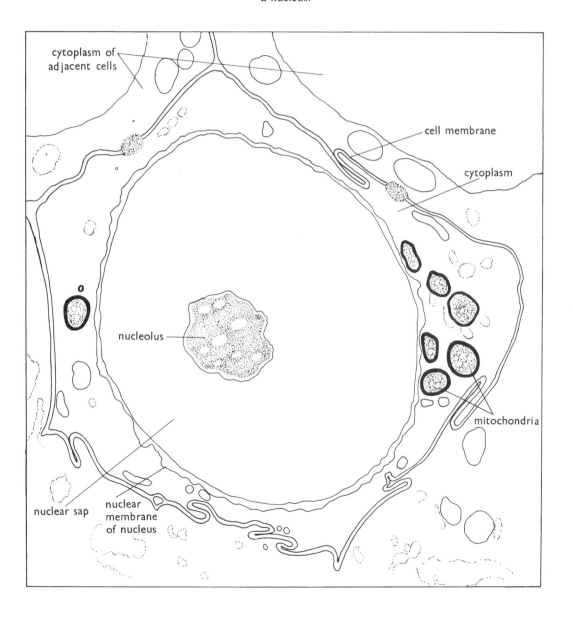

Fig. 2.2. Cells from human intestine. In cells the living protoplasm consists of cytoplasm containing a nucleus.

Plate 8 and Fig. 2.1 show part of a rat liver cell magnified many times by the electron microscope and, like Plate 9, it is given here chiefly to show the great advance in the study of cells made possible by the development of that instrument. Before the invention of the electron microscope cytoplasm was thought to be structureless but as the photograph shows this is far from true. There is present within the cell a distinct *endoplasmic reticulum* which is formed by an intucking of the cell membrane and which contains, at intervals along it, *ribosomes*—structures closely associated with the manufacture of proteins in the cell. This Plate also shows quite clearly that the mitochondria are surrounded by a two-layered membrane, the inner layer projecting at intervals towards the centre of the mitochondrion. The fact that the membrane round the mitochondria is two-layered cannot be clearly seen in Plate 9 which is at a lower magnification. In other words, greater magnifications on improved instruments are continually yielding new and exciting facts.

Cell Differentiation and Organisation

Cells can be grown in culture solutions in isolation, when they tend not to have any special shape or function, but in the living body they become *differentiated*. That is they each take on a definite shape reflecting their use for a particular function. In becoming specialised cells may lose some of their powers: thus a nerve cell, while being highly specialised for carrying messages, loses power to contract, and muscle cells in developing the power to contract lose some of their sensitivity.

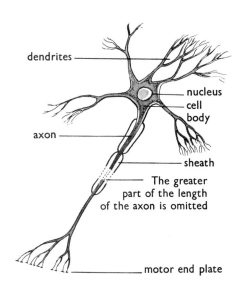

FIG. 2.3. A TYPICAL MOTOR NEURONE.

Neurones are special cells for carrying messages from one part of the body to another.

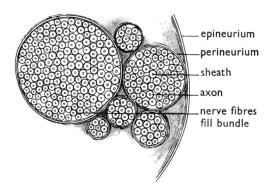

FIG. 2.4. NERVOUS TISSUE IN TRANSVERSE SECTION.

Nervous tissue is made of many neurones or nerve cells. These are seen cut across; several nerve fibres (neurones) are seen bundled together.

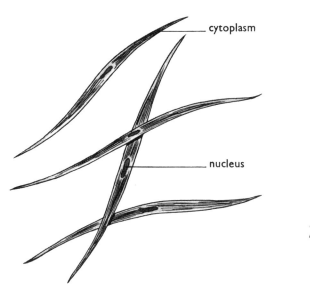

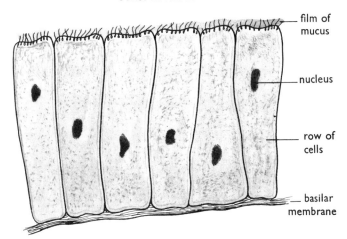

FIG. 2.5. INVOLUNTARY MUSCLE CELLS.

Muscle cells are of three kinds, one of which is shown (see also page 70).

FIG. 2.6. INVOLUNTARY MUSCLE TISSUE.

Muscle tissue is also of three kinds, each kind corresponding to one of the types of muscle cell (see also page 70). Muscle tissue is specialised to contract in order to move something, e.g. two bones in relation to one another.

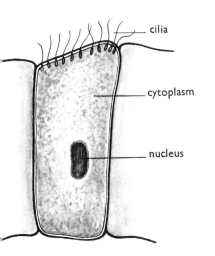

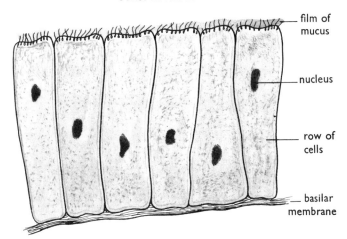

FIG. 2.7. CILIATED CELLS.

These cells have a little hair-like projection of protoplasm which can beat to and fro.

FIG. 2.8. CILIATED EPITHELIUM.

This tissue has the function of moving liquids. The little projections (cilia) beat vigorously to make a current of water over a surface. It is found, for example, lining the nose.

33

Organs

These will be dealt with in appropriate parts of the book but it may be useful to mention a few here in order to emphasise their compact structure and specialised functions: the *eye* receives light waves, the *ear* receives sound waves, the *kidney* is specialised for removing nitrogenous waste and for keeping the correct amount of water and salts in the body, and the *ovary* produces eggs in order that the race may be continued.

Systems

These are as follows:

System	Function
1. Skeletal	Support and Movement
2. Muscular	Support and Movement
3. Circulatory	Transport of materials round the body
4. Respiratory	Obtaining energy for metabolic processes
5. Digestive	Nutrition
6. Nervous	Receiving stimuli and carrying messages
7. Endocrine	Carrying messages, controlling growth
8. Excretory	Removal of useless or harmful matter from the body
9. Reproductive	To ensure that a new generation is produced

Integration

It must not be thought that these body systems exist and function independently of one another: they all work together for the good of the whole animal. Man is not a number of separately functioning parts but is a unified whole, all of his systems being wonderfully co-ordinated.

PRACTICAL WORK ON 1 AND 2

1. In order to get a real impression of *live* protoplasm watch an *Amoeba* under a microscope for some time. Notice how the *protoplasm flows*, how structures in it move, how the pseudopodia form, and how the contractile vacuole functions. Then (a) draw a large diagram of your specimen and (b) make a series of diagrams to show how *Amoeba* moves.

2. Examine and draw a prepared slide of *Amoeba* under the high power of the microscope. Notice how the nucleus stains darkly in prepared specimens.

3. Carefully scrape the inside of your cheek with the *blunt* end of a scalpel. Place the scrapings in a drop of saliva on a glass slide. Draw the cells under the high power of the microscope having first covered them with a cover slip. These cells are called *pavement epithelium*.

4. Microscopically examine and draw two or three slides of different cells, e.g. ciliated epithelium, muscle cells and fat cells.

THINKING POINTS

1. Just how far can we consider the division of matter into living and non-living to be a strict one in the light of recent work on viruses?

2. To what extent do you consider men to be justified in using animals for experimental work, bearing in mind that the results are of benefit to mankind?

QUESTIONS

1. What do you understand by the terms *anatomy*, *histology*, *physiology* and *hygiene*?

2. With reference to either Man or *Amoeba* give an account of the characteristic activities of living things.

3. Give a concise account of the properties of protoplasm.

4. State concisely the meanings of the words *cell*, *tissue*, *organ* and *system*. What is meant by saying that the systems of the body are integrated?

3. Man and his Environment

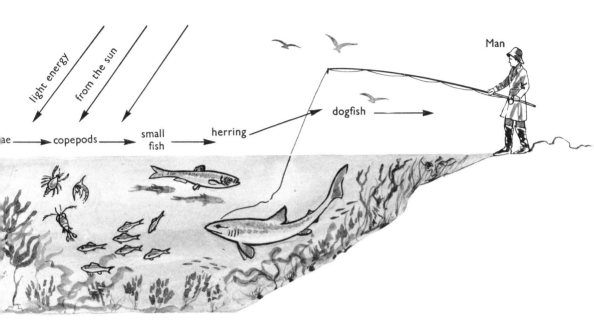

Fig. 3.1. A food chain showing Man's dependence on other organisms and upon the sun.
(*Not drawn to scale*)

Interdependence

Man must not be thought of as existing on his own. There is a constant interaction between Man and his environment. Man takes in and incorporates into himself many substances from the world outside and similarly gives substances to it. In addition Man can mould his surroundings to a large extent to suit himself and hence he can live in places as contrasting as the tropics and the poles.

Human beings also depend upon one another for material things, sharing the work of the community for the good of the whole society. They depend also upon one another for comfort, help, friendship and love.

Man feeds either on plants or on animals which have used plants for food. Thus ultimately we depend for our existence on the green colouring substance, *chlorophyll* which is found in most plants. It is chlorophyll which enables plants to use the sun's

35

PLATE 10. The main crop of the West—wheat.

energy to make sugars from water and carbon dioxide. Man depends not only on these sugars but also upon the oxygen which plants give out while making their food. Plates 10 and 11 show two crops which together form the main food supply of the world. The pro-

PLATE 11. The main crop of the East—rice.

cess of food manufacture by green plants which use the sun's energy is called *photosynthesis*.

A *food chain* such as that shown in Fig. 3.1 indicates how closely human beings depend upon other animals and plants for their life.

The Carbon Cycle. The element carbon, C, is one of the most important to Man for, as we have seen, it is vital in the formation of protoplasm. Fig. 3.2 shows how carbon circulates in nature and again we see the interdependence of living things.

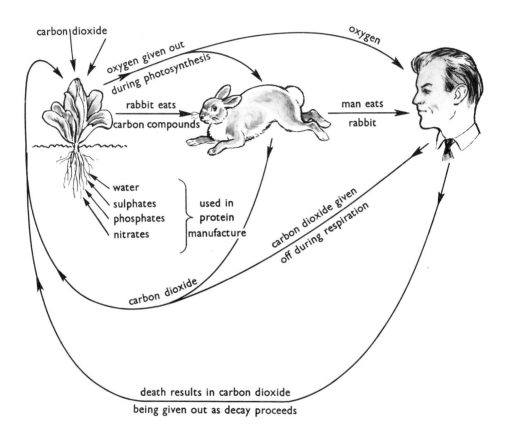

FIG. 3.2. The Circulation of Carbon in nature.

The Circulation of Nitrogen. As in the case of carbon we have in nitrogen an element vital in the manufacture of protoplasm. Fig. 3.3 shows how nitrogen circulates in nature and yet again emphasises the way in which the life of plants and animals is interdependent.

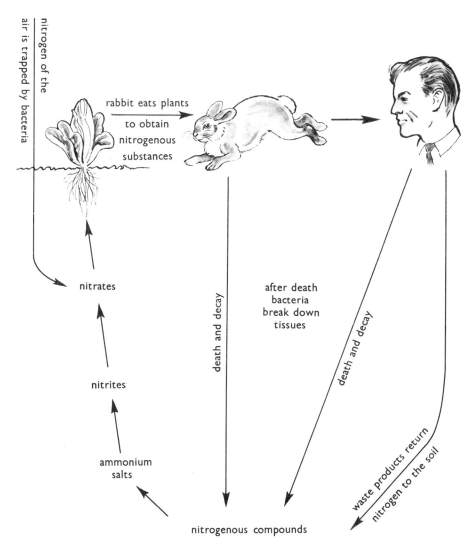

FIG. 3.3. The Circulation of Nitrogen in nature.

Factors of the Environment

Men and other animals are subject to the influence of their environment, as we have seen in the last section. Plants play an important part in the life of animals by making food and by giving out oxygen; animals give out carbon dioxide which is needed by plants; bacteria in the soil affect the life of both plants and animals—and so on. The separate influences acting on plants and animals in any particular environment are known as *factors*.

Factors are of two main types—*physical* and *biological*. Examples of physical factors are temperature, humidity, water content of the soil, acidity of the soil and light intensity. Biological or *biotic* factors include the influence of other plants and animals on an organism.

The influence of temperature is easily observed both in the case of Man and animals. It affects, for example, the distribution of reptiles, confining these cold-blooded animals to the warmer parts of the globe.

The physical factors of the environment play an important part in deciding which crops Man may grow in different parts of the world. Wheat must have sufficient sunshine to ripen the ears, rice must have enough water to germinate the seeds and to swell the grains, while many tropical plants which are able to grow well in northern regions during the summer are unable to survive the winter.

Both physical and biotic factors vary considerably from place to place and not all of them are operating at the same time. This has given rise to quite distinct types of environment such as hedgerows, woods, streams and the seashore. Any such environment is called a *habitat*. Each type of plant and animal lives in the habitat which suits it best. Thus we would not expect to meet a polar bear in the tropics or to find fish living on dry land.

Animals react to factors in the environment in such a way as to make the best use of the conditions available. An *equilibrium* between each individual and its habitat exists and if this equilibrium is disturbed there may be far-reaching changes in the environment. For example, many environments were much changed in Britain as a result of the destruction of most of the rabbit population in 1954 by the disease known as *myxomatosis*. On the one hand there was more food available for other species, while, on the other, animals which normally eat many rabbits found themselves short of food. Foxes raided chicken farms for food. There seemed also to be a marked drop in the buzzard population of Wales, for young rabbits had formed a large part of their food.

This equilibrium, or 'balance of nature' as it is called, has frequently and sometimes disastrously been upset by Man himself. The introduction of the rabbit into Australia about a century ago led to tremendous damage to crops. The rabbit, which is not a native of that continent, multiplied rapidly as it had no natural enemies to keep it in check. In addition to loss of crops, many million pounds have to be spent each year in controlling the growth of the rabbit population.

Another serious pest was unwittingly introduced into Australia in 1870. It was a cactus known as 'prickly pear' and the factors of the environment were ideal for its spread. It soon made large areas unsuitable for sheep pasture. Study showed that in the country of its origin there was a moth whose caterpillars feed on the plant. Introduction of the moth into Australia soon reduced the amount of prickly pear. This forms an example of what is called 'biological control'—a method of controlling a pest by using another organism to destroy it. Such methods have to be used with extreme caution: it would be disastrous to introduce an organism which fed on the main crop of the country concerned!

The Differences Between Plants and Animals

Because Man is so dependent on plants for food, clothing, building materials, etc., it is worth noting the ways in which he differs from even the most complex plants. Not only does Man exhibit much more *movement* than plants but also, as we have just seen, his method of *nutrition* is entirely different. This is true of other animals also for they all feed by taking in complex substances and breaking them down to release energy, whereas plants take in simple substances and build them into more complex forms using energy, from the sun, in the process. Most of this food is stored but some is broken down releasing energy used in metabolic processes in the plant. No animals contain chlorophyll.

The structure of plant cells is different from that of animal cells—plant cells are surrounded by a hard wall of *cellulose* but animal cells have no cell wall, their limits being formed by the protoplasm itself. The support given to plant cells by their walls means that the *cytoplasm* is not as firm as in animal cells. Plant cells have a *vacuole* in their centre. This cavity is filled with cell sap. The diagrams—Fig. 3.4—of plant cells should be

FIG. 3.4. TYPICAL PLANT CELLS.

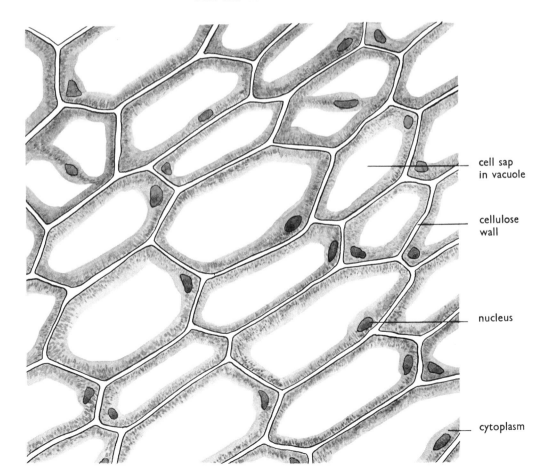

cell sap
in vacuole

cellulose
wall

nucleus

cytoplasm

compared with those of animal cells already given on pages 32 and 33.

Fig. 3.5 shows an interesting little organism —*Euglena*. It is interesting because it exhibits some plant and some animal features. It swims, has an eyespot which is sensitive to light and has no cellulose wall. On the other hand it possesses chlorophyll and manufactures its own food by photosynthesis.

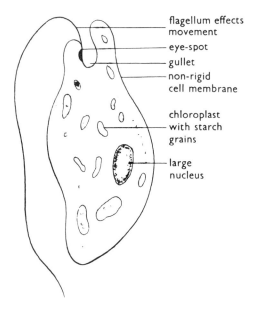

flagellum effects movement

eye-spot

gullet

non-rigid cell membrane

chloroplast with starch grains

large nucleus

FIG. 3.5. *Euglena*

1. Strip the epidermis from the inside of an onion scale. Place it in a drop of iodine solution on a slide and look at it under the microscope. Cell walls, cytoplasm and nuclei (stained brown) should be visible. Starch grains, if present, will be stained blue-black by the iodine. Draw.

2. Mount a moss leaf on a slide in a drop of water. Under the microscope the *chloroplasts* should be clearly visible. These chloroplasts manufacture sugar. Draw.

THINKING POINTS

1. How far is it possible to get along without our fellow men? Is your answer to this question any different from what it might have been had you lived before the invention of rapid means of travel and communication such as the jet plane, television and Telstar?

2. Is it possible in the light of modern knowledge to draw a very clear distinction between plants and animals?

QUESTIONS

1. 'The existence of human beings depends on the sun.' Discuss this statement.

2. Describe how carbon and nitrogen circulate in nature. Why is this circulation important to Man?

3. Give a brief description of the differences between plants and animals using a tree and a human being as examples.

4. Man as a Mammal

The Characteristics of Mammals

Man belongs to the large group of vertebrate animals known as *mammals*. Plates 12–16 show some of the other animals which belong to the same group and you may like to see how many of the mammalian characters listed below you can find in the photographs.

The eggs of mammals are not laid but develop inside the mother's body, in a structure called the *uterus*, until they are ready to be *born*. During the time it is inside the parent the young mammal is attached by an organ called the *placenta*. After birth the baby mammal is fed on *milk* which is a fluid

PLATE 12. A lion.

PLATE 13. A rhinoceros.

PLATE 14. Elephants.

produced in *mammary glands*. Mammals also show some degree of *parental care* after the young have been born: this reaches its most developed form in human beings, young children being cared for over a period of many years.

Man, in common with other mammals, possesses *hair*, *sweat glands*, a *four-chambered heart*, a *diaphragm* separating the thorax from the abdomen and an external ear or *pinna*.

In mammals a *hard palate* separates the nasal from the food passage and this enables us to bite up our food and to breathe at the same time. Mammals also have differentiated teeth.

Lastly mammals have a more *highly developed brain* than any other animals, and in Man the brain reaches a degree of development not found in any other mammal.

PLATE 15.
A chimpanzee.

45

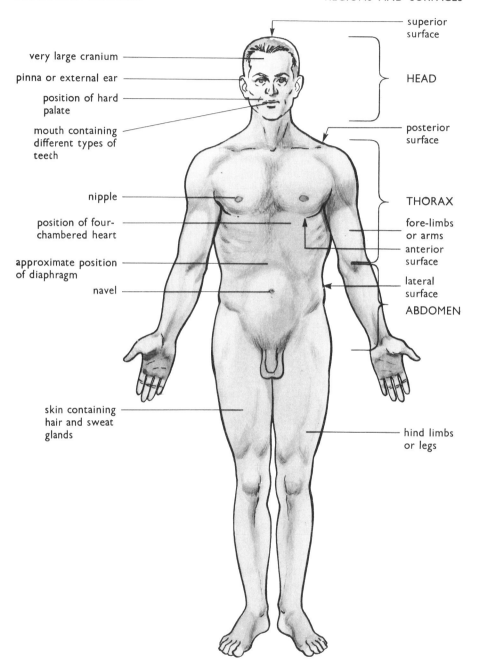

very large cranium

pinna or external ear

position of hard palate

mouth containing different types of teeth

nipple

position of four-chambered heart

approximate position of diaphragm

navel

skin containing hair and sweat glands

superior surface

HEAD

posterior surface

THORAX

fore-limbs or arms

anterior surface

lateral surface

ABDOMEN

hind limbs or legs

FIG. 4.1. Man's most obvious mammalian features are shown on the left of the page. The labelling on the right shows some useful descriptive terms used in anatomy. These terms enable the view of any structure shown in a diagram to be quickly described. For example a vertebra drawn looking upon it from above would simply be described as seen in 'superior aspect'; if drawn from below—'inferior aspect'.

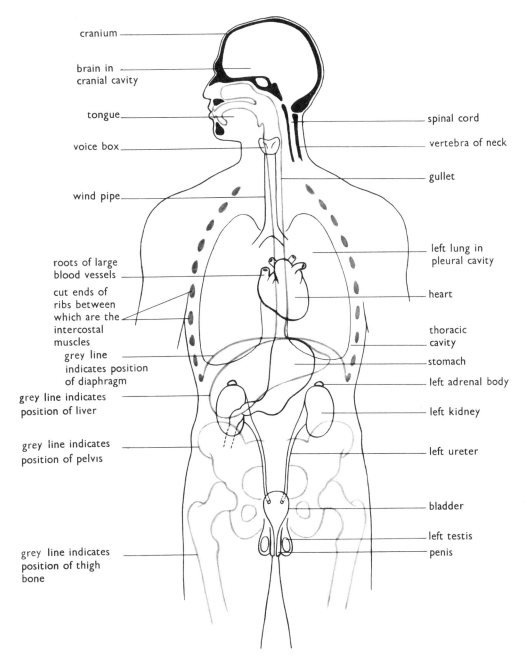

cranium

brain in cranial cavity

tongue

voice box

wind pipe

roots of large blood vessels

cut ends of ribs between which are the intercostal muscles

grey line indicates position of diaphragm

grey line indicates position of liver

grey line indicates position of pelvis

grey line indicates position of thigh bone

spinal cord

vertebra of neck

gullet

left lung in pleural cavity

heart

thoracic cavity

stomach

left adrenal body

left kidney

left ureter

bladder

left testis

penis

FIG. 4.2. Some of the more important cavities and body structures in Man. The intestines, spleen and pancreas are not shown.

General Structure

Fig. 4.1 shows the general external features of Man and Fig. 4.2 gives an idea of how the organs and cavities are arranged. This should be compared with the rabbit in Fig. 4.3. The rabbit is chosen for dissection because it is readily available whereas the human being is not!

The Head is the part of the body which houses the *brain* and the main *sense organs*—the *eyes* and *ears*, the *nose* and the *tongue*. It is also the place for entry into the body of both food and air.

The Neck. This forms a connection between the head and thorax which enables the former to be moved easily in relation to the latter. It contains important nerves and blood vessels and the food and air passages.

The Trunk is the name given to the thorax and abdomen together. Both parts contain vital organs, which can be seen in Figs. 4.2 and 4.3.

The *thorax* is separated from the abdomen by a muscular sheet of tissue called the *diaphragm*. This structure forms the floor of the thorax while its walls are formed by the *thoracic vertebrae*, the *ribs*, the *intercostal muscles* and the *sternum*. The *thoracic cavity* contains the *heart*, the *lungs*, part of the *gullet* and certain important *nerves* and *blood vessels*.

The *abdomen*, whose walls are formed by the *lumbar vertebrae* and the soft *abdominal muscles*, contains the *stomach* and *intestines*, the *pancreas*, the *liver*, the *spleen*, the *kidneys* and *bladder*, part of the *reproductive organs* and, of course, many nerves and blood vessels.

The Limbs. All mammals have four limbs and most use all four for locomotion. Man, however, is able to walk on the hind pair only, thus leaving the front pair—the arms—free for other work.

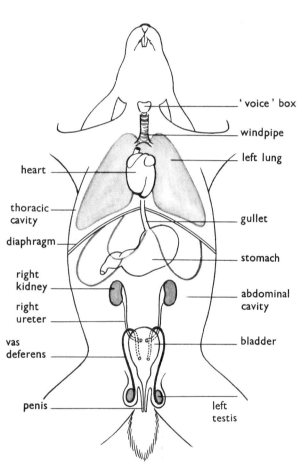

FIG. 4.3. Ventral view of a rabbit with the abdominal and thoracic cavities opened to show some of the organs.

48

5. Man's Place in Nature

The Idea of Evolution

Some animals are much more complex than others in both their structure and functioning. Non-cellular animals such as *Amoeba*, for example, are much less complex than even the simplest multicellular animals like sea-anemones.

It has been found possible to arrange animals into groups according to their complexity of structure, all animals in the same major group having certain structural features in common. Some examples are given below starting with the simplest and proceeding to the most complex:

Invertebrates (animals without backbones)
    Non-cellular animals, e.g. *Amoeba*
    Sponges
    Sea-anemones
    Earthworms
    Crabs
    Spiders
    Insects

Vertebrates (animals with backbones)
    Fish
    Amphibians
    Reptiles
    Birds
    Mammals

Fig. 5.1 shows some animals of different degrees of structural complexity.

PLATE 16. A ring-tailed lemur.

Fossil evidence suggests that the more advanced animals have developed from the simpler types over the course of millions of years. Physiological and other evidence also points to the same conclusion. This process of gradual development of new types over very long periods of time is known as *evolution*. Table 2 will help you to see Man's position in perspective. Man as we have already seen is a mammal and belongs therefore to the most recently evolved group. Within this group Man has been in existence for a *relatively* short period—perhaps one or two million years.

49

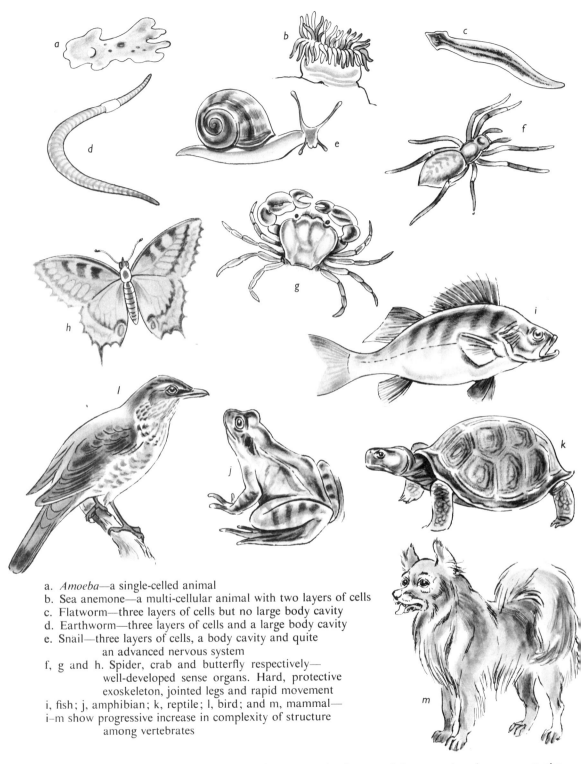

a. *Amoeba*—a single-celled animal
b. Sea anemone—a multi-cellular animal with two layers of cells
c. Flatworm—three layers of cells but no large body cavity
d. Earthworm—three layers of cells and a large body cavity
e. Snail—three layers of cells, a body cavity and quite
       an advanced nervous system
f, g and h. Spider, crab and butterfly respectively—
       well-developed sense organs. Hard, protective
       exoskeleton, jointed legs and rapid movement
i, fish; j, amphibian; k, reptile; l, bird; and m, mammal—
i–m show progressive increase in complexity of structure
       among vertebrates

FIG. 5.1 Animals of different complexity of structure. At the top of the page *Amoeba* represents the simplest type and at the bottom the dog represents the most complex.

Time (in millions of years)	Eras	Epochs	First Appearance
1		Pleistocene	Man
10		Pliocene	
30		Miocene	
40	Cenozoic	Oligocene	
60		Eocene	
75		Paleocene	Flowering plants
135		Cretaceous	Mammals
165	Mesozoic	Jurassic	
205		Triassic	
230		Permian	Conifers
250		Pennsylvanian	Reptiles
325		Devonian	Amphibians
360		Silurian	Insects
	Paleozoic		Fish
425		Ordovician	Ferns
			Algae
500		Cambrian	Many invertebrates
3,000		Proterozoic	First fossils and first life on earth
	Precambrian		
10,000		Archeozoic	Origin of the earth

TABLE 2. THE HISTORY OF LIFE ON EARTH.

Note the very small time for which Man has been on the earth. If a film were made of the history of the earth and if the film lasted 24 hours Man would appear for only the last minute of the film!

Evolution and Religious Controversy

Although the essence of the idea of evolution is very old—it appears in Greek writings several centuries B.C.—it was not until the nineteenth century that it was fully propounded as a scientific theory. The publication of a book in 1859 entitled *On the Origin of Species by Natural Selection* by Charles Darwin (Plate 17) not only formulated a theory of evolution, and suggested the way in which it came about, but also wrought a change in men's thinking in scientific and intellectual circles the world over.

Before the publication of Darwin's ideas, it had been generally accepted that God created separately each individual species of plant and animal—a theory known as Special Creation —and that each went on to produce offspring like itself with little or no variety. The publication of Darwin's book, backed up as it was by a mass of evidence accumulated during many years of painstaking effort, led to a tremendous outcry from the Christian Church which saw Darwin as an evil force trying to undermine its power and authority. The story of Man's creation as it was given in the Bible had been too literally interpreted and many churchmen were unable or unwilling to adopt the new ideas. Their stubborn and continued refusal to face the evidence laid before them led to many bitter arguments and to much intellectual intolerance between scientists and churchmen, and lowered the esteem in which the church had previously been held, leading finally to an unfortunate divorce between science and religion. This breach continued for many years and indeed it is only recently that a reconciliation has been attempted to any serious extent. Nowadays many sincere Christians have accepted the fact of evolution and look upon it as a more wonderful process than Special Creation, feeling that it supports rather than detracts from belief in some Creator behind the universe. Some Christians now regard the story of the Creation as given in Genesis as an attempt by early Man to account for his presence on earth, as he strove to meet and to understand the God in whom he believed.

PLATE 17. Charles Darwin.

52

Primate Characteristics and the Evolution of Man

Man belongs to a mammalian group known as the *primates*. The primates are distinguished from all other groups by features which include the following:

1. Hands, feet and limbs well adapted for living in trees.

2. Well-developed eyes and ears with a corresponding development of the areas of the brain which deal with vision and hearing.

3. An enlargement of the frontal region of the skull to accommodate the large brain.

Primates are divided into two groups:

(a) Primitive primates—this group includes such unusual and interesting animals as the tarsiers of the East Indies and the lemurs (Plate 16) and aye-ayes of Madagascar; and

(b) Advanced primates which comprise the New and Old World monkeys, the apes and, lastly, Man himself.

The similarities in structure between Man and the apes has, of course, been noted for many years and strongly supports the theory that both animals had a common ancestor. (Note that this is contrary to a popular belief that Man is descended *from* apes: the true view is that *both* Man and present-day apes had a common ancestor many millions of years ago.) Recent fossil findings in Tanzania have shown that there existed, between one and two million years ago, a creature very like modern Man in appearance. He was, however, only about one metre tall, he made tools from stone and he lived on a diet of fruit, vegetables and meat. The chief difference between him and ourselves was in brain size: his being very much smaller. He has been named *Homo habilis*, which name means 'handy man', because of his ability to make tools. Since he first appeared on earth he has given rise to generations which have gradually

PLATE 18. A comparison of the hands of Man and ape.

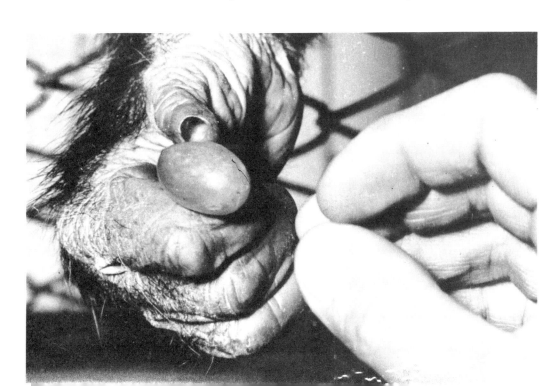

developed both in physical stature and in brain size until modern Man himself finally developed. This, of course, is a very simplified account and it must be emphasised that many gaps in the story remain to be filled.

PLATE 19. Monkey showing threatening attitude.

Man's Distinctive Features

Although Man is closely related to present-day apes—gorilla, orang-utan and chimpanzee—and to fossil forms of apes and ape-men, he has none the less some features which distinguish him from them all. The chief of these distinctive features is his brain size. Brain size is expressed as 'cranial capacity'—that is the size of that part of the skull which houses the brain. It is found that modern Man has a cranial capacity of some 1600 cm^3 whereas that of the apes is only about 600 cm^3. Man is also strongly bipedal (two-legged) in his method of walking and this is reflected in certain features of his skeleton (Fig. 5.2). It is only by Man that we find an extensive use and *manufacture* of tools. This may be partly due to Man's ability to oppose fingers and thumb in order to grip and to manipulate skilfully things which he is holding (Plate 18).

Man is also the only animal to use spoken language of a very complex kind and to pass thoughts on to the next generation in writing. Some monkeys show ability to communicate to each other, by a variety of postures, gestures and calls, such attitudes as attack, fear, threat, friendship and courting (Plate 19).

Man's more efficient brain coupled with his ability to use language and tools led at an early stage to attempts at painting and writing. As Man became more efficient at catching his food and at performing the other necessary tasks of life he gradually found himself with more time to devote to cultural activities and this led finally to great works of art, literature, drama and music—activities not pursued by other animals.

FIG. 5.2. Parts of the skeletons of Man and ape compared.

APE   MAN

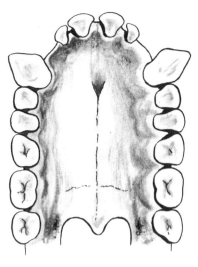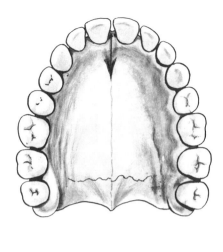

a. Upper jaw showing teeth. Notice the large canine teeth of the ape.

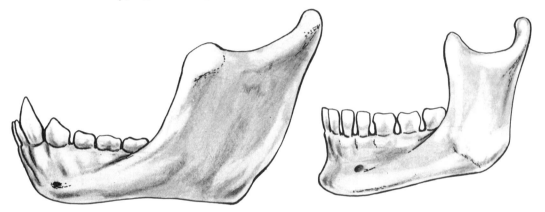

b. Side view of left lower jaw. That of the ape is much more powerful than is Man's.

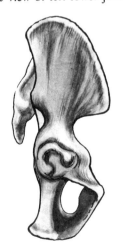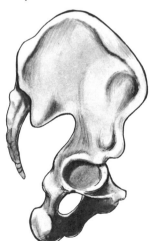

c. Side view of right pelvis. The short broad structure of Man's pelvis is an adaptation for walking upright.

PLATE 20. Elizabeth Fry.

Spiritual Needs

Not only has Man felt a great desire to express his thoughts and feelings on canvas or paper or upon the stage, and thus to reach out towards his fellow men, but throughout the ages, from the earliest times, he has sought to commune with something or someone greater than himself, something to which he has given the name 'God'. Desire for religious experience is not found in other animals as far as we know and is therefore a unique feature of Man. Perhaps it is his highest attribute, for while it is true that organised religion has often throughout history stood in the way of progress, it is also true that many social reformers who have striven to improve the lot of their fellow men have been deeply religious people—William Wilberforce (Plate 22) (anti-slavery), Elizabeth Fry (Plate 20) (prison reform), Hack Tuke (Plate 21) (mental health) and Seebohm Rowntree (factory reform) are names which quickly come to mind.

PLATE 21. Hack Tuke.

PLATE 22. William Wilberforce.

PLATE 23. Man can live in cold places.

The Dominance of Man

Human beings are today the dominant creatures of the earth, having power over all others even to the extent of using many animals to work for them. This control over Nature by Man is not confined to animals but extends over the whole of his environment so that he can adapt the conditions around him in order to live in the hottest or the coldest (Plate 23), the wettest or the driest places of the earth.

This century has seen a tremendous quickening of Man's control over Nature through the expansion of scientific research so that Man can now live for considerable periods below the sea in submarines or above the earth in satellites.

Races of Man

In a previous section of this chapter we saw that Man has characteristic features which distinguish him from all other animals: in fact he has been given a special name—*Homo sapiens*. But are all men exactly alike? Study reveals that differences of structure do occur between different men and this has given rise to the idea of 'race'. There are, for example, European, Negroid and Mongoloid races, each distinguished by their particular features. Men can also be grouped according to the colour of their skin—white, black, red and yellow (Plate 24).

Most of the differences are superficial and should not be allowed to obscure the funda-mental similarity of all men. As in other animals some of the variations are of direct physiological importance to the men concerned and are adaptations to a particular environment. The heavy pigmentation of dark-skinned people is a protection against the possible harmful effect of some of the sun's rays. Thick layers of fat under the pale skins of Eskimoes act as a good insulator against heat loss. In spite of these slight differences in structure the basic similarity of men of all types, and the fact that intermarriage occurs, makes any strict definition of a particular race difficult: much overlapping occurs.

PLATE 24. There is no colour-bar between young children.

Racial Prejudice

The small differences between men of different races have frequently been much exaggerated by various groups at different times in order to try to prove their superiority. Often the basic cause behind such attempts is *fear* or greed—or both. One group may fear that another race may obtain the best posts, may revolt against being slaves, or may come to have an equal standard of living. This doctrine reached its greatest development in Nazi Germany and it resulted in the most terrible persecution of Jews and finally to the death of many millions of them.

The deep-rooted nature of these attitudes has been clearly seen in America where there has been great opposition in the Deep South to integration of the white and black population.

The attitude that one race is inferior to another is called *racial prejudice*.

Tolerance and understanding in matters connected with race are one of the greatest needs in the present age. Television and newspapers give ample evidence of the crisis in human affairs when tolerance is lacking.

PRACTICAL WORK ON 4 AND 5

1. Dissect—or ask your teacher to dissect for you—a rabbit. Identify as many of the organs and other structures as possible. Draw. List all the mammalian features that you can see on the rabbit.

2. Draw various specimens of animals of different degrees of complexity. If they are not available at your school you may be able to find them at a museum.

3. Visit a museum to see fossil evidence of Man's evolution.

4. Visit a zoo to see *living* specimens of animals of different degrees of complexity and to observe the behaviour of apes.

THINKING POINTS ON 4 AND 5

1. Darwin's theory of evolution angered many churchmen. Does this mean that the whole of the Bible is now of no value? Try to find out whether Darwin's theory affected other people besides scientists and churchmen.

2. Consider carefully the importance of Man's ability to manufacture tools. How does this ability help Man to have more leisure time? Why is the correct use of leisure time rapidly becoming an important problem?

3. What was the driving force behind many attempts by social reformers to improve the conditions under which their fellow men worked?

4. Man now has a tremendous control over the forces of nature. Is there any danger in this? If so, can you make any suggestions towards overcoming the dangers?

5. Racial prejudice is a serious problem in the world today. Can you suggest ways in which the problem can be tackled? Is there any scientific foundation for racial prejudice?

QUESTIONS ON 4 AND 5

1. What is a mammal? List the main mammalian characteristics and give a large labelled drawing of the external appearance of a named mammal.

2. Make a large fully labelled drawing to show the position of the main body structures within the thoracic and abdominal cavities of *either* the rabbit *or* Man.

3. Write brief notes on the following:
   (a) The History of Life on the Earth
   (b) Evolution and Religion
   (c) Man's Dominance over Nature.

4. Give an account of the problems of 'race prejudice'. How do you think you can play a part in solving them?

5. Write an essay on the chief features that distinguish Man, the upright animal, from the four-footed creatures. (J)

Summary of 1 to 5

1. *Human physiology* is the study of how our bodies function. It is impossible to study physiology without some knowledge of *anatomy* and *histology*.

2. *Hygiene* is concerned both with *personal* health and cleanliness and with *social* health on a wide scale.

3. All living things show common characteristics. Viruses represent an ill-defined position between living and non-living.

4. Living material is called *protoplasm*. It shows many *metabolic* activities. Its chemical and physical properties are very complex.

5. Protoplasm is divided into units called *cells*. Cells are differentiated and grouped to form *tissues* which in turn make up *organs*. There are nine body *systems integrated* together.

6. Human beings are dependent on their environment—e.g. on plants, on air, on soil and on their fellow men. The different items of the environment are called *factors*.

7. There are definite differences between plants and animals of which the mode of nutrition is the most important.

8. Man has *evolved* from less complex organisms over the course of millions of years. Man belongs to a group of animals known as *primates*. He is distinguished from even the most advanced apes by his *larger brain* and by his *ability to use and to manufacture tools*.

9. Man is also distinguished from other animals by his *cultural* and *spiritual* needs and activities.

10. The human being is today the *dominant animal* of the world having tremendous power over nature. He can live in places all over the world owing to his ability to *adapt* his environment to suit his needs.

11. Different *races* of men exist in spite of their basic similarity. Differences are found to be adaptations to living in different parts of the globe. *Racial prejudice* is a serious and difficult problem in many parts of the world.

6. Support and Movement—1

Introduction

Most animals need to move to obtain their food. In all but the simplest animals, e.g. *Amoeba*, movement is brought about by the contraction of *muscle cells*. In many of the smaller invertebrate animals, because the rate of movement is slow and the body weight is small, no special supporting structures are needed, the muscles alone being sufficient to effect movement.

In larger animals—and especially in fast-moving types—a *skeleton* of some kind is necessary. This provides not only a *support* but also a *system of levers* which, working in conjunction with the muscles, enables rapid *movements* of limbs to be made. The skeleton also provides *protection* either for the whole body or for some of its parts.

Aquatic animals are partly supported by the water in which they live. You may have noticed how heavy your body and limbs feel when you proceed on to dry land after a swim in the sea. This is because salt water, with its high density, helps to buoy you up. Animals which live on land need to have very strong skeletal tissues if they are to be of any large size. The size to which a skeleton could grow is limited for if it became too big it would also become too heavy to carry the animal's weight without an uneconomic use of energy. The elephants (Plate 14), and their extinct relatives the mammoths, probably represent the limit to which a land animal can grow. In water, where the buoyancy helps to support the animal, a larger size can be reached and here the size limit is found in the largest whales (Plate 25). In this connection it is interesting to note that while the maximum size of an elephant is about six megagrammes a Blue Whale may weigh up to 120 megagrammes.

PLATE 25. A whale.

In some animals the skeleton is largely for protection. For example, the shells of snails and clams protect the soft parts of their bodies.

The insects are amongst the most efficient and fast-moving animals: they have a skeleton round the *outside* of their bodies. This *exoskeleton*, as it is called, not only forms an excellent protective covering but also provides a system of levers upon which the muscles can pull to effect movement. Fig. 6.1 will help to make this clear.

The skeleton in Man and other mammals is *inside* the body and it is known as an *endoskeleton*. Whether the skeleton of an animal be an exoskeleton or an endoskeleton it must, since it is made of a rigid substance, have a number of *joints* to enable the animal to move.

Bone and Cartilage

Because bone remains intact for a long time after an animal has died we tend to think of it as a dead tissue. In fact bones in a living animal are themselves live structures containing cells whose function is to produce the hard non-living part of bone. This hard substance is largely *calcium phosphate* and it is this which makes bones into hard rigid structures. Fig. 6.2 is a drawing of part of Plate 26 which shows a photograph of bone seen in transverse section under a microscope. Plate 27 shows the appearance of bone cut longitudinally. Tiny threads of protoplasm extending through the hard substance of the bone link together the bone-forming cells. At the centre of the concentric rings is a canal containing blood vessels which bring the necessary materials for bone formation to the cells.

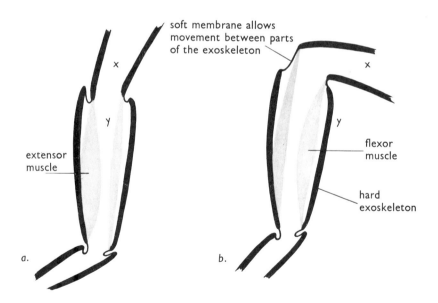

FIG. 6.1. JOINTS IN AN INSECT'S LEG.

a. Shows the extensor muscle contracted. In b. the extensor has relaxed and the flexor muscle has contracted, closing the two parts of the exoskeleton marked *x* and *y* together.

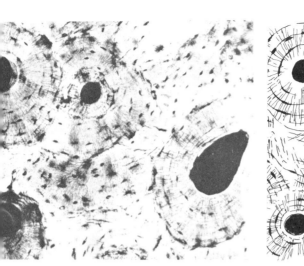

PLATE 26. A transverse
section of bone.

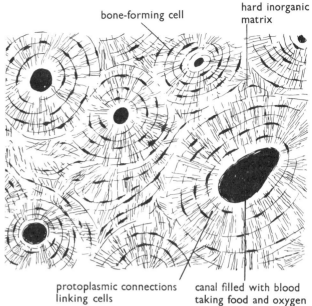

bone-forming cell

hard inorganic
matrix

protoplasmic connections
linking cells

canal filled with blood
taking food and oxygen
to the cells

FIG. 6.2. A small portion of bone as
seen in transverse section drawn
from Plate 26.

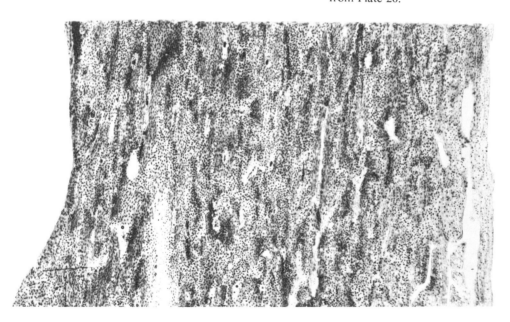

PLATE 27. A longitudinal section of bone.

Bones form a useful reserve of *calcium* and *phosphorus* for the body.

Cartilage, Fig. 6.3 and Plate 28, is produced in a similar way to bone but it is flexible instead of rigid.

Bones are very strong structures. Plate 29 shows a human thigh bone undergoing a test of its strength. The test showed that when placed vertically it could stand a force of 60 000 newton. Placed horizontally a force of 4000 newton was needed to break the bone. If bone is such a strong substance why do people so often break them? The answer is that a particular bone is made to withstand certain strains and stresses in certain directions only. Sudden strains in unusual directions—such as a strong kick on the side of a leg—may snap the bone. Bones become more brittle as age advances and many old people break bones merely by falling over. (With age some calcium is lost from the bones.)

Fig. 6.4 shows the external appearance of a bone. The *periosteum* is the membrane round the outside of the bone which gives rise to the bone-forming cells. Another function of the periosteum is to act as a place for attachment of muscles. The bone consists of a *shaft* with an *epiphysis* at each end. The layer of cartilage between the epiphysis and the shaft allows the bone to grow in length. Growth in diameter is brought about by the bone-forming cells under the periosteum. The *marrow cavity* is filled with a substance called *marrow*. It is rich in blood vessels. It is the marrow of the bones which produces red blood cells (see also page 94).

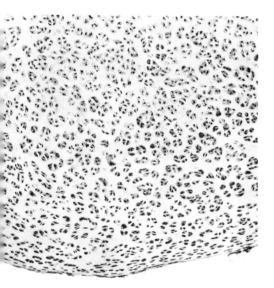

PLATE 28. A transverse section of cartilage.

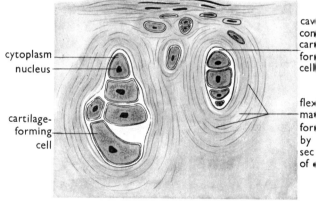

cytoplasm
nucleus

cartilage-
forming
cell

cav
con
car
for
cell

flex
ma
for
by
sec
of

FIG. 6.3. A small portion of cartilage as seen in transverse section drawn from Plate 28.

PLATE 29. Testing the strength of a bone.

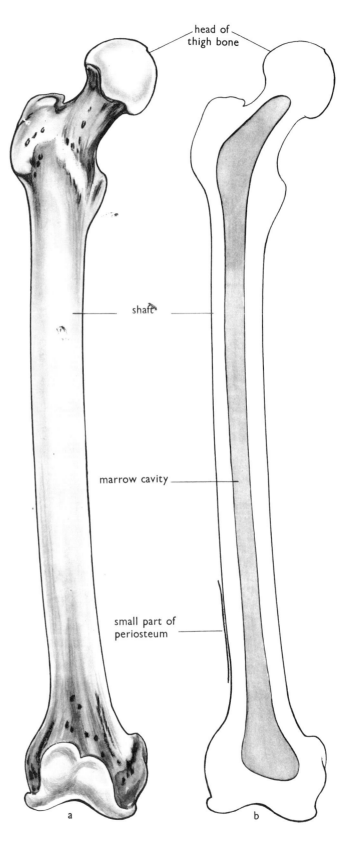

head of
thigh bone

shaft

marrow cavity

small part of
periosteum

a

b

FIG. 6.4. THE STRUCTURE OF A BONE.

    a. External view of thigh bone

    b. Longitudinal section of
       thigh bone

c

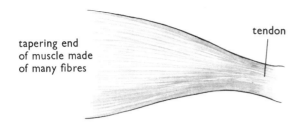

tapering end
of muscle made
of many fibres

tendon

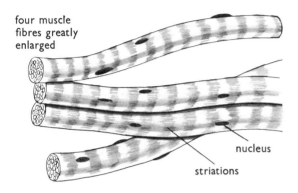

four muscle
fibres greatly
enlarged

nucleus

striations

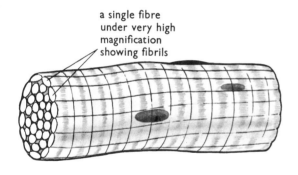

a single fibre
under very high
magnification
showing fibrils

Physiology of Muscle Contraction

The function of muscle is to *contract* in order to bring about movements. Contraction requires energy and this is supplied by our food. *Glucose* from the food is carried in the blood to muscle fibres where it is stored in the form of *glycogen*. This glycogen forms a store of potential energy for muscle contraction. The protoplasm of each muscle fibre contains proteins which have strong contractile ability. The exact mechanism of muscle contraction is not fully understood although several theories have been put forward to explain it. One of these theories, based on electron microscope photographs, is illustrated simply in Fig. 6.5.

The metabolic processes involved in muscle contraction are very complex and the following account is simplified. For the shortening of the chains of amino-acids to take place energy is required and this is obtained from the substance adenosine triphosphate (see also page 24) or A.T.P., as it is called, which

FIG. 6.5. STRIATED MUSCLE.

Diagrammatic representations of a portion of a fibril, in A a relaxed muscle, and in B a contracted muscle. It is thought that the plates of amino-acid molecules slide over each other when contraction takes place. The exact details are unknown.

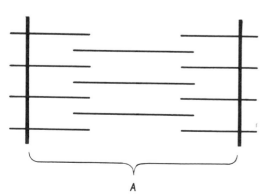

A

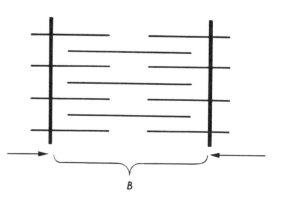

B

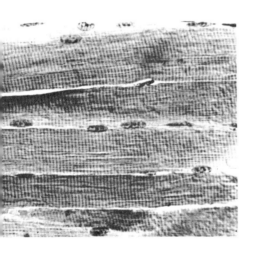

ADP. + Phosphoric acid + Energy for Muscle Contraction

A.T.P. reformed using Energy derived from Glycogen. $CO_2 + H_2O$ are given off as waste products

FIG. 6.6 The Release of Energy.

acts as an energy carrier. The A.T.P. is broken down to adenosine diphosphate (A.D.P.) and phosphoric acid which causes a sudden release of energy. It is this energy which is used for contraction. After contraction of the muscle fibre, A.T.P. is re-formed and this process also requires energy. In this reaction the energy is obtained from the breakdown of glycogen stored in the muscle cells. Carbon dioxide and water are formed as by-products and heat is given off. This is why we feel hot after vigorous muscular activity. Fig. 6.6 will help to make this clear.

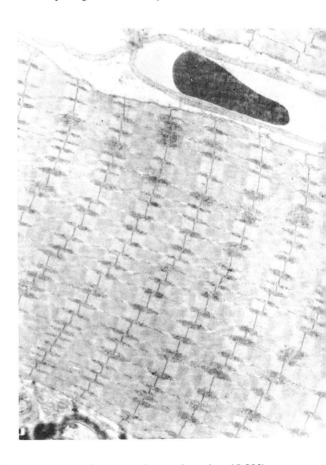

PLATE 30. Striated muscle under the light microscope.

PLATE 31. Striated muscle under the electron microscope (approximately × 10,000).

67

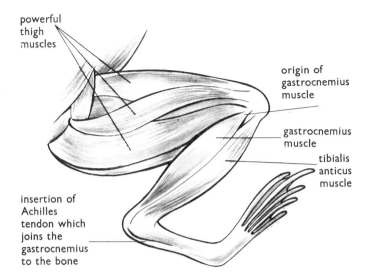

Fig. 6.7. Dorsal view of right leg of a frog with the skin removed to show the muscles. The gastrocnemius is the extensor of the ankle-joint and the tibialis anticus is the flexor.

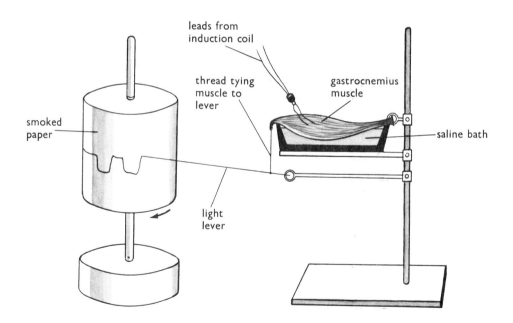

FIG. 6.8. Making a muscle-nerve tracing.

Greater activity needs a greater supply of oxygen so that when we run, for example, both our heart beat and breathing rates are increased. There is, however, a limit to the amount of oxygen which can be passed to the cells in a given time so that if activity continues a lack of oxygen—known as the *oxygen debt*—occurs. You will all have seen people panting after a race. *Rest* is then essential to give the blood time to get more oxygen to the cells.

We also get tired because increased activity leads to the collection in the cells of a substance called *lactic acid* under conditions of oxygen debt. This leads to *fatigue* and rest is again needed to allow removal of lactic acid. It is removed by being converted to glycogen, the energy for this process being derived from the oxidation of glucose.

A muscle can only contract if it is stimulated to do so by a nerve message. Each *fibre* of the muscle is stimulated by a message which comes along a tiny branch of a larger nerve.

An interesting physiological experiment can be carried out quite easily on the calf muscle of the frog. The calf muscle (gastrocnemius) together with part of the nerve which serves it—the *sciatic nerve*—is removed from an anaesthetised frog (Fig. 6.7). One end of the muscle is fixed to a firm support while the other end is attached by a thread to a light lever (Fig. 6.8). The other end of the lever touches lightly a piece of smoked paper which is fastened to a revolving drum. The muscle must be immersed in saline solution to prevent it from drying up. The sciatic nerve is connected to two electrodes leading from an induction coil. When a current is passed for a moment the nerve receives a stimulus which is passed to the muscle. The muscle reacts by contracting and the movement shown by the lever is recorded on the smoked paper.

The type of tracing obtained on the paper is shown in Fig. 6.9. Notice that there is a small *latent period* before contraction starts. This is followed by the *period of contraction* followed by the *period of recovery*. A number of stimulations results in a number of contractions but gradually these become weaker as the muscle becomes *fatigued*.

A muscle *fibre* always contracts to the full: it cannot give a half-hearted contraction. This is often referred to as the 'all or nothing' law. *Muscles*, however, can contract strongly or weakly. This is because the *number* of fibres contracting can vary—according to the number or strength of the stimulations.

FIG. 6.9. The kind of tracing obtained in the muscle contraction experiment described above.

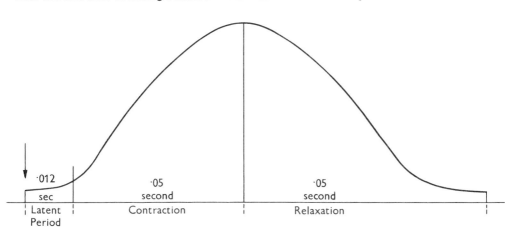

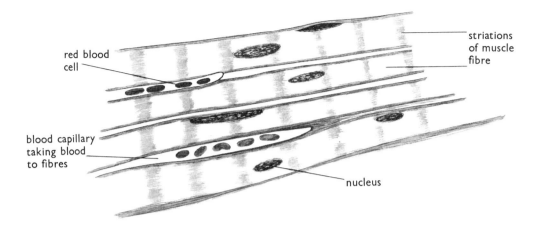

red blood cell

striations of muscle fibre

blood capillary taking blood to fibres

nucleus

FIG. 6.10. Striated muscle showing how blood vessels take food and oxygen very close to each fibre.

Types of Muscle

Although all muscle cells have contraction as their function there are different types of cells, each of which is suited to a particular type of contraction.

The muscle used in the experiment just described is known as *striated*, *voluntary* or *skeletal muscle* (Plates 30 and 31). Different names have been given to the same cells according to the aspect under consideration: 'striated' refers to the muscle fibre's appearance, 'voluntary' to the fact that it is under the control of the 'will' and 'skeletal' to its chief function in vertebrates, namely to move the bones of the skeleton. Fig. 6.10 shows the appearance of striated muscle under the microscope. Notice the blood capillaries (see page 100) which take glucose and oxygen to the cells. Fig. 6.5 shows how a muscle is made of fibres and how the fibres are marked with striations. These striations are due to the presence of the amino-acid molecules mentioned on page 66. Fig. 6.10 shows how the muscle is served by tiny blood vessels.

Skeletal muscle can contract and relax very quickly. For example, in the fingers of a pianist, the wing of a bird and—fastest of all—in the wings of insects. A bee's wing beats about 400 times every second.

Smooth muscle is shown in Fig. 2.5. Each cell is separate from those next to it and each contains one nucleus. Smooth muscle is found where a sustained contraction is required, e.g. in the walls of the intestine and in the bladder.

Cardiac muscle is only found in the heart. Here a need for rhythmical contractions and relaxations is present throughout the life of the animal. The heart can never rest.

Joints: Muscles and Bones working Together

As already mentioned, the function of muscles of the skeletal type is to move bones in relation to each other. This is only possible because *joints* occur between bones. Where two bones fit together in such a way that they can move in relation to one another they are said to *articulate*. The elbow joint, Fig. 6.11, is a good example of the way in which muscles and bones work together to produce movement.

The articulation at the elbow joint is be-

70

tween the upper arm bone (the *humerus*) and the two bones of the lower arm (the *ulna* and *radius*). The main articulation is with the ulna.

The muscles, which are attached to the periosteum of the bones by non-elastic tissues called *tendons*, are the *biceps* and the *triceps*. Their positions can be seen in the figure. The *origin* of a muscle is in the periosteum of the bone which remains stationary (in this case the shoulder blade) while the end which is attached to the bone which moves—here it is

the ulna—is called the *insertion*.

Now in all movements two opposing sets of muscles are involved. At the elbow, for example, contraction of the biceps muscle causes the arm to bend while the opposing sets of muscles—the triceps—straighten it. The bending of the elbow joint is called *flexion* and the reverse is *extension*. While one set of muscles is contracting, the opposing set is gradually relaxing, thereby exerting a breaking influence on the movement.

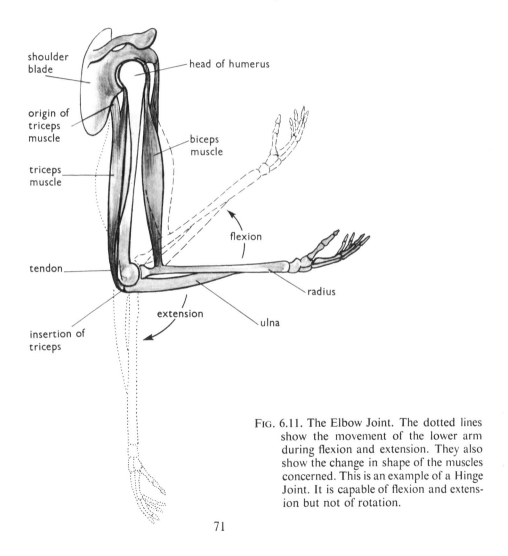

shoulder blade

head of humerus

origin of triceps muscle

biceps muscle

triceps muscle

flexion

tendon

radius

extension

insertion of triceps

ulna

FIG. 6.11. The Elbow Joint. The dotted lines show the movement of the lower arm during flexion and extension. They also show the change in shape of the muscles concerned. This is an example of a Hinge Joint. It is capable of flexion and extension but not of rotation.

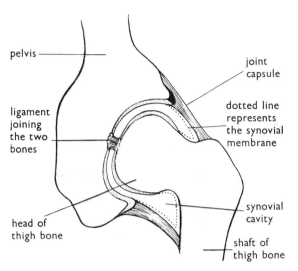

pelvis

joint capsule

ligament joining the two bones

dotted line represents the synovial membrane

head of thigh bone

synovial cavity

shaft of thigh bone

FIG. 6.12. The Hip Joint to show internal structure. This is an example of a Ball and Socket joint and is capable of rotary movement.

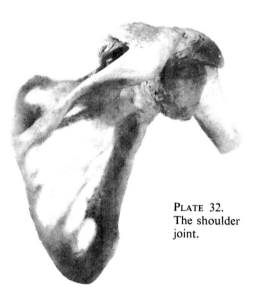

PLATE 32. The shoulder joint.

Detailed Structure of a Joint

Reference to Fig. 6.12 will help you to understand the actual structure of a joint: the drawing shows part of the pelvis and part of the thigh bone cut through to show the internal structure of the *hip joint*.

The actual surfaces of the two bones are covered with cartilage: this is a softer substance than bone and there is less friction at the joint, therefore, than if the actual bone material were touching. Round the inside of the joint is a *synovial membrane* which holds a lubricating liquid—the *synovial fluid*—which helps to lessen friction between the cartilage surfaces as they move over one another. The bones are held together by tissue of an elastic nature known as *ligament*. These ligaments can stretch when the bones move. The whole joint is surrounded by a *joint capsule* (Plate 32).

Types of Joints

The elbow joint just described is a typical *synovial joint*, i.e. one which allows very free movement. There are several kinds of synovial joint of which the three most important are the *hinge joint*, the *gliding joint* and the *ball and socket joint*. Examples of these are:

Hinge joint—the *elbow* and the *knee* joints.
Gliding joint—the joint between the articular facets of vertebrae (page 79).
Ball and socket joint—the shoulder and hip joints.

In addition to synovial joints there are other kinds such as *immovable* joints, like those occurring between the bones of the skull, and joints which allow *slight movement* only as, for example, between vertebrae. (This last must not be confused with the gliding joints which occur between the *articular* facets of the vertebrae.)

Kinds of Movement at Synovial Joints

There are three types of movement possible at synovial joints: to help when describing movement these have been named as follows.

Angular movements: flexion and *extension.*

Abduction and *adduction*—moving the part concerned away from or towards the mid-line respectively.

Gliding movements: one bone or one of its parts slides over another.

Rotary movements: moving a limb round in a circular way. This is possible at the shoulder and hip joints. Also the head moves in a rotary fashion on the vertebrae. Fig. 6.13 will make these terms clearer.

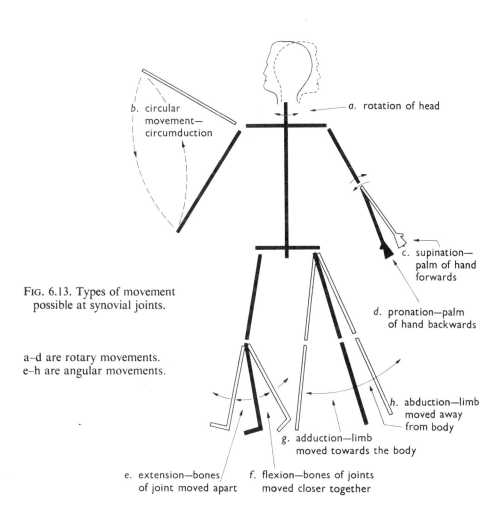

Fig. 6.13. Types of movement possible at synovial joints.

a–d are rotary movements.
e–h are angular movements.

b. circular movement—circumduction

a. rotation of head

c. supination—palm of hand forwards

d. pronation—palm of hand backwards

h. abduction—limb moved away from body

g. adduction—limb moved towards the body

e. extension—bones of joint moved apart

f. flexion—bones of joints moved closer together

73

7. Support and Movement—2

THE SKELETON

The General Plan of the Human Skeleton

Fig. 7.1 is a simple plan of the way in which parts of the skeleton are arranged. The two main divisions under which it is usual to consider the skeleton are firstly the *axial skeleton* and secondly the *appendicular skeleton*. The axial part, as the name implies, forms a strong axis for the support of the body and its organs, and consists of the *skull*, the *backbone* or *vertebral column* and the ribs. The appendicular part is formed by the *limb girdles* (the *shoulder blade* and *collar bone* and the *pelvis*) and the bones of the *limbs*.

The skull is formed by a number of bones fused together, the joints being of the immovable kind and being referred to as *sutures*. Its main regions are the *cranium*, which houses the brain, and the *upper* and *lower jaws*.

The main axis of the body is formed by the *vertebrae*—the individual bones of the backbone. There are thirty-three of these altogether. The *ribs* are articulated to some of these vertebrae.

The two limb girdles provide strong structures on which the limbs can articulate. The pelvic girdle, which has to support the whole weight of the body, is actually fused to the backbone. The shoulder blade is not fused to the vertebral column but is attached instead by powerful muscles.

The bones of the arm consist of the *humerus*, the *radius* and the *ulna*. To these last two bones are articulated the bones of the wrist (*carpal bones*) which in turn articulate with the *metacarpal* bones in the palm of the hand. Finally the metacarpals articulate with the *phalanges*—the small bones of the fingers or *digits*.

The lower limb or leg is constructed in much the same way as the arm but the bones are given different names. The thigh bone is called the *femur* and the bones of the lower part of the leg are the *tibia* and *fibula*. With these the *tarsal* bones of the ankle articulate. Last are the bones of the foot—the *tarsals* and *metatarsals* followed by the *phalanges* of the toes.

FIG. 7.1. The basic plan of the human skeleton.

74

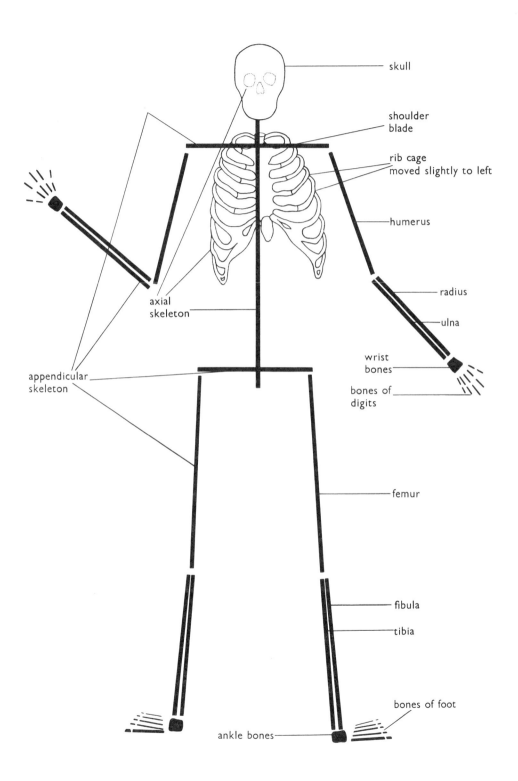

skull

shoulder blade

rib cage
moved slightly to left

humerus

radius

ulna

wrist bones

bones of digits

axial skeleton

appendicular skeleton

femur

fibula

tibia

bones of foot

ankle bones

The Skull and Teeth

The skull, Figs. 7.2 and 7.3 and Plate 33, is formed from a number of bones which arise separately in the baby before it is born. After birth the bones gradually become more and more firmly fused together at the *sutures* until the hard, strong skull of the adult is fully formed. There are quite large gaps in the skull of the newly born baby: these gaps are known as *fontanelles* (Fig. 7.3) and it is possible to feel them on a baby's head. They are all closed up before the baby is two years old.

The *cranium* is formed from a number of bones which fuse firmly together to form a very strong box-like structure which protects the brain. On the inferior side of the cranium is a large hole for the exit of the spinal cord.

The upper jaw, which is firmly fused to the cranium, provides a strong structure to hold the *teeth*. The lower jaw, which is, of course, also equipped with teeth, can move up and down owing to its articulation with the underside of the cranium.

As the teeth are firmly rooted in both jaws food of a hard nature may be chewed safely or *masticated*. Each tooth, Fig. 7.4, is composed of a *crown* connected by a short *neck* to strong *roots*. The crown, which is the part of the tooth exposed above the gum, is covered by a very hard substance called *enamel*. Beneath the enamel is the *dentine*—a hard substance which forms the major part of the tooth. Within the dentine is a soft area known as the *pulp cavity*: this contains nerves and blood vessels. Damage to the enamel, such as may occur when one is using the teeth to crack a nut, results in a small hole through which food particles may penetrate to the dentine. Bacteria then cause the food to decay with the formation of acids which gradually erode the dentine—Fig. 7.4. In time

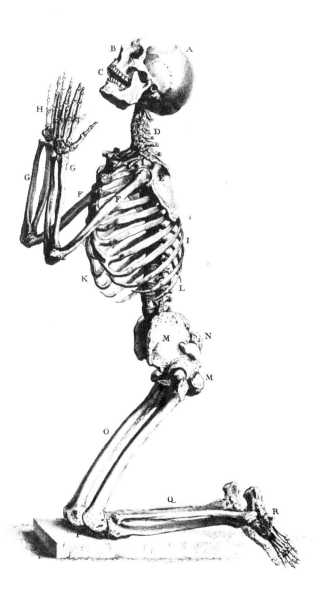

PLATE 33. The skeleton from Vesalius.

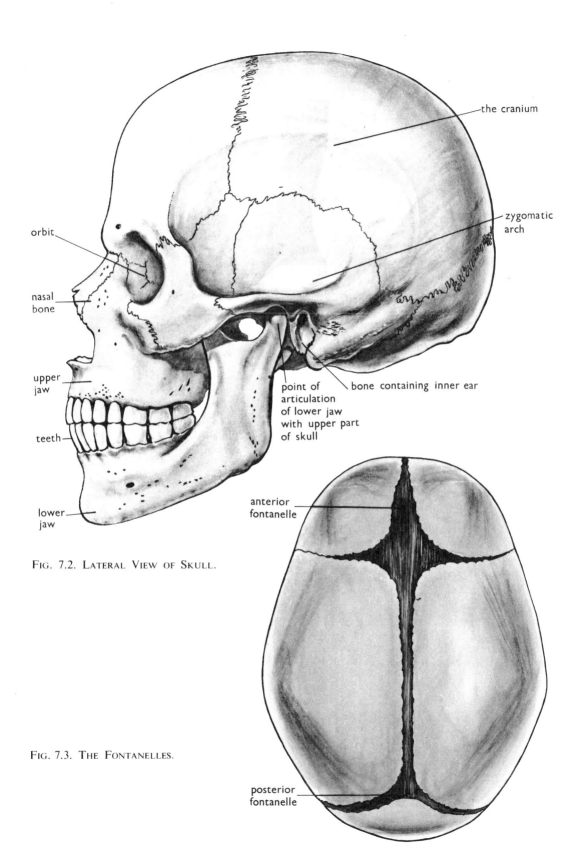

the cranium

zygomatic arch

orbit

nasal bone

upper jaw

teeth

lower jaw

point of articulation of lower jaw with upper part of skull

bone containing inner ear

Fig. 7.2. Lateral View of Skull.

anterior fontanelle

posterior fontanelle

Fig. 7.3. The Fontanelles.

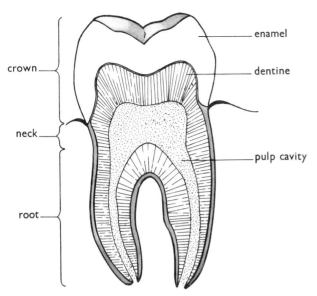

FIG. 7.4. a. The structure of a healthy tooth.

b. A tooth attacked by decay.

the acids penetrate near to or actually into the pulp cavity and this brings on an attack of toothache. Foods containing sugar are particularly likely to bring about tooth decay and hence the continual eating of sweets is harmful.

Man, in common with other mammals, has during his life two sets of teeth. The first, or *milk dentition*, as it is called, consists of twenty teeth and lasts only until the child is six or seven years old. The *permanent dentition* then forms, the new teeth pushing out the milk teeth as they grow. There are thirty-two in the permanent set.

The teeth are of four kinds: the *incisors* for cutting, the *canines*—which are used for stabbing by animals which hunt their food—and the *premolars* and *molars*, both of which are used to grind the food (Fig. 7.5).

The number of teeth is frequently and conveniently expressed as a *dental formula* in which the letters stand for the type of teeth while the figures refer to the number of teeth in each jaw.

(a) Milk dentition:

$$\text{i } \frac{2}{2}, \text{ c } \frac{1}{1}, \text{ pm } \frac{0}{0}, \text{ m } \frac{2}{2} = 10 \text{ per side} = 20 \text{ in all}$$

(b) Permanent dentition:

$$\text{i } \frac{2}{2}, \text{ c } \frac{1}{1}, \text{ pm } \frac{2}{2}, \text{ m } \frac{3}{3} = 16 \text{ per side} = 32 \text{ in all}$$

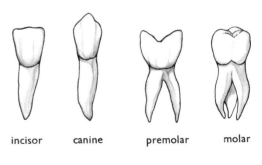

incisor canine premolar molar

FIG. 7.5. The four types of teeth found in Man.

78

The Vertebral Column

The *vertebral column* or backbone consists of thirty-three separate bones or *vertebrae* which articulate in such a way that slight movement between them is possible—with the exception of some of the lower vertebrae which have fused together.

Fig. 7.6 shows the basic plan on which each vertebra is built. The main strength of the vertebra lies in the *centrum*. Behind the centrum the *neural arch* forms a strong protection for the spinal cord—the main nerve of the body—which runs beneath it. The neural arch is surmounted by a *neural spine* to which strong muscles are attached in the living animal.

The two *transverse processes* projecting laterally from the centrum provide further surfaces for the attachment of muscles. Also present on the vertebra are the *superior* and *inferior articular facets* which, as the names imply, help two successive vertebrae to articulate together. The superior articular facet of one vertebra articulates with the inferior articular facet of the vertebra immediately above it.

A large disc of cartilage situated between each vertebra and its neighbours acts as a shock absorber by preventing the bones from jarring on each other when movement takes place. Each disc is called an *intervertebral disc*.

All the vertebrae are built on this basic pattern, each varying from it to suit the particular function it fulfils.

Before studying the different types of vertebrae, note first the number of each kind:

Cervical or Neck vertebrae	7
Thoracic or Chest vertebrae	12
Lumbar vertebrae	5
Sacral vertebrae, fused together	5
Coccygeal vertebrae, fused together	4

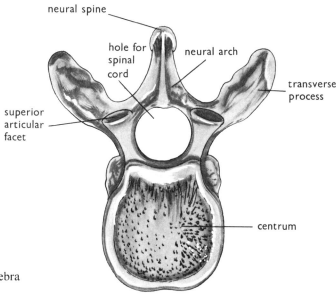

neural spine

hole for spinal cord

neural arch

transverse process

superior articular facet

centrum

FIG. 7.6. The basic plan of a vertebra seen in superior aspect.

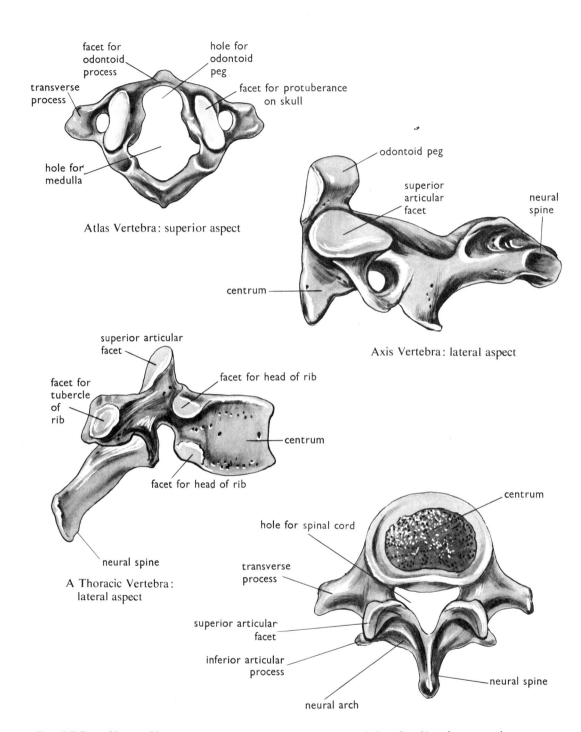

facet for
odontoid
process

hole for
odontoid
peg

transverse
process

facet for protuberance
on skull

hole for
medulla

Atlas Vertebra: superior aspect

odontoid peg

superior
articular
facet

neural
spine

centrum

Axis Vertebra: lateral aspect

superior articular
facet

facet for head of rib

facet for
tubercle
of
rib

centrum

facet for head of rib

neural spine

A Thoracic Vertebra:
lateral aspect

centrum

hole for spinal cord

transverse
process

superior articular
facet

inferior articular
process

neural spine

neural arch

FIG. 7.7 SOME HUMAN VERTEBRAE.

A Lumbar Vertebra: superior aspect

80

Cervical Vertebrae (Fig. 7.7). Of the seven cervical vertebrae the first two are especially modified to enable the head to move.

The first, or *atlas vertebra*, is a ring of bone surmounted by a small neural spine and bearing two broad transverse processes each of which has a hole through it for the passage of an artery. The superior articular facets are large and concave to receive two protuberances situated on the inferior side of the head. This articulation enables the head to be moved up and down as when nodding 'yes'.

The second cervical vertebra, or *axis* as it is called, bears upon its centrum a small peg —the *odontoid peg*—which articulates with the atlas vertebra and enables the head to be moved with a rotary motion as when one indicates 'no'. To prevent the spinal cord being damaged by the odontoid peg a *transverse ligament* passes across the atlas vertebra from side to side.

The remaining five cervical vertebrae are less modified and specialised than the two just described: their main purpose is to give greater movement to the head. It is interesting to note that in birds, where a large number of neck vertebrae are found, the head can be rotated much farther.

Thoracic Vertebrae (Fig. 7.7). These vertebrae are very similar to each other. Their particular function is to support the ribs. Each has a strong centrum, stout transverse processes and a long neural spine. There are two facets for the articulation of the ribs, the *head* of the rib fitting against the centrum and the *tubercle* articulating with the transverse process.

Lumbar Vertebrae (Fig. 7.7). The lumbar vertebrae are the largest and strongest in the body: they have to support the whole weight of the person. The centrum of each is massive and the neural spines and transverse processes are well developed in order to provide strong areas for muscle attachment.

Sacral Vertebrae (Fig. 7.8). The five sacral vertebrae are strongly fused together to form the *sacrum*. This is a very strong and important structure for it is to the sacrum that the pelvis is fused and this in turn articulates with the leg bones.

Coccygeal Vertebrae. Each coccygeal vertebra is little more than a very reduced centrum. In the human these vertebrae are all fused together to form the *coccyx*—a structure representing the tail of other animals. A few people are actually born with a short tail!

superior end

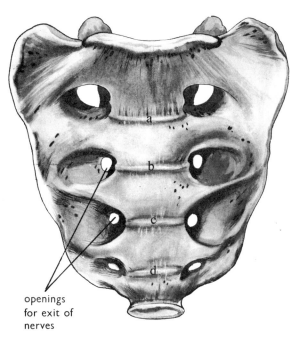

openings
for exit of
nerves

inferior end

Fig. 7.8. The Sacrum
a–d are ridges between the five fused vertebrae.

81

The Thoracic Cage (Fig. 7.9)

The skeleton of the thorax acts as a protective cage round the heart and lungs. Its anterior face is formed by the *breast-bone* or *sternum*, and its sides by the ribs, while posteriorly it is closed by the vertebral column.

The sternum consists of a superior *manubrium*, a middle *body*, and an inferior *xiphoid process*. To it are fused the *costal cartilages* of the ribs. Each rib is a curved bone with ridges on it to which the *intercostal muscles* (see page 157) are attached. At the posterior end of each rib is found a short *tubercle* which articulates with the transverse process of a thoracic vertebra, and a head which fits into a hollow formed by shallow facets in two adjacent vertebrae.

There are twelve pairs of ribs in all. The last two pairs are called *floating ribs* because their anterior ends are not attached to the sternum. The costal cartilages of the five pairs immediately superior to the floating ribs are fused together, while those of the first five pairs fuse separately with the sternum.

The flexibility of the cartilages of the sternum and of the costal cartilages, together with the joints where the ribs articulate on the vertebrae, enable the ribs to move, when the intercostal muscles contract, thus allowing the volume of the thoracic cavity to be increased.

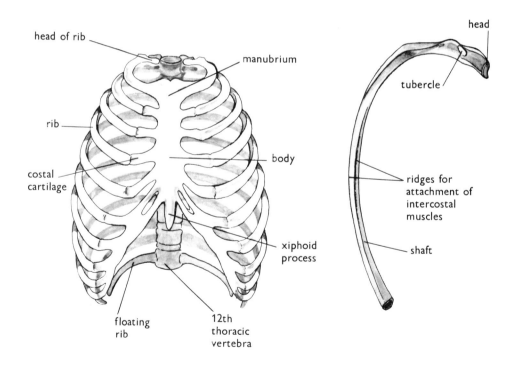

FIG. 7.9. The thoracic cage and a left rib.

82

The Limb Girdles (Fig. 7.10)

As we have seen, the limb girdles are those bones to which the limbs are articulated. They are two in number: the *pectoral* or *shoulder girdle*, and the *pelvic girdle* or *pelvis*. The position of the girdles can be seen in Figs. 7.1 and 7.13.

The *pectoral girdle* is divided into two halves, the left and the right, and each half is composed of two bones: the *scapula*, or *shoulder blade*, at the back; and the *clavicle*, or *collar bone*, at the front. The scapula and the clavicle articulate at the side with one another. Each clavicle is joined anteriorly to the sternum and each scapula is strongly fastened to the backbone by muscles—there being no actual fusion between the scapula and the vertebrae, in contrast to the position in the pelvic region.

At the side of the scapula is a knob and a shallow *glenoid cavity*; the head of the upper arm bone, the humerus, fits into the cavity and is held there by ligaments, muscles and the suction of the air-tight joint. The knob is used for the attachment of the biceps muscles. The two halves of the pectoral girdle act entirely independently of each other.

The *pelvic girdle* (Plate 34) consists of right and left halves fused firmly together and to the backbone. This gives a very strong construction by means of which the whole weight of the body may be borne by the legs. Each half of the girdle consists of three bones, an upper *ilium*, an outer *ischium* and an inner *pubis*. The *acetabulum* is a deep hollow, formed from part of each of the three bones, into which the head of the femur fits.

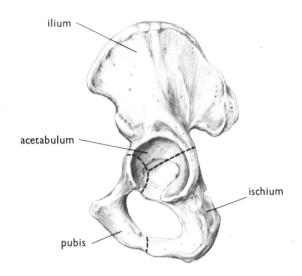

FIG. 7.10. a. The left half of the pelvic girdle.

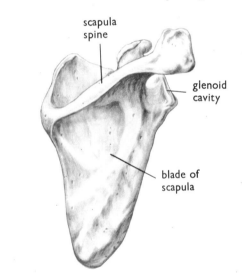

FIG. 7.10. b. The right scapula, dorsal side.

PLATE 34. The pelvic girdle.

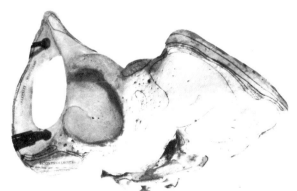

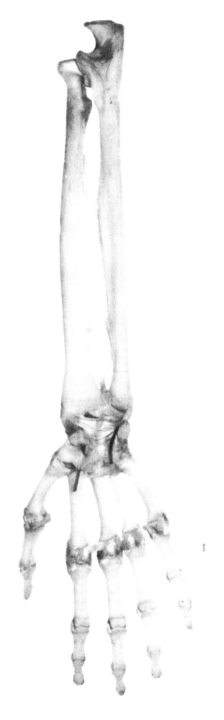

The Limbs

The limb bones may be seen in Fig. 7.13 and Plates 35 and 36. The basic pattern is the same in arm and leg but different names are, of course, given in each case. The *upper arm* is formed from a single bone, the *humerus*, whose head fits into the *glenoid cavity* of the *scapula* while the *lower arm* is supported by two bones, the *radius* and the *ulna*. The chief articulation of the humerus is with the ulna. The radius rotates against the lower end of the humerus when the palm of the hand is rotated. At their lower ends the radius and ulna articulate with a number of wrist bones. These wrist bones, or *carpals* as they are called, in turn articulate with the *metacarpals* —the bones in the palm of the hand. The bones of the *digits* or fingers are called *phalanges*.

In the leg the thigh bone, or *femur*, fits into the *acetabulum* of the pelvis forming a ball and socket joint (see page 72). At the knee the lower end of the femur articulates with the *tibia* which in turn articulates, at its lower end, with a large ankle bone. On the outer side of the tibia is a bone called the *fibula*. In the human there is no articulation between the femur and the fibula. The sole of the foot is formed by *metatarsals* and the bones of the toes are *phalanges*.

PLATE 35. The bones of the arm and hand.

PLATE 36. The human skeleton.

84

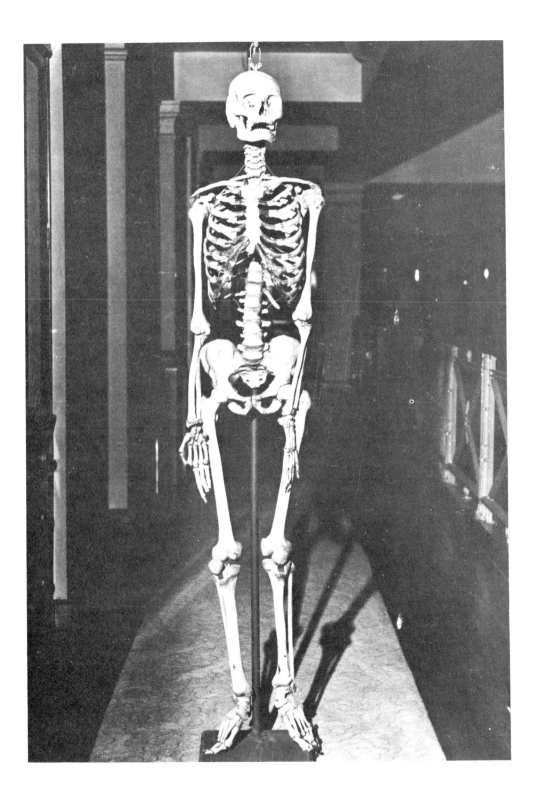

MUSCLES OF THE BODY

Good Posture and Standing

It is only comparatively recently in his evolutionary history that Man has assumed an upright posture. Within his own lifetime each person has to learn to walk erect, for at birth he cannot walk at all and as a baby he first learns to crawl and then to walk.

When the body is correctly held there is only slight tension on the skeletal muscles: this is called *muscle tone*. Muscle tone is only present during our waking hours. When we are asleep our muscles relax—with the exception of those concerned with breathing and heart beat.

As Man is normally erect, the whole weight of his head, trunk and arms has to be borne by the pelvic girdle and legs. Provided the vertical axis of the body and the axial skeleton nearly coincide, good posture can be maintained without undue effort in spite of the great weight of the head, trunk and arms. As long as the centre of gravity is held directly over the feet, an erect position may be held without strain for a long time. As an exercise, by referring to Fig. 7.12, try to find out which muscles are at work when you are standing well.

Bad posture such as that shown in Fig. 7.11 frequently results in poor health. It may, for example, lead to disorders of the digestive and breathing systems as well as bringing strains to the back and abdomen. Poor posture in childhood will lead to poor posture in the adult and hence we can see the importance of early training in good habits.

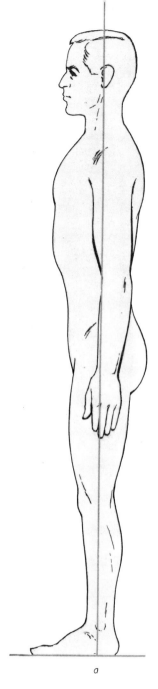

a

FIG. 7.11. GOOD AND BAD POSTURE.

a. *Good Posture.* Notice that the vertical axis of the body and the axial skeleton nearly coincide. Note the position of the ear, the hand and the foot.

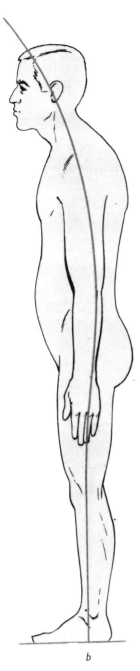 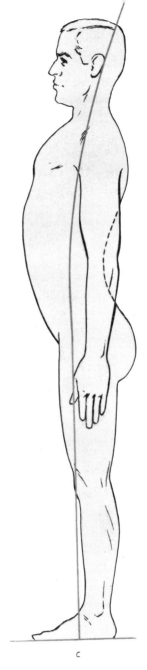

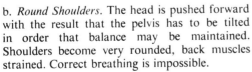

b. *Round Shoulders.* The head is pushed forward with the result that the pelvis has to be tilted in order that balance may be maintained. Shoulders become very rounded, back muscles strained. Correct breathing is impossible.

c. *Hollow Back.* The shoulders are held back and the person may imagine that he is standing well. In fact his abdomen is thrust forward and his abdominal muscles become slack. This may result in digestive and respiratory troubles.

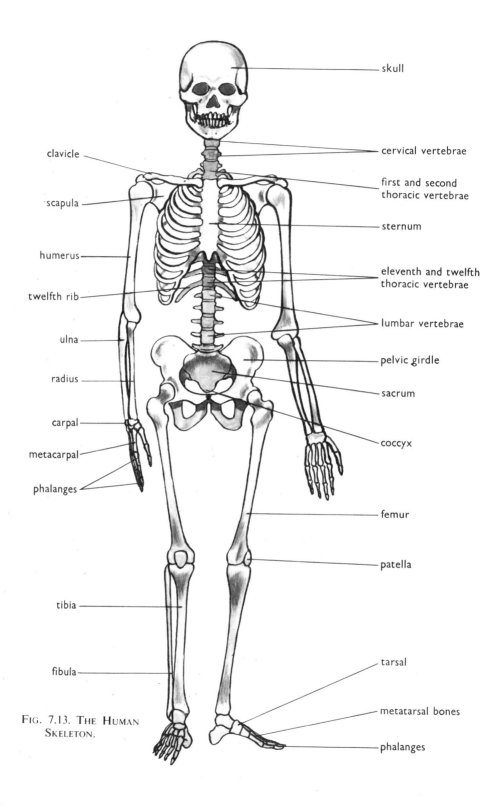

skull

cervical vertebrae

first and second
thoracic vertebrae

clavicle

scapula

sternum

humerus

eleventh and twelfth
thoracic vertebrae

twelfth rib

lumbar vertebrae

ulna

pelvic girdle

radius

sacrum

carpal

coccyx

metacarpal

phalanges

femur

patella

tibia

fibula

tarsal

metatarsal bones

FIG. 7.13. THE HUMAN
SKELETON.

phalanges

Walking

The main muscles used in running are shown in Fig. 7.12. Notice, as was the case with the arm—pages 70 and 71—that the muscles work in sets in opposition to each other. There is, for example, opposition between the *quadriceps* and the *biceps*, between the quadriceps and the *gluteals* and between the *gastrocnemius* and the *tibialis anterior*.

Notice also that one set of muscles may have more than one function. The quadriceps, for example, not only moves the femur forward when we walk but is also responsible for extending the leg at the knee. Similarly the gluteals move the leg backwards—and hence the body forwards—and also straighten the body by rotating it on the head of the femur.

The *gastrocnemius* muscle at the back of the lower leg is responsible for raising the heel off the ground—the first stage of a step forward in walking. It is attached to one of the heel bones by the famous Achilles' tendon.

Grasping

To perform the delicate movements of which our fingers are capable it is obviously necessary for our arms and hands to be equipped with a large number of muscles and tendons. It is not necessary for you to know the names of these but the general pattern upon which they work is as follows: the muscles on the inner surface of the lower arm have long tendons which cross the palm of the hand and run along the inner surface of the fingers. When the muscles contract they pull on the tendons causing the fingers to curl in towards the palm in a grasping action. Similarly the muscles on the outer surface of the arm cause the fingers to be extended thus straightening the hand. The tendons are held in position at intervals along the fingers and in the palm of the hand by loops of fibrous tissue which thus prevent their slipping out of place.

FIG. 7.12. Some important muscles used in locomotion.

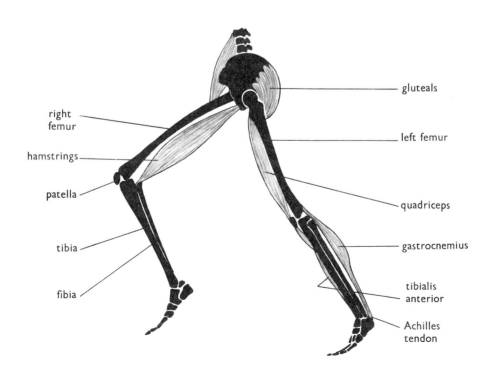

1. Visit a zoo and study the animals with protective exoskeletons—insects, snails, fish with heavy scales, tortoises and armadillos. Consider whether or not it would be an advantage to Man if he possessed an exo-skeleton.

2. Visit a museum and study the skeletons of different animals in order to compare them with Man. Notice especially the simi-larities and differences between the skeletons of Man and the great apes.

3. Examine with a microscope or micro-projector prepared slides of bone and cartilage in transverse section. Examine also slides of muscle preparations.

4. Soak a small bone in hydrochloric acid for several days. Notice how soft it becomes as the acid dissolves the inorganic salts.

5. Examine a 'shoulder of lamb' obtained from a butcher's shop. After it has been cooked the muscles may be easily separated from the bones and eaten in order not to waste the meat. Notice the smooth, glistening head of the humerus where it fits into the glenoid cavity. This may be done after the synovial capsule has been opened. Examine the ligaments holding the humerus to the girdle. Notice the periosteum. Make drawings as your investigation proceeds.

6. Remove the skin from the leg muscles of a frog after it has been killed by chloro-form. Carefully part the muscles noticing how neatly they are fitted together. Note the origin and insertion of some of the muscles and the strong tendons which hold them to the bones.

7. Ask your teacher to perform the frog muscle experiment described on page 69.

8. Carefully examine the elbow joint of a friend. Notice how the muscles change shape as the joint is flexed or extended.

9. Perform all the kinds of movement described on page 73. How many of your joints move in each way described?

10. Examine a human skeleton. If the human skeleton is not available, make use of a rabbit skeleton instead. Using individual bones, try to see how they are arranged on the complete skeleton. Draw as many in-dividual bones as time allows.

11. Examine a set of human teeth. Draw one tooth of each of the four kinds.

12. Feel the thorax of a friend noting the position of the ribs. Notice how the ribs move when a deep breath is taken.

13. Examine your posture. Place your back against a wall. If your posture is good the following parts of the body should be touch-ing the wall: the head, the flat part of the shoulder blades, the buttocks and the heels. In this position it should be possible *just* to slide your hand between your back and the wall at waist level: there should *not* be a large gap. Viewed from the side the tip of the lobe of the ear, the point of the shoulder, the back of the wrist and ankle should be in a vertical line—as in Fig. 7.11. The position should be fairly relaxed and held without strain.

14. Try to analyse a single step forward by feeling your leg muscles or those of a friend.

1. Describe, as clearly as possible, the position in which the body is held in good posture. What harmful effects may result if a child is allowed to develop a bad posture when standing, sitting or walking? (RSA)

2. Describe the structure of the vertebral column. What is a good posture, and why is it important to health? (W)

3. What kind of tissues enter into the formation of a limb joint? Show how each tissue contributes to a function of the joint as a whole. (C)

4. Describe a typical voluntary muscle and how it causes movement. Discuss the importance to the body of exercise, fatigue and rest. (S)

5. Explain how the human skeleton protects delicate tissues of the body, and helps in the absorption of shocks. Illustrate your answer with some simple labelled diagrams. (L)

6. What are the functions of the human skeleton? Describe an example to illustrate each function. (O)

7. The framework of the body is made up of bones and muscles, the bones being connected by joints. Explain carefully why these three structures are necessary. List the *main* types of joint; state the purpose, and give an example, of each. Choose *either* the knee *or* the elbow *or* the shoulder joint; state which type it is and give a simple, but fully labelled, diagram of the joint you have chosen, in order to show the main features of its type. (RSA)

8. Describe and compare the joints of the shoulder, hip and elbow and discuss the ways in which they are adapted to perform particular functions. (S)

9. Give the functions of the pelvic (hip) girdle and make a list of the organs contained in the cavity formed by this girdle in a woman. Describe the nature and functions of *two* of the organs you mention. (RSA)

10. Discuss the occurrence and nature of (a) cartilage, (b) bone, in relation to their functions in the body. (C)

11. By means of a labelled diagram show the general arrangement of the human skeleton. What is the importance of the skeleton in the life of Man? (S)

12. By means of a labelled diagram show the structure of a voluntary muscle fibre. Why do muscles show fatigue after strenuous exercise, and how is their recovery brought about? (L)

13. With the aid of a diagram showing the main bones and muscles concerned, describe how the arm is bent and straightened. Name four other types of joints that occur in the arm, and describe the situation and movements of each. (O)

14. Distinguish between smooth and striated muscle. Give two examples of each type. What kind of muscle is the diaphragm? Describe its actions. (L)

15. Describe with diagrams the main muscles involved in raising the foot to take a step. (L)

16. Describe the term 'synovial joint'. Give an account of the characteristics of synovial joints and indicate the functions of the different parts. How are synovial joints classified? (L)

17. Describe a named example of (a) a hinge joint, (b) a ball and socket joint in the human body to show how the construction of each, with its associated muscles, fits the functional needs of its situation. (J)

18. Name and describe the types of muscle tissue found in the body, pointing out how each serves efficiently the function it has to perform. (J)

8. Our Transport Fluids—Blood and Lymph

Introduction

In a small unicellular animal such as *Amoeba*, substances passing into the protoplasm, from the water in which the animal lives, have only a short distance to travel to the centre of the cell. The same is true of substances moving in the opposite direction. Thus *Amoeba*, and other animals of a similar size, can obtain their food and oxygen and remove their waste materials by simple diffusion. In a number of the simpler multicellular animals such as *Hydra* (Fig. 8.1) and the sea-anemones (Fig. 5.1) simple diffusion still suffices. But in larger multicellular animals where the cells in the centre of the body are some distance from the outside environment, the distance becomes too great for the substances concerned to pass quickly enough through the tissues by diffusion alone. Cells in the centre would soon become starved of food and oxygen.

Thus because every cell, however deeply it lies in the body, needs a continual supply of food and oxygen and is continually producing substances which must be removed from the protoplasm, a transport system is necessary. In the higher animals this system takes the form of a *vascular system* which consists, in Man, of a *blood system* and a *lymphatic system*. The fluids found in these two systems are called respectively *blood* and *lymph*.

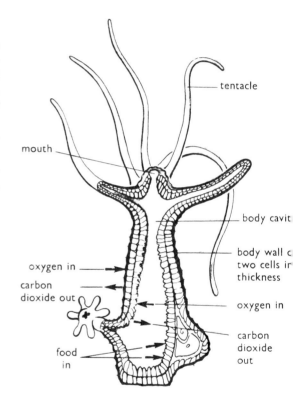

FIG. 8.1. Hydra—a simple multicellular animal in which diffusion of substances from the environment to the cells and vice versa is possible without the aid of a transport system.

92

Substances can only be passed into and out of cells in solution, so that the living cells themselves must be bathed in a liquid: this liquid is called *tissue fluid*. It is important to remember that all our cells must be kept moist. (See page 114.)

Thus we see that water is a substance of the very greatest importance to Man, for a man weighing 70 kilograms contains in his body about 46 litres of water—that is, about 70% of his weight. Of this 46 litres about 30 litres are *within* the cells (you will remember that protoplasm is largely composed of water) and 16 litres are outside the cells. This volume—16 litres—is divided into approximately 11 litres of tissue fluid and 5 litres of blood.

The presence of blood in the body necessitates a series of tubes through which the blood can pass to and from the different organs and tissues: these tubes are called *blood vessels*. The presence of a fluid transport substance implies the need for a pump to make it circulate and this in Man is, of course, the *heart*.

The Composition of the Blood

Those of you who have received a cut at some time must have noticed that blood is a bright-red, sticky fluid. Blood is also salty to the taste and slightly alkaline and it has a smell unlike that of any other substance. If you were to smear some of the blood from the cut on to a microscope slide and look at it under the high power of the microscope you would find that it contains many round disc-like cells which appear pale yellow in colour. A specially stained slide of blood will show more clearly that these cells are biconcave discs and that they lack a nucleus. These are the *red blood cells* or *red corpuscles*. They are also known as *erythrocytes*. They are shown in Fig. 8.2 and Plate 37. The slide will

PLATE 37. Human blood.

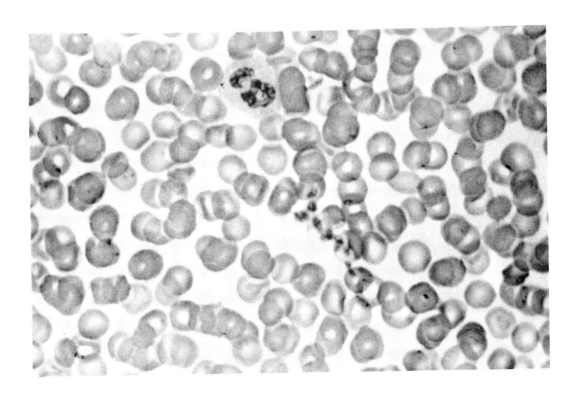

also show a second type of cell which is larger than the red cells and which contains a nucleus. *These cells are white blood cells.* They are present in far fewer numbers than the red cells—the ratio being about one white blood cell to every 500 red cells. The white blood corpuscles are also known as *leucocytes.*

In addition to the red and white cells, the blood contains numerous very small structures called *blood platelets* or *thrombocytes.* The liquid in which the cells and the platelets are carried is called *plasma.*

Red Blood Cells are present in the body in very vast numbers: each cubic *millimetre* of our blood contains about five million red cells! The cell is elastic in nature and can therefore change its shape in order to squeeze through tiny blood vessels, the smallest of which are even smaller in diameter than the red cells themselves. Once a red cell has passed into a slightly larger vessel, its elastic nature enables it to return to its normal shape —a biconcave disc. The biconcave shape is due to the lack of a nucleus. Although these blood cells appear yellow when seen unstained under a microscope, they give a red colour to the blood when it is seen in the mass: the colour is due to the pigment *haemoglobin.* This is a substance of the utmost importance, for it acts as an oxygen carrier.

Erythrocytes originate in the marrow of certain bones (see page 64). The red blood cells are not able to divide, for they do not contain a nucleus. They are short-lived, lasting for about three months only. They are then destroyed in the liver or the spleen, some of the useful substances which they contain being retained in the body.

White Blood Cells are irregular in shape, being rather like *Amoeba* in appearance. They possess a nucleus although, like the red blood cells, they are incapable of dividing.

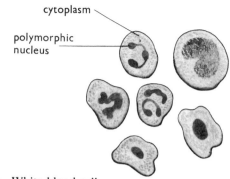

a. White blood cells

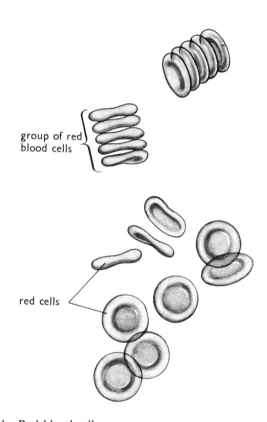

group of red blood cells

red cells

b. Red blood cells

FIG. 8.2. HUMAN BLOOD CELLS.

They are of especial interest for they are capable of moving through the tissues of the body, having passed through the walls of the blood vessels in order to do so. The reason for this peculiar ability will become apparent later (page 98).

There are two main types of white blood corpuscle. *Granulocytes*, which are formed in the bone marrow, have granular cytoplasm, and frequently they have a lobed nucleus (Fig. 8.2). *Lymphocytes* are produced in *lymph nodes* (page 114), and have clear cytoplasm and a rounded nucleus.

The Blood Platelets are minute structures found in the blood. They are not cells but are fragments of cytoplasm from certain large cells found in the bone marrow.

Plasma is the name given to the fluid in which the blood cells are found. It is a complex mixture of substances which include inorganic salts as well as proteins. The salts account for about 1% of the weight of the plasma, sodium chloride and sodium bicarbonate being the most important. It is the presence of these salts which gives the blood its alkaline reaction.

The most important blood protein is, perhaps, *fibrinogen*. The blood plasma also carries other important substances such as fats, glucose, amino-acids, hormones (see page 221) and waste substances such as urea (page 174).

The Functions of the Blood

The functions of the blood are of two kinds: one is to act as a transport system for the body, ensuring that every cell is supplied with the food, oxygen and other substances that it requires for its efficient working, and removing waste substances from it; the second is to act as a defence system against disease.

Oxygen. As we saw on page 22, a source of energy is necessary for all living things. This is usually obtained by the oxidation of sugars during the process called respiration. One of the most important functions of the blood is to transport oxygen from the lungs, where it has been absorbed, to the tissues requiring it. Under conditions of high oxygen concentration haemoglobin combines with the oxygen, forming oxyhaemoglobin. This substance is carried in the red blood cells to regions of lower oxygen concentration where it dissociates, giving up the oxygen to the cells. This is explained in more detail on page 153. The oxyhaemoglobin is bright red in contrast to the haemoglobin which gives the blood a darker red colour.

Carbon Dioxide. This is, of course, a waste substance produced during the respiration of living cells. It is carried to the lungs for removal from the body. Most of the carbon dioxide—about 80%—is carried in the plasma in the form of sodium and potassium bicarbonates. About 10% is in solution in the plasma, i.e. not in chemical combination, and the remaining 10% is in the red blood cells.

Food Substances. Those which have been absorbed from the small intestine into the blood are transported to all the cells of the body. Details of the fate of the different food substances absorbed are described in Chapter 12.

Waste Substances. One of the most important functions of the blood is to transport waste substances from the cells, where they are produced by the metabolic activity of the protoplasm, to the kidneys to be excreted. See also page 174.

Heat. Metabolic activities such as muscle contraction produce heat. The amount of heat produced varies in different parts of the body, being large, for example, in the liver and in the muscles. The blood distributes the heat produced evenly round the body so that an even temperature is maintained.

The blood, therefore, plays an important part in the control of body temperature. In addition to carrying heat evenly throughout the body, the blood carries excess heat to the skin, from which the heat may be easily lost (see page 168).

Hormones. These substances are described more fully in Chapter 19, page 221. Here it is sufficient to say that they are chemical messengers carrying messages from one part of the body to another and that they are transported freely in the blood.

PREVENTION OF DISEASE

When the skin is cut or bruised the body is exposed to two kinds of danger: firstly there may be serious or even fatal loss of blood, and secondly bacteria may invade the tissues and cause infection.

The Danger from Loss of Blood. The body has an automatic defence against loss of blood: this consists of a mechanism by means of which a *scab* or *clot* forms over a wound. The clot itself consists of a mesh-work of fibres which traps both types of blood cell. This is shown simply in Fig. 8.3 The mesh is formed from a substance called *fibrin*. Fibrin is not normally present as such in the blood—otherwise all the blood might clot—but is formed from another substance known as *fibrinogen*. This is changed in-directly to fibrin by the action of another substance which is given off from the walls of damaged blood vessels—vessels which have become broken when the wound was inflicted.

The exact series of actions leading to the formation of a clot is complex but is some-what as follows. As was mentioned in the preceding paragraph fibrin itself is not normally present in the blood but is formed under certain conditions from fibrinogen. This occurs when the fibrinogen is itself acted upon by an enzyme (page 130) called *thrombin*. Thrombin is not normally present in the blood as such but in an inactive form known as *prothrombin*. Prothrombin is prevented from acting, except when wounding occurs, by an enzyme—*anti-prothrombin* or *heparin*—which causes it to be destroyed. How then does the series of events leading up to the formation of a clot begin? It is 'triggered off' by a substance given off from the walls of the damaged vessels. This 'triggering' sub-stance is *thrombokinase*, or *thromboplastin* as it is sometimes called. Besides being produced from the walls of the damaged blood cells, it is also formed by the blood platelets. The thrombokinase destroys anti-prothrombin, thus allowing prothrombin to act.

Fig. 8.4 may help to make the process of clot formation clear.

The removal of fibrin from the plasma leaves a colourless liquid known as *serum*: this is, of course, unable to clot and is of con-siderable medical importance (see page 302). Serum may sometimes be seen oozing out of the scab which has formed over a cut.

Thrombosis is a condition in human beings in which the blood clots within the blood vessels causing them to become blocked. Treatment consists of injecting the patient with heparin. The heparin for this purpose is extracted from the liver of other mammals.

Haemophilia is an interesting condition in Man in which the ability of the blood to clot has been lost. Even a small cut may lead to severe and even fatal bleeding.

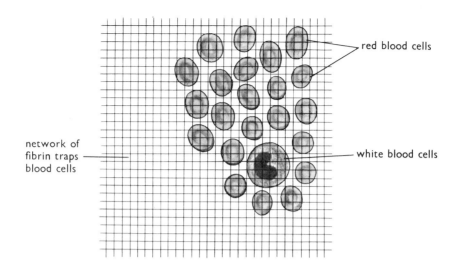

FIG. 8.3. Diagrammatic illustration of a blood clot.

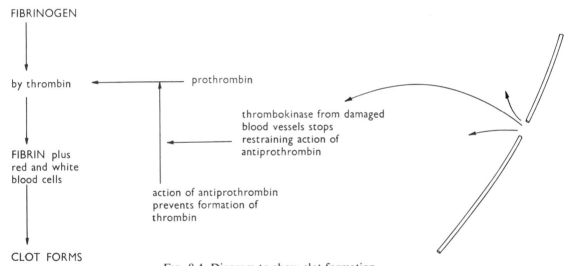

FIG. 8.4. Diagram to show clot formation.

The Danger from Infection. Normally disease-causing *bacteria* or *germs*, as they are commonly called, have some difficulty in entering the body because externally our skin forms a protective barrier while internally the chemicals of the alimentary canal provide a chemical defence. If the skin is broken, however, germs may easily gain entry to the body. Bacteria may also enter the body in other ways (see page 298).

97

Bacteria may be harmful in two ways. Firstly, certain proteins occurring in bacteria are dangerous to human beings and secondly the waste substances—*toxins*—produced by the metabolic activities of the bacteria themselves are harmful.

The human body has means of dealing with both the bacteria and the toxins they produce. When bacteria gain entrance through a wound certain white blood cells migrate through the walls of the blood vessels near the site of infection and invade the surrounding tissues, ingesting and destroying the harmful bacteria as they go. These bacteria-killing white blood cells are called *phagocytes* and the process is known as *phagocytosis*. As a result of this activity, assisted as it is by the formation of clots—which prevent free circulation—the site of infection is restricted and the bacteria are destroyed before they enter the general circulation. However, any bacteria which do manage to enter the blood circulation are dealt with by white blood cells in the liver, spleen and lymph nodes. Sometimes the invading bacteria kill large numbers of white blood cells and these accumulate, forming *pus*.

Certain bacteria are resistant to phagocytosis until they have been acted upon by chemicals known as *antibodies* (see also page 300). Substances which stimulate the production of antibodies are called *antigens* (see page 300).

The harmful toxins produced by bacteria are neutralised by *antitoxins*. These antitoxins are produced largely by the liver.

Blood Transfusion and Blood Groups

Blood transfusion is a medical process which has saved very many lives: severe loss of blood may lead to death and this is frequently prevented by injecting into the patient blood donated by another person.

Blood may not be given to anyone at random. Blood of one type may be incompatible with that of another type, that is, the two will not mix satisfactorily. In some cases when blood of one type comes into contact with blood of another type the red blood cells stick together in clumps—a process known as *agglutination*.

In human beings it has been found that the blood of any individual may be placed into one of four groups referred to as O, A, B and AB. These groups are present in the population of Britain as 48%, 40%, 10% and 2% respectively. Scientists by careful research have found out which blood group is compatible with which, hence allowing transfusion to be safely carried out. If transfusion is necessary the first step is to ascertain the patient's blood group. Blood of a compatible group may then be given with complete safety.

The red blood cells may contain substances known as *agglutinogens* (or *antigens* as they are sometimes called). There are two of these in human blood known respectively as antigen A and antigen B. In the plasma there may be two other substances known as *agglutinins* or *antibodies* and referred to as antibody a and antibody b. In the case of both antigens and antibodies the blood from any one person may contain one, both or neither of the substances. Table 3 shows the exact position:

Blood Group	Antigen	Antibody
O	Neither	a and b
A	A	b
B	B	a
AB	A and B	Neither

TABLE 3. BLOOD GROUPS

Recipients				
Donors		O (a, b)	A (A, b)	B (B, a)	AB (AB)
O (a, b)	S	S	S	S
A (A, b)	NS	S	NS	S
B (B, a)	NS	NS	S	S
AB (A, B)	NS	NS	NS	S

Key: A—antigen A   a—antibody a
     B—antigen B   b—antibody b
     O, A, B and AB—the four blood groups
     S—transfusion may safely be performed
     NS—transfusions may not be safely performed

TABLE 4. TABLE OF BLOOD TRANSFUSIONS

Agglutination will occur if blood containing antigen A is mixed with blood containing antibody a. Similarly if antigen B comes into contact with antibody b the red blood cells will stick together.

Since blood from persons in Group O contains both antibodies a and b it might be expected that agglutination would occur whenever Group O blood was used for transfusion. This does not occur, however, and persons with Group O blood are, in fact, known as *universal donors* since their blood may be mixed with that of any other group. Table 4 shows which blood groups can be mixed. You will notice that persons with blood of group AB may be called *universal recipients*.

The O, A, B, AB blood grouping is not the only one. Another which is well known is the *Rhesus* group, so called because it occurs in the little Rhesus monkey as well as in human beings. Detailed description of this group is beyond the scope of this book but it should be mentioned that it is of particular importance to pregnant women for should a woman in such a condition be given the incorrect kind of blood the result might be fatal to the developing baby.

Lymph

The term 'lymph' is used to refer to the liquid found in lymphatic vessels (page 114). The term tissue fluid refers to the liquid bathing the tissues. Lymph is not very different in composition from tissue fluid. Excess tissue fluid drains into the lymphatic vessels and is then known as lymph.

Lymph, tissue fluid and blood are fluids working together to take substances to and from the cells of the body.

99

9. Our Transport System—Its Structure and Function

The need for a transport system in the multicellular animals was mentioned on page 92. In the human being there are two parts to the transport system—the *blood system* and the *lymphatic system*.

PLATE 38. William Harvey.

THE BLOOD SYSTEM

Introduction

The blood system in vertebrate animals including Man is a *closed system* formed of a vast number of *blood vessels* through which the blood is pumped by a muscular *heart*. The circulation of the blood through the heart was first described by William Harvey, 1578–1657, whose portrait may be seen in Plate 38.

Vessels which carry blood away from the heart are called *arteries* while those taking blood towards the heart are *veins*. Arteries become smaller and smaller the further they are from the heart while the veins become bigger and bigger as they approach the heart, the smaller ones joining together like the tributaries of a river to form vessels of ever-increasing size. Very small arteries and veins are called *arterioles* and *venules* respectively. The finest arterioles end in even smaller *capillaries* which link them to the venules. Thus the whole system of vessels forms a closed circuit through which the blood is pumped (see Fig. 9.2). Blood never leaves the vessels except when wounding occurs.

Blood vessels penetrate to every part of the body and it is helpful to remember that every organ and tissue is served by both an artery and a vein.

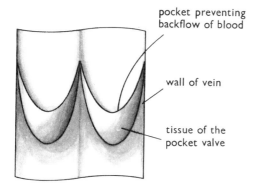

a. A vein opened out to show the pocket valves

Arteries have to withstand a higher blood pressure than do veins and hence it is not surprising to find that they possess thicker walls—relative to the size of their cavity or *lumen*—than veins. Fig. 9.3 and Plate 39 show this difference quite clearly.

The walls of arteries are more elastic than are those of the veins.

Veins have pairs of pocket-like valves at intervals along their length to prevent the back flow of blood (Fig. 9.1).

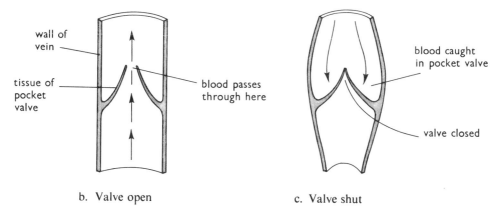

b. Valve open   c. Valve shut

FIG. 9.1. Diagrams to show the action of pocket valves in veins.

FIG. 9.2. A simple diagram to show a closed blood system.

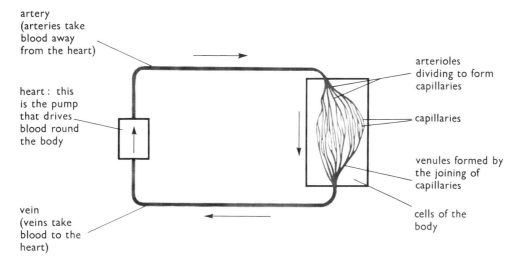

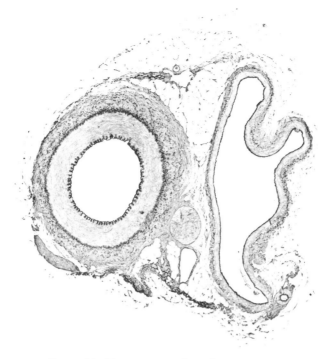

PLATE 39. Transverse section of an artery and vein.

FIG. 9.3. A transverse section through an artery and a vein.

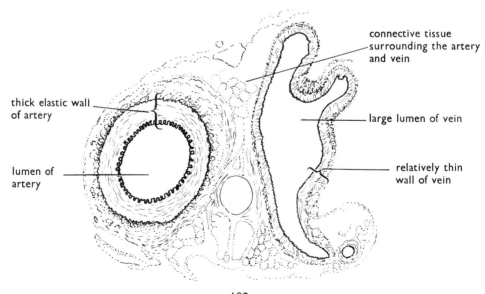

connective tissue
surrounding the artery
and vein

thick elastic wall
of artery

large lumen of vein

lumen of
artery

relatively thin
wall of vein

The Heart

The heart is a very muscular organ about the size of a clenched fist. It lies in the thorax above the diaphragm and between the lungs (Fig. 4.2, page 47). It is covered by a two-layered sack called the *pericardium*. Between the two layers of the sack is a liquid known as *pericardial fluid*. This fluid reduces friction as the heart moves during its beating.

Both the structure and the functioning of the heart are a little difficult to understand but reference to the figures in this chapter will help you to get a clear idea of its action, especially if you first master the terms in the very simple Fig. 9.4. Notice that all the figures, except Fig. 9.7, show the heart in anterior aspect so that the right-hand side of the heart appears on your left-hand side, while the left of the heart is upon your right, as you look at the drawings.

Fig. 9.4 shows the basic parts of the heart and the main vessels entering and leaving it. It is seen to consist of four chambers—the right and left *atria* and the right and left *ventricles*. The auricles *receive* blood and the ventricles pump blood *from* the heart. Notice that the right and left sides of the heart are completely separated from one another by a *median septum*. Each atrium communicates with the ventricle below it by openings guarded by valves which allow the blood to pass in one direction only.

The right atrium receives blood from the body by means of the great veins known as the *superior* and *inferior venae cavae*. The left atrium receives blood from the lungs through *pulmonary veins*. When the atria contract they send blood through the valves into the ventricles. The right ventricle sends blood along the *pulmonary arch* to the lungs, and the left ventricle pumps blood to the whole of the body, apart from the lungs, along the *dorsal aorta*.

There now follows a more detailed description of the heart which should be read in conjunction with a study of Figs. 9.5, 9.6 and 9.7 and Plates 40, 41 and 42, together with a *practical examination of a sheep's heart purchased from a butcher's shop*.

Fig. 9.5 is a diagram showing the internal structure of the heart as seen when it has been

FIG. 9.4. A purely diagrammatic representation of the heart and main vessels.

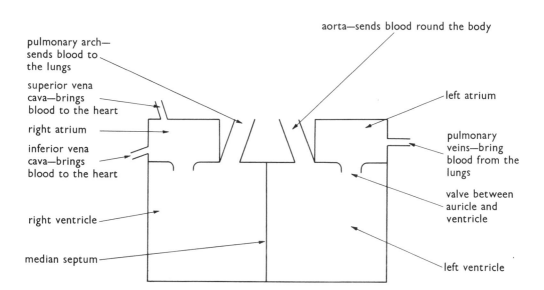

cut vertically. Both atria are fairly thin-walled structures because they do not have to pump the blood far—merely to send it on to the ventricles: their muscles are not therefore nearly as thick as those of the ventricles. Notice that the muscular walls of the left ventricle are thicker than those of the right: this is because while a strong pressure is needed to send blood through the fine capillaries of the lungs, an even greater force is required to propel it through the whole body.

The dorsal aorta arises from the left ventricle: its walls are very strong for it has to withstand the full force of the ventricular contraction, and indeed it is elastic so that it can swell to accommodate all the blood forced into it. When the contraction of the ventricle stops the elastic nature of the aorta's walls helps force the blood on its course. In the human being the dorsal aorta is usually called the *ascending aorta* where it

leaves the heart and the *descending aorta* where it passes downwards from the *arch of the aorta* (Fig. 9.6).

The pulmonary arch arises from the right ventricle and takes blood to the lungs. Like the ascending aorta it is powerful in structure. It divides into two, sending one vessel to each lung. The pulmonary arteries are the only arteries in the whole body carrying deoxygenated blood (see page 156).

Blood from the lungs is returned to the heart through the pulmonary veins which enter the left atrium. This blood is rich in oxygen, having obtained this vital element from the lungs. The pulmonary veins are the only veins in the body to carry oxygenated blood.

Deoxygenated blood returning from the tissues and organs of the body apart from the lungs, enters the right atrium by the venae càvae.

PLATE 40. The heart in vertical section.

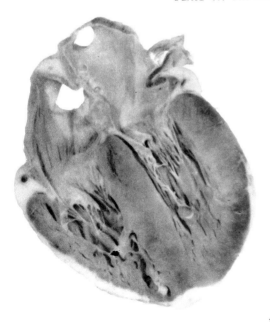
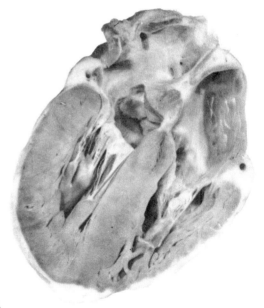

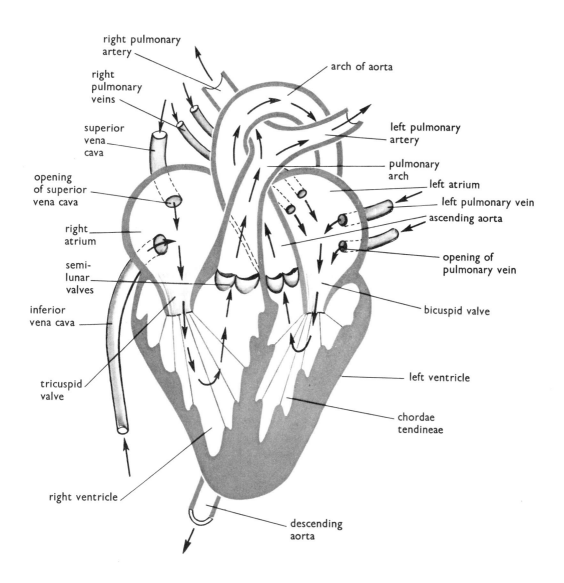

right pulmonary artery

right pulmonary veins

superior vena cava

opening of superior vena cava

right atrium

semi-lunar valves

inferior vena cava

tricuspid valve

right ventricle

arch of aorta

left pulmonary artery

pulmonary arch

left atrium

left pulmonary vein

ascending aorta

opening of pulmonary vein

bicuspid valve

left ventricle

chordae tendineae

descending aorta

FIG. 9.5. Heart. Diagrammatic vertical section. Heavy arrows indicate direction of blood flow.

105

Semi-lunar valves are present, of course, in the veins entering the heart and are also found in the pulmonary arch and in the ascending aorta.

Valves also occur between the atria and the ventricles—that on the left side of the heart being known as the *bicuspid* or *mitral* valve, while that on the right is called the *tricuspid* valve. These valves prevent blood from returning to the atria when the ventricles contract. The valves themselves are prevented from turning inside-out by strong strands known as *chordae tendineae* which are attached firmly at one end to the valve and at the other to the ventricle wall.

To summarise: the passage of blood through the heart is as follows. Blood from the body enters the right atrium through the venae cavae, passes through the tricuspid valve into the right ventricle, is pumped up the pulmonary arteries to the lungs, returns to the heart along the pulmonary veins and enters the left atrium, passes through the bicuspid valve to the left ventricle from where it is forced up the aorta to the body tissues. During its passage through the lungs the blood becomes oxygenated and during its passage round the body it gives up the oxygen to the cells (see page 95 and page 153).

The heart is essentially a pump. Notice that the left side of the heart has only oxygenated blood passing through it while the right side deals only with deoxygenated blood.

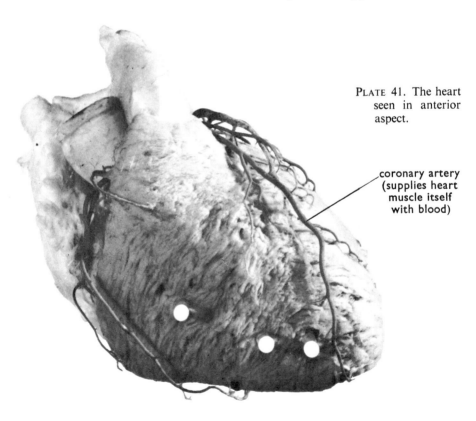

PLATE 41. The heart seen in anterior aspect.

coronary artery (supplies heart muscle itself with blood)

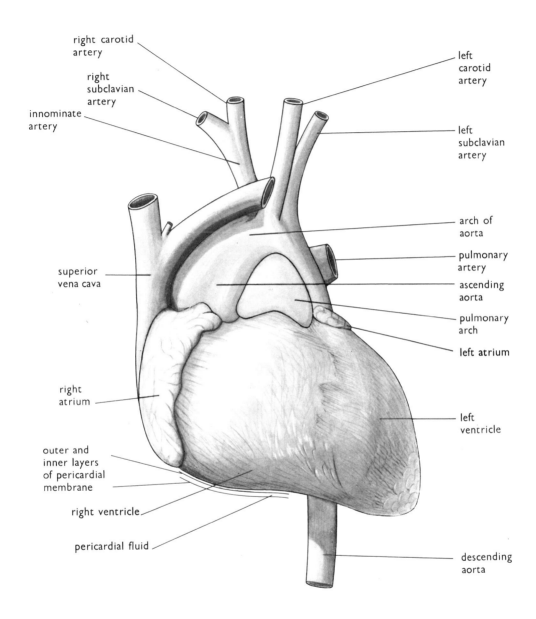

right carotid artery

right subclavian artery

innominate artery

left carotid artery

left subclavian artery

arch of aorta

pulmonary artery

superior vena cava

ascending aorta

pulmonary arch

left atrium

right atrium

left ventricle

outer and inner layers of pericardial membrane

right ventricle

pericardial fluid

descending aorta

FIG. 9.6. The heart seen in anterior aspect. Only a small portion of the pericardium is shown.

107

PLATE 42. The heart
seen in posterior aspect.

As we have seen, it is the contraction of the powerful heart muscles which pumps the blood round the body. Not all the chambers contract simultaneously, however. The two atria contract together and, as they do so, the ventricles relax. The ventricles then contract—both at the same time—whilst the atria relax. The whole heart then rests for nearly half a second after which the process is repeated. This series of events constitutes the *heart beat*. Contraction of the ventricles is known as *ventricular systole* and contraction of the atria as *atrial systole*. The period of relaxation of the whole heart is called *diastole* (Fig. 9.8). The rate of the heart beat varies with age, being about 140 beats per minute at birth and gradually slowing down to about 75 beats per minute in the adult. Vigorous exercise increases the rate of heart beat. In fact the rate may become almost twice its normal speed. The volume of blood passing through the heart also greatly increases during vigorous exercise—sometimes to as much as 30 dm³ a minute instead of the normal 5 or 6 dm³.

The noise made by the heart beat, which may be heard clearly with the aid of an instrument called a *stethoscope*, is due to the closing of the valves. The sound is frequently described as 'lubb-dup', the first sound is long and is caused by the closure of the bicuspid and tricuspid valves while the second is short and sharp and is due to the closing of the semi-lunar valves.

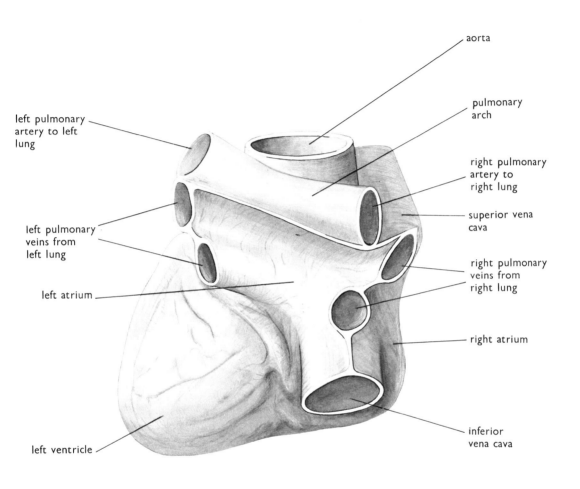

left pulmonary
artery to left
lung

aorta

pulmonary
arch

right pulmonary
artery to
right lung

superior vena
cava

left pulmonary
veins from
left lung

left atrium

right pulmonary
veins from
right lung

right atrium

left ventricle

inferior
vena cava

FIG. 9.7. The heart: posterior aspect seen slightly from above.

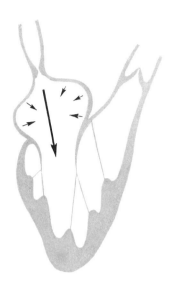

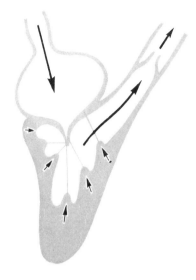

FIG. 9.8. AURICULAR AND
VENTRICULAR SYSTOLE.

Auricular systole. Small arrows indicate contraction of auricle which forces blood into the ventricle as indicated by the large arrow.

Ventricular systole. Small arrows indicate contraction of ventricle. Large arrows show direction of blood flow. Semi-lunar valves open; valves between auricle and ventricle shut.

The Arteries and Veins

Fig. 9.9 shows in a simple way the main blood vessels of the human body. Notice how every part is served by both a vein and an artery, the former taking blood towards the heart and the latter carrying it away from the heart. As Fig. 9.9 is a diagram it has been simplified; for example, arteries are shown on one side and veins on the other. Do not imagine that this is the condition in the real body or that arteries only take blood downwards! More realistic drawings may be seen in Figs. 9.10 and 9.11. Notice in Fig. 9.9 that there is an unusual position with regard to the vessels serving the liver and gut. Blood is taken to the liver by the hepatic artery and from it by the hepatic vein but there is an additional vessel entering the liver—the *hepatic portal vein* bringing blood to it from the gut. A system where a vessel takes blood from one organ to another instead of return-ing the blood direct to the heart is called a *portal system*.

Fig. 9.9 makes clear, if it has not already been noticed, that there are really two circula-tions: one is the *pulmonary circulation* con-sisting of the right side of the heart, the pulmonary arteries and the pulmonary veins, while the other consists of the left side of the heart, the aorta and the vena cava together with all the arteries and veins connecting them. This second circulation is known as the *systemic circulation*. This double circulation is found in all mammals and birds and enables every part of the body of these animals to receive a good supply of oxygen. This in turn enables them to have a high metabolic rate (see page 24) and thus to maintain a high body temperature, irrespective of the temperature of the environment, and thus to lead very active lives.

110

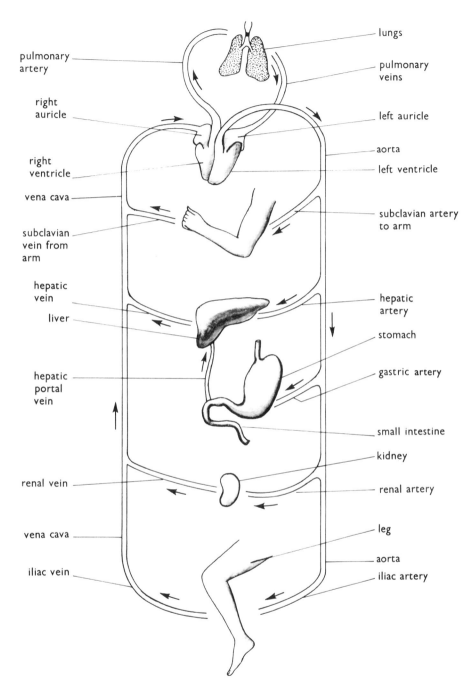

FIG. 9.9. The main blood vessels shown diagrammatically.

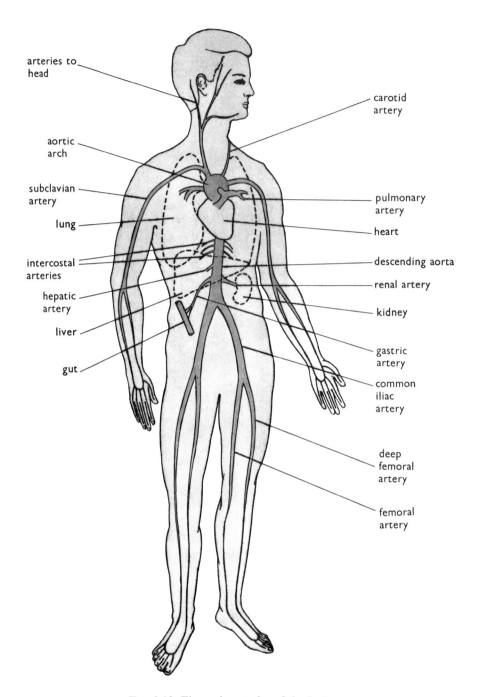

arteries to head

carotid artery

aortic arch

subclavian artery

lung

intercostal arteries

hepatic artery

liver

gut

pulmonary artery

heart

descending aorta

renal artery

kidney

gastric artery

common iliac artery

deep femoral artery

femoral artery

FIG. 9.10. The main arteries of the body.

112

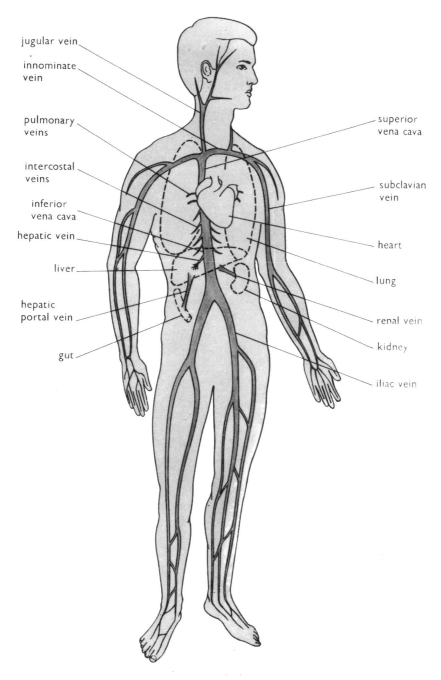

jugular vein

innominate
vein

pulmonary
veins

intercostal
veins

inferior
vena cava

hepatic vein

liver

hepatic
portal vein

gut

superior
vena cava

subclavian
vein

heart

lung

renal vein

kidney

iliac vein

FIG. 9.11. The main veins of the body.

113

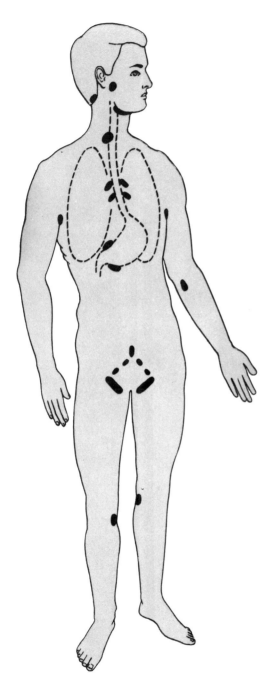

The part played by lymph in the body was mentioned on page 99. Substances needed by cells must be able to diffuse out of capillaries through the tissue fluid and into the cells. Excess tissue fluid drains into lymph vessels. These vessels gradually join together and finally join the venous system by entering the innominate veins. Lymph contains more waste substances and less food than does plasma.

Before joining the veins the lymph passes through structures called *lymph nodes* which act as filters collecting, and rendering harmless, poisonous substances which have gained entry to the body perhaps through a cut or bruise. Fig. 9.12 shows the position of the main lymph nodes in Man.

The lymph vessels, like the veins, are equipped with valves (Fig. 9.13).

In spite of the large number of substances entering and leaving the body the tissue fluid is maintained at a remarkably steady composition and, indeed, if it were not so the cells would die. The maintenance of 'steady state' in a system is called *homeostasis*. The system here is the internal environment and in particular the tissue fluid, the steady composition of which is maintained by the correct and inter-related functioning of various organs and systems such as the kidneys, liver and ductless glands. (See pages 136, 169, 174, and 222.

FIG. 9.13. A lymphatic vessel showing valves.

FIG. 9.12. The positions of the main lymph nodes.

PRACTICAL WORK ON 8 AND 9

1. Examine a prepared slide of human blood. Observe the red and white blood cells. Notice the shape of the nuclei in the white blood cells. Draw.

2. One drop of blood may easily be obtained from the lobe of the ear using a sterilised needle. Place a drop on a microscope slide and observe it at intervals for about twenty minutes. Notice the threads of fibrin which slowly form as the blood clots.

3. Obtain about 250 cm³ of blood from a slaughter house. Nearly fill two test-tubes with some of the blood and add about 3 cm³ of 10% sodium citrate solution to one of the tubes. Then leave the tubes for about half an hour. Notice that the tube with the sodium citrate solution does not clot. This is because the sodium citrate precipitates the calcium which is essential for clot formation.

4. Take two more test-tubes of blood and bubble oxygen through one and coal-gas through the other. (Both tubes must contain a little sodium citrate solution.) Notice that the blood in the tube through which oxygen is passing turns red as oxyhaemoglobin is formed. Coal-gas, which contains carbon monoxide, turns the blood a very bright red colour due to the formation of carboxy-haemoglobin. This substance prevents the erythrocytes from carrying oxygen: death from carbon monoxide poisoning would quickly occur if coal-gas were inhaled.

5. Anaesthetise a frog with ether and stretch one of the hind feet over a hole cut in a piece of cardboard, using cotton tied to the ends of the digits. Observe the web of the foot under the low power of the microscope and note the flow of blood in the capillaries.

6. Obtain a sheep's heart from the butcher and examine it carefully, making drawings to show the position of the great vessels. Open the heart carefully from the ventral side, washing out the blood clots as you proceed. Notice the valves and all the other structures you can find. Make drawings to show the structures.

7. Try to borrow a stethoscope from your doctor and listen to a friend's heart beat.

8. Try to find the pulse of a friend by placing the finger lightly upon the inner surface of the wrist slightly towards the pre-axial border. Time the pulse before and after exercise.

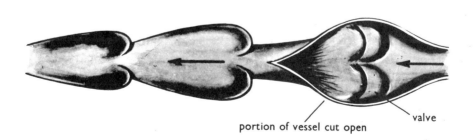

portion of vessel cut open   valve

QUESTIONS ON CHAPTERS 8 AND 9

1. Give a large, well-labelled diagram of the heart, showing clearly the blood vessels that enter and leave it. Briefly describe the path of the two main blood circuits; explain the purpose of each, stating the main organ or regions of the body with which each is concerned. (R.S.A.)

2. Write a concise account of the structure and functions of human blood. Outline the path taken by a red corpuscle moving away from the head to enter the right arm. (W)

3. What changes take place in the blood as it traverses (a) the lungs, (b) a contracting muscle, (c) the liver? Show how these changes are related to one another. (C)

4. Describe the mechanism and importance of (a) antibodies, (b) haemorrhage, (c) blood clotting, (d) blood groups. (S)

5. Trace the path taken by red corpuscles in passing from the leg to the brain. Describe any changes which occur in their composition during the journey. Discuss the factors influencing the return of venous blood from the leg to the heart. (L)

6. Draw a diagram to show the structure of the human heart. Name the major blood vessels supplying the brain with oxygen, and describe how the oxygen reaches the brain cells. (O)

7. Answer both (a) and (b).

(a) Give a fully-labelled diagram to show the path of the Pulmonary blood circuit and that of the General (Body or Systemic) blood circuit. State the purpose of each of these circuits.

(b) Describe how the lymph and blood circuits are connected and explain how the lymph (tissue fluid) helps in transporting substances about the body. (RSA)

8. What do you understand by blood groups? Explain the importance of this knowledge in relation to blood transfusion. How are stocks of blood established and maintained for transfusion purposes? (J)

9. Where are valves found in the circulatory system? Explain their mechanism and importance. (J)

Summary of 6 to 9

1. All mammals possess a *skeleton* which confers certain advantages upon them—*protection* of internal organs, *support* for the body, a *system of levers* upon which muscles can act during movement.

2. The skeleton is composed of *bone* and *cartilage*. Bone is hard and rigid: cartilage is soft and flexible.

3. Bone forms a *reservoir* for *calcium* and *phosphorus* and in its marrow the *red blood cells* are formed.

4. Movement of the skeleton is possible because the bones *articulate at joints*. The joint is lubricated by *synovial fluid* which is contained in a *synovial capsule*. The bones are held together by *ligaments*.

5. There are several kinds of joints—*synovial* (*hinge, gliding, ball-and-socket*); *immovable* and those which *allow slight movement*.

6. Synovial joints allow *angular movements; abduction* and *adduction; gliding movements* and *rotary movements*.

7. The human skeleton comprises the *axial* and the *appendicular* parts, both of which consist of many bones.

8. Movements are brought about by the *contraction* of *muscles*. Energy for this process is derived from glucose. *Rest* is necessary after muscle contraction to allow the removal of *lactic acid*.

9. Muscle is of three types—*striated, smooth* and *cardiac*.

10. Muscles enable us to stand correctly. Bad posture may lead to ill health.

11. A *transport system* is essential in all large animals. In Man this takes the form of a *blood vascular system* and a *lymph system*.

12. The blood system comprises *arteries, veins* and *capillaries* and a muscular *heart*.

13. Blood is a fluid *plasma* containing *red* and *white cells* as well as many substances in solution—*hormones, food substances* and *enzymes* for example.

14. White blood cells *engulf bacteria*; red blood cells *carry oxygen* in combination with *haemoglobin*.

15. Blood plasma contains *fibrinogen* which is precipitated as *fibrin*, in the formation of a *clot*, when wounding happens.

16. Lives may be saved by *blood transfusions*, but care must be taken to check *blood groups*.

10. Food

Introduction

We discovered on page 22 that all living organisms need a supply of food and on page 36 that plant nutrition is entirely different from that of animals. Animals are dependent upon plants for their food as they themselves are not able to manufacture nutritional substances. Plants are able, it will be remembered, to take in inorganic substances—water, carbon dioxide and mineral salts—and produce organic food substances from them. Animals either eat the plants or feed on other animals. Human beings eat both plant and animal matter including the products of animals, such as milk and eggs. In both plants and animals the necessity of taking in materials from the environment is evident.

Food is required for a number of purposes the chief of which are firstly the production of *energy*, secondly the manufacture of new body material, i.e. for *growth*, and thirdly for the repair of worn out cells. Certain substances known as *vitamins* are needed to prevent disease.

Food Substances

Although there is an infinite number of what are commonly called 'foods'—cake, bread, jam, butter, milk, eggs, meat, apples, etc.—there are only six basic food substances from which all the 'foods' are made. These six substances are:

1. Carbohydrates 4. Mineral Salts
2. Fats 5. Vitamins
3. Proteins 6. Water

We will consider each in turn.

Carbohydrates. These chemical substances are composed of the three elements: carbon, hydrogen and oxygen. The last two elements are always present in the same proportions as in water. In the carbohydrates there are six, eleven or many carbon atoms joined together in one molecule. A single molecule of carbohydrate may therefore contain many atoms for each carbon atom may be linked to two hydrogen and one oxygen atom. A simple carbohydrate in which only six carbon atoms are present is the simple sugar *glucose* whose formula is $C_6 H_{12} O_6$, the atoms being linked together thus:

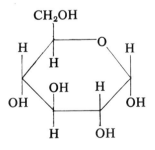

H—C=O
glucose

118

There are many carbohydrates with only six carbon atoms and they are known as *simple sugars, monosaccharides* or *hexoses*. Glucose is the most important; another is *fructose*—common in fruits.

The group of carbohydrates with eleven carbon atoms have the general formula $C_{12}H_{22}O_{11}$ and are known as *disaccharides*. Well-known disaccharides are *lactose* or *milk sugar*, *maltose* or *malt sugar* and *sucrose* or *cane sugar*. This last is the common table sugar used for sweetening tea, coffee, etc.

A third group of carbohydrates are the *polysaccharides*. Their general formula is $(C_6H_{10}O_5)_n$, n being often very large—perhaps as high as 200. This means that polysaccharide molecules are very large. Two important polysaccharides are *plant starch*—found in most plants—and *animal starch* or *glycogen* as it is usually called, which occurs in the liver and muscles.

Both monosaccharides and disaccharides are usually soluble in water although monosaccharides are the only sugars which can be absorbed into the blood (page 141). Polysaccharides are insoluble in water.

Disaccharides and polysaccharides can be changed into simple sugars by a process known as *hydrolysis*. A little acid must be present to assist the reaction. For example, if a few drops of dilute hydrochloric acid are added to a test-tube containing sucrose solution and the mixture is then warmed, the two simple sugars glucose and fructose are formed.

$$C_{12}H_{22}O_{11} + H_2O = C_6H_{12}O_6 + C_6H_{12}O_6$$
cane sugar water glucose   fructose

In other words hydrolysis consists of the breaking down of complex molecules to simple ones by the addition of water. Another example of hydrolysis is changing starch (a polysaccharide) to glucose (a simple sugar).

$$(C_6H_{10}O_5)_n + n\ H_2O = n\ C_6H_{12}O_6$$
starch   water   glucose

The importance of hydrolysis will become clear when we study digestion in Chapter 12, for it is the means of breaking down the complex carbohydrates we eat to simple substances which can be absorbed into the blood.

Carbohydrates form a very important part of our diet for they are energy-providing substances. It is the basic substance glucose —to which all carbohydrates taken into the body are broken down—which combines with oxygen to release energy (see page 151).

Common foods containing carbohydrates are bread, flour, potatoes (starch) and fruit (simple sugars). Carbohydrate is stored in the body as glycogen by the liver and muscles.

Table 6, page 124, shows some of the common sources of carbohydrate and other foods.

Fats. These organic substances contain the same elements as carbohydrates but the proportion of oxygen in them is smaller. Compare, for example, the proportion of hydrogen to oxygen in the carbohydrate glucose, $C_6H_{12}O_6$, and the fat *tristearin*, $C_{57}H_{110}O_6$. Fats are insoluble in water. Fats which are liquid at about $15°$ C are called *oils*. These will solidify at colder temperatures. Fats and oils are important storage substances in human beings and form a useful reserve of potential energy, for they can be changed into carbohydrates when needed. Fat is stored not only under the skin but also around some of the internal organs such as the kidneys.

Common foods with a high proportion of fat are lard, butter, margarine, bacon and cheese. Milk contains about 4% fat.

119

Proteins. Like fats and carbohydrates proteins consist of carbon, hydrogen and oxygen but in addition they also contain the element nitrogen. Frequently they contain phosphorus or sulphur or iron as well. Protein molecules are very large and may be made up of as many as 40,000 atoms! The important thing to remember is that they are made up from simpler substances called *amino-acids*. The simplest amino-acid is *glycine* which has the formula CH_2NH_2COOH. The —COOH group of atoms is acidic and the —NH_2 group basic so that amino-acids have both acidic and basic properties.

When proteins are taken into the body they are broken down to amino-acids which are later recombined to form different proteins.

Proteins from animal sources are often called *first-class proteins* and those from plants *second-class proteins*. Examples of first-class protein sources are cheese, beef and fish while second-class proteins are oatmeal, flour and cabbage.

Proteins are the basic substances of which protoplasm is made (see also page 26) and hence it is of great importance to see that they are included in the diet. They are used not only for the manufacture of new living material but for the repair of worn-out tissues as well. It has been estimated that all the cells of which a man is made are replaced every seven years. This replacement is a continuous process, of course, going on all the time. It becomes more important as age increases. In the growing child most of the protein will be used for growth. Proteins can also be oxidised to provide energy.

Mineral Salts. We need a considerable number of elements in our bodies besides those already mentioned in connection with fats, carbohydrates and proteins. Some of these are required in minute quantities only

and are hence known as *trace elements*. Others are needed in considerable quantities and these—in order of the amount needed, starting with the greatest—are *calcium, phosphorus, potassium, sulphur, chlorine, sodium, magnesium* and *iron*. The trace elements are chiefly *fluorine, iodine, zinc, copper, cobalt* and *manganese*. Of these fluorine is necessary for the formation of the enamel of the teeth, iodine for the manufacture of the hormone *thyroxin* (page 224) and zinc for the production of *insulin* (page 227).

Returning now to the main mineral elements, we will take each jn turn. For details of foods containing the elements see Table 6.

Calcium is essential for proper bone formation as bone is largely made of calcium phosphate (see also page 62). Lack of calcium in the diet, especially of very young children, leads to malformed bones. This disease which was common in the last century is known as *rickets*. Calcium is also necessary for the formation of dentine in the teeth and as has been already mentioned for clotting of the blood. Cheese is rich in calcium.

Phosphorus is needed, of course, for bone formation. It is also essential for cell division, being an important element in the proteins of the nucleus.

Potassium is required for both blood and muscle cells.

It has already been mentioned that sulphur is necessary for protein formation.

Both sodium and chlorine are essential elements for body fluids such as blood. In addition sodium is required for the formation of sodium bicarbonate used to transport carbon dioxide to the lungs (see page 95). Chlorine is needed for the manufacture of the hydrochloric acid found in the stomach.

Iron is an element essential for the formation of *haemoglobin*. Lack of iron results in

Saturday
2nd June
Edinburgh

a condition known as *anaemia* which is characterised by paleness of appearance and general tiredness.

Vitamins. It has been known for many years that a lack of certain foods leads to serious diseases. There was published, for example, as early as 1757, a book entitled *A Treatise on Scurvy* which had been written by a captain in the Royal Navy. In this book he described experiments with the diet provided on board ship. He showed that the disease known as *scurvy* could be prevented by including oranges and lemons in the diet. Captain Cook (Plate 43) was another seaman who used to give his crew lemons to prevent their getting scurvy.

Rickets is a disease which also became associated in people's minds with food, for it was observed that in the slums of the large industrial towns the disease was very common during the latter part of the nineteenth century. It was known that the disease was rare amongst Eskimoes and this it was suggested could possibly be accounted for by the fact that Eskimoes ate large quantities of fish-liver oils. Subsequent experiment showed that this was indeed the case.

These observations on scurvy, rickets and other diseases suggested that there were other essential food substances besides fats, proteins and carbohydrates but it was not until 1906 that it was scientifically proved by experimental methods. Gowland Hopkins took two groups of rats and fed one group on a diet of pure fat, protein and carbohydrate. The second group had the same pure diet except that a small quantity of milk was added to it. Hopkins observed that the first group of rats soon became ill and lost weight. The second group grew normally. Then Hopkins interchanged the diets and the first group of rats quickly recovered their condition but the second group began to lose weight and to become very ill. Something was present in the milk which was essential for the normal healthy functioning of the animal body. Hopkins's work was soon confirmed by other workers who discovered that there was more than one essential substance. To these substances the name *vitamin* was given. Their discovery has brought great benefit to mankind, for by their use disease can be prevented and a better understanding of the essentials of a good diet has been obtained. Diseases resulting from lack of a particular vitamin are called *deficiency diseases*.

Vitamins are complex organic compounds some of which are water-soluble and others fat-soluble.

Table 5 shows the main vitamins, their deficiency effects and the principal food sources from which they may be obtained.

Water. Of all the substances taken into the body water must be considered the most important. We have already seen that it forms about 70% of the total body weight and that it forms the basis of blood and other body fluids. It is in a watery medium that the chemical processes of the body take place and it is water which removes waste materials.

PLATE 43. Captain Cook.

121

By its evaporation from the skin water cools the body thereby helping us to maintain a constant body temperature irrespective of the temperature of the air around us.

Water is taken into the body not only in liquid form but in solid foods such as vegetables and fruit. It is lost from the body through the lungs and as sweat as well as in urine.

Milk

Milk is such an important food that it warrants a small section on its own. It is produced in all mammals and these animals do in fact take their name from the mammary glands which produce the milk in the female of the species. The milk is used, of course, to feed the new-born young for a longer or shorter period according to the animal concerned. Because it is used for this purpose it needs to contain all the food substances required for growth. For this reason milk is sometimes spoken of as the *ideal food*.

Milk contains both protein and fat as well as the carbohydrate lactose or milk sugar. It is rich in calcium and potassium—elements essential for the formation of bone, teeth and blood. Cow's milk contains a higher percentage of all these substances, with the exception of lactose, than does human milk. The percentage of lactose is about 2% higher in human milk. Vitamins A, B and D are present in milk but it is lacking in vitamin E, and also in iron.

The *mammary glands* consist of numerous *secretory lobules* each of which opens into a *lactiferous duct* which in turn opens into *lactiferous sinuses* which open at the *nipple*— through which the milk is sucked by the baby. The lobules are enormously enlarged at the time they are producing milk.

Food Energy Values (Calorific Values)

It will have already become clear that different foods have different values. One important aspect of food is the amount of energy which it gives us: we have seen that fats and carbohydrates supply us with energy. Not all foods contain the same amount of energy for us to use: some are better than others. The unit of energy used for measuring the energy value of a food is the joule.

The energy given out by one gram of food is calculated by use of a special instrument called a *bomb calorimeter*. It consists, in principle, of a closed metal container (immersed in water), in which a known quantity of the food under consideration is rapidly fired by an electric element. As the food burns it gives out heat which causes the temperature of the surrounding water to rise. The rise in temperature is measured and the amount of heat given out by one gram of food is calculated.

It has been found that on the average the food energy values for fats, carbohydrates and proteins are 39, 17 and 17 kilojoules respectively. Normally proteins are not used greatly as a source of energy, being needed for growth and repair of tissues, but under starvation conditions, once the reserves of fat and glycogen have been exhausted, proteins of the actual flesh may be used. This is why people who have been starved for any length of time appear emaciated.

Foods of high energy value are naturally those made from fats or containing a high proportion of fat. Cooking fat, butter, bacon and cheese all have high energy values. The carbohydrate sucrose is also very valuable. Glucose, which also has a high energy value, can be absorbed quickly into the blood stream as it needs no digestion. For this reason it is given to invalids and may be taken by athletes shortly before a race.

Vitamin	Deficiency Effects	Source
A—fat soluble	Poor skin and mucous membranes. Night and day blindness.	Green vegetables, carrots, milk, butter, fish liver-oils.
B complex B1—thiamine B2—riboflavin	'Beri-beri'—nervous upsets, muscular weakness, heart failure. Skin and digestive disorders; anaemia.	Yeast, whole-meal bread, peas and beans. Yeast, lean meat, milk, liver, eggs, green vegetables.
C—Ascorbic acid, water soluble	Scurvy—internal bleeding; gums swell and bleed.	Oranges, lemons, green vegetables.
D—fat soluble	Rickets in children—bones do not develop correctly.	Fish liver-oils, butter and eggs. Formed by action of sunlight on skin.
E—fat soluble	Embryos fail to develop fully in female; loss of fertility in male.	Wheat germ oil, eggs, liver, green vegetables.

TABLE 5. THE MAIN VITAMINS, SOURCES OF VITAMINS AND DEFICIENCY DISEASES.

Food Substance	Formula or Symbol	Use	Source
Carbohydrates Glucose	$C_6H_{12}O_6$	Provides energy	Grapes, animal tissues, carrots
Fructose	$C_6H_{12}O_6$	Provides energy	Honey, fruits
Lactose	$C_{12}H_{22}O_{11}$	Provides energy	Milk, cheese
Maltose	$C_{12}H_{22}O_{11}$	Provides energy	Malt; is a breakdown product of starch
Sucrose	$C_{12}H_{22}O_{11}$	Provides energy	Sugar cane, sugar beet
Starch	$(C_6H_{10}O_5)n$	Provides energy	Potatoes, wheat, rice
Glycogen	$(C_6H_{10}O_5)n$	Provides energy	Liver, lean meat
Fats	—	Provide energy, can be stored in the body under skin, etc.	Butter, lard, cheese, suet, fish oil, nuts, olives
Proteins	—	Body-building food, used in manufacture of protoplasm	Lean meat, poultry, fish, milk, eggs, cheese, cabbage, peas, wheat and potatoes

TABLE 6. A SUMMARY OF FOOD SUBSTANCES, THEIR USE AND SOURCE.

Food Substance	Formula or Symbol	Use	Source
Mineral Salts Calcium	Ca	Bone formation, teeth formation, blood clotting	Cheese, milk, bread, herring, cabbage
Phosphorus	P	Bone formation, cell division	Most foods containing proteins
Potassium	K	Formation of new protoplasm especially blood and muscle cells	Meat and most vegetables
Sulphur	S	Protein formation	Any diet containing sufficient proteins will also contain sufficient sulphur
Chlorine	Cl	Used in body fluids and in the manufacture of hydrochloric acid	Common salt
Sodium	Na	Used in body fluids and in transport of carbon dioxide	Common salt
Magnesium	Mg	Formation of bones and teeth	Most foods will contain some magnesium

TABLE 6. A SUMMARY OF FOOD SUBSTANCES, THEIR USE AND SOURCE (*contd.*)

Food Substance	Formula or Symbol	Use	Source
Iron	Fe	Formation of haemoglobin	Liver, kidney, eggs, watercress
Fluorine	Fl	Formation of enamel	A trace element in natural water. Some Water Boards add fluorine to the water
Iodine	I	Production of thyroxin	Seaweeds and other plants
Zinc	Zn	Production of insulin	As trace element from plants
Copper	Cu	Formation of haemoglobin	As trace element from plants
Cobalt	Co	Formation of haemoglobin	As trace element from plants
Water	H_2O	Dissolving foods; carrying substances in blood; metabolic processes occur in solution; removing waste; formation of protoplasm, etc.	Normally from rain—see page 349 for work done by Water Boards
Vitamins—see Table 5			

TABLE 6. A SUMMARY OF FOOD SUBSTANCES, THEIR USE AND SOURCE (*contd.*)

Metabolic Rate

The *metabolic rate* is used to express the rate at which the tissues 'burn' sugar and oxygen. It varies with activity and occupation. Metabolic rate is lowest, of course, when the body is at rest—when we are asleep for example and only our heart and breathing mechanisms are at work, i.e. those cells which are working all the time to keep us alive. This low rate is known as the Basal Metabolic Rate or B.M.R. The B.M.R. of an individual is measured when he is in bed, preferably asleep, inactive and fasting. The B.M.R. for a normal person weighing about 65 kg is usually found to be between 6000 and 8500 kilo-joules per 24 hours. This figure varies with age, sex and climate. This is partly because some energy is lost from the body as heat and this figure will obviously vary according to size—because of different surface areas from which the heat is lost—sex (for the same reason) and environmental temperature: there will be less heat lost in some parts of the world than in others.

If less food is taken in than is demanded by a person's B.M.R., starvation will commence. As soon as a resting person starts to move or work more energy is used and hence more food is required. Any food taken in above that required to satisfy the B.M.R. is used to supply energy for work in its various forms. Heavy manual work demands the most energy and it is perhaps disappointing to the scholar to learn that an increase in mental work hardly affects the metabolic rate!

Table 7 gives some idea of the amount of energy required by different people at different ages.

A Balanced Diet is Necessary

It will have become evident that different foods serve different purposes—carbohy-drates and fat give energy; proteins are necessary for body-building; vitamins prevent the development of deficiency diseases; mineral salts take part in the formation of many vital substances; water is required for a wide variety of purposes. Since no one food contains all the necessary materials it is obvious that a varied diet is more likely to be of value than one consisting of one substance only. A diet containing too much carbohydrate is likely to be deficient in proteins for muscle building and a child fed on such a diet will tend to be fat rather than muscular; lack of fruit and vegetables may lead to deficiency diseases, and so on.

Thus we see that the individual's daily food requirements should be obtained by eating well-balanced meals which contain the essential *protective* and *body-building* sub-stances as well as those which give *energy*.

One other aspect of our food must be mentioned. Much of the food taken into the alimentary canal is not absorbed and passes out of the body in the *faeces*. This material is essential to good health, although it is removed, because it supplies us with *roughage*. Roughage is composed mainly of the cellulose cell walls from the plant material we ingest. Its value is that it makes bulk in the intestine and stimulates *peristalsis* (see page 141), so preventing constipation. By eating plenty of vegetables, fruit and brown bread we obtain sufficient roughage.

It should be noted that proteins and fats are more expensive than carbohydrates and this should be remembered when planning a family diet. It makes a problem for those who have to live on a low income, especially at a time when the mother is nursing or pregnant, as she may develop the child at the expense of her own tissues. More may be read about this aspect of nutrition in a later chapter (page 368).

Person	Occupation	Daily Food Energy Requirements in Kilojoules
New-born baby	Sleeping, wriggling	1900
Person in bed	Resting	7600
Girl age 8 years	Very active in play and other physical activities	8000
Boy age 8 years		8400
Woman	Light work, e.g. factory	8800
Man	Light work, e.g. secretary	10 500
Pregnant woman	Food needed for foetus	10 500
Girl age 15 years	Active games, e.g. tennis	11 800
Woman during lactation period	Requirement for milk production	12 600
Man	Moderate work, e.g. carpenter	14 300
Boy age 15 years	Active in games, etc.	14 700
Man	Heavy work, e.g. labouring	18 900

The figures are approximate, of course, and vary widely according to the exact nature of the work and according to the individual.

TABLE 7. DAILY ENERGY REQUIREMENTS

Food Tests

The different carbohydrates, the fats and the proteins may be detected in foods by chemical means. These tests are interesting to perform and are described in the section on practical work at the end of this chapter.

PRACTICAL WORK ON 10

FOOD TESTS

1. *Glucose.* Dissolve a little glucose in a test-tube one-third full of water. Add Fehling's solution A until the blue colour of copper sulphate is obtained. Then add Fehling's solution B until a clear deep blue colour forms. Boil the mixture. A brick-red precipitate is obtained. Repeat the test with a small piece of onion crushed in water and again using carrot.

2. *Sucrose.* Dissolve a little cane sugar (normal table sugar) in water. Divide into two equal parts in two test-tubes. Apply Fehling's Test to one of the portions. No precipitate is formed. Add a few drops of dilute hydrochloric acid to the second portion. Boil for one minute and leave to stand for ten minutes. Perform Fehling's Test. A red precipitate is obtained this time. This is because glucose is now present, having been formed by hydrolysis when the sucrose was boiled with the acid.

3. *Lactose.* Perform experiment as described under 2. Write down your observations.

4. *Starch.* Add a few drops of iodine solution to some starch powder in a test-tube. A deep blue-black colour is obtained. Try this test on potatoes, bread and flour.

5. *Glycogen* (animal starch). Add a few drops of iodine solution to some glycogen.

A red colour is obtained. Repeat this test using fresh liver.

6. *Cellulose.* Add a few drops of Schultze's solution to a thin section of a dead-nettle stem. Mount the sections on a microscope slide and look at them under the medium power of the instrument. Notice some areas of the sections have turned purple indicating the presence of cellulose. Then add some Schultze's solution to a little cotton wool. Cotton wool consists of pure cellulose: a purple colour will be obtained.

7. *Proteins.* (a) Xanthroproteic Test. Add a little concentrated nitric acid to a small amount of milk in a test-tube and boil the mixture. Cool the mixture well and carefully add *one or two drops* only of strong ammonia solution by allowing the drops to slide down the side of the test-tube while it is held in a sloping position. An orange ring is formed where the ammonia meets the milk/acid mixture. (b) Millon's Test. Add a few drops of Millon's reagent to a little milk in a test-tube and warm the mixture. A red precipitate is obtained.

8. *Fats.* Press a piece of cheese or smear a little butter on a piece of paper and hold the paper up to the light. A translucent mark appears. Add a few drops of ether and the mark almost disappears: ether dissolves fats.

9. *Water.* Add a drop of water to some dry white copper sulphate: the copper sulphate turns blue.

Add a drop of water to dry blue cobalt chloride paper: the paper turns pink.

10. Test different foods such as bread, milk, egg, potato, cheese, etc. for each of the main food substances.

N.B. When performing all the experiments just described make careful note of both what you do and what you observe.

129

11. Enzymes and Accessory Glands

Introduction

Before undertaking a full study of the structure and functions of the digestive system, it is necessary to consider some of the glands with which it is associated and without a knowledge of which a complete understanding of the work of the alimentary canal is impossible. It is also necessary to know something about the substances which these glands produce.

The glands are frequently called *accessory glands* and they are the *salivary glands*, the *liver* and *gall bladder* and the *pancreas*. The *spleen* is not an accessory gland of the digestive system, strictly speaking, but it is usual to consider it in conjunction with those glands owing to its close proximity to the stomach and pancreas in the body.

The liver and gall bladder produce *bile*, the salivary glands manufacture *saliva* and the pancreas secretes *pancreatic juice*.

Full descriptions of these organs, and of the spleen, are given later.

It is worthwhile to pause here to note the difference between *secretion* and *excretion*— two terms which are frequently confused with one another. Both terms refer to substances produced by living cells, but whereas secretion refers to the production of useful substances, excretion describes the production of waste or harmful chemicals.

Thus, for example, the kidney cells *excrete* the waste substance *urea* but the salivary glands *secrete saliva*—a useful substance.

Enzymes and Digestion

Both the saliva and the pancreatic juice contain important chemicals known as *enzymes*. These substances are also produced by the cells forming the lining to the walls of the stomach and intestine. Enzymes are very important for they bring about the breaking down of complex carbohydrates, fats and proteins to simple substances which are readily absorbed by the intestine. They can be thought of as organic catalysts, i.e. they speed up the process of breakdown of the food substances, making them soluble and diffusible.

Enzymes possess the following characteristics:

1. Enzymes are produced by living cells.

2. They are specific in their action, one enzyme acting on one of the main food substances only.

3. As the enzyme molecule is itself only temporarily changed during its action and can be used repeatedly, large quantities of enzyme are not necessary.

4. Enzymes work within only a narrow range of acidity or alkalinity: great variation in acidity stops the enzyme action.

5. Enzymes are quickly destroyed by heat and work only within a narrow range of temperature.

6. Chemically the basis of every enzyme is a protein: this is possibly why their action is destroyed by heat, for heat coagulates proteins.

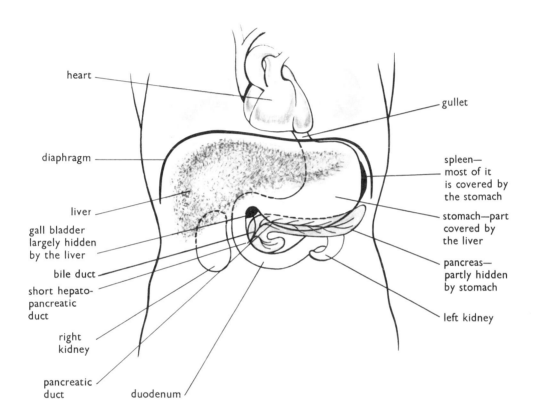

heart

gullet

diaphragm

spleen—
most of it
is covered by
the stomach

liver

stomach—part
covered by
the liver

gall bladder
largely hidden
by the liver

pancreas—
partly hidden
by stomach

bile duct

short hepato-
pancreatic
duct

left kidney

right
kidney

pancreatic
duct

duodenum

FIG. 11.1. THE ACCESSORY GLANDS OF THE DIGESTIVE SYSTEM.

Note: Where part of an organ is covered by another its hidden portion is indicated by dotted lines. The liver, gall bladder and pancreas are the accessory glands of the digestive system. The spleen is more closely associated with the blood system in its function but is shown here because of its proximity to the stomach. The heart and kidneys are shown as 'land-marks'.

131

Experiments demonstrating the action and properties of enzymes

Preparation. Make a paste up from a little starch powder and cold water. Pour the paste into a beaker of boiling water. Boil for one minute. Cool the solution and make it up to about 500 cm³. About 2 gm of starch powder is required to make this quantity of solution. Also prepare a saliva solution by rinsing the mouth out with about 50 cm³ of cold water.

To show the hydrolysis of starch by ptyalin. (*Ptyalin* is an enzyme contained in saliva and maltose. Ptyalin is also called salivary amylase.)

Add a few cm³ of the starch solution to a test-tube together with a small quantity of the saliva solution. After about 10 minutes add one drop of iodine solution to the test-tube. A blue-black colour is *not* obtained, showing that the starch has been changed to another substance by the ptyalin. When no saliva is used in a control experiment, a blue-black colour, indicating presence of starch, is obtained.

To show the effect of acid on the action of ptyalin. Repeat previous experiment but add a drop or two of dilute hydrochloric acid to the test-tube before adding the saliva solution. When a drop of iodine is added after about 10 minutes, the blue-black colour is obtained, indicating that the action of ptyalin was stopped by the acid.

To show the action of heat on enzymes. Repeat first experiment yet again but boil the saliva solution before adding it to the starch solution. Test with a drop of iodine solution after 10 minutes. A blue-black colour is obtained, indicating that heat destroyed the ptyalin.

To ascertain the temperature at which ptyalin works fastest. (Enzymes work best at a certain temperature although they act to some extent over quite a range of temperatures. The temperature at which they work best is called the *optimum temperature*. Note that this is not the same as the *maximum* temperature at which they will act. At what temperature would you expect enzymes to work best?)

Take six test-tubes and add 1 cm³ of saliva solution to each. Then to each add about 10 cm³ of the starch solution. Place each tube in a separate water-bath kept at the (constant) temperatures of 15° C, 25° C, 35° C, 45° C, 65° C and 100° C.

On a white tile place a large number of single drops of iodine solution in rows. Using a clean glass rod *each time*, place a drop of the solution from each test-tube on a drop of the iodine solution on the white tile at intervals of 1 min., 2 min., 4 min., 8 min., 16 min. and 32 min. From the results you will be able to see at which temperature the enzyme acts most quickly. Fig. 11.2 indicates the method employed in this experiment.

To show the action of pepsin on egg-white. (Pepsin is an enzyme acting on proteins.)

Prepare a suspension of egg-white particles by adding the egg-white to distilled water and bringing it quickly to the boil while stirring vigorously. Cool the suspension and then add equal quantities of it to each of five test-tubes. Label the tubes 1–5. Add to tube 1 a little pepsin; to tube 2 a little dilute hydrochloric acid; to tube 3 pepsin and hydrochloric acid; to tube 4 some sodium bicarbonate; and to tube 5 some *boiled* pepsin solution and hydrochloric acid.

Place all the tubes in a beaker of water whose temperature is kept steady at about 35° C for 30 minutes. After this time the liquid in tube 3 is found to be clear. Try to explain these results yourself. Write down your conclusions.

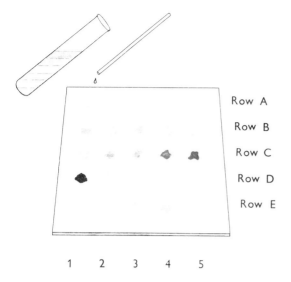

Row A
Row B
Row C
Row D
Row E

1   2   3   4   5

The Salivary Glands

Fig. 11.3 shows the position of the salivary glands on one side of the head. There are three glands on each side, making three pairs in all. The *parotid glands* open into the mouth on the upper side, near the second molar tooth. The *sublingual glands* secrete their products by twelve small ducts which open on a fold of tissue at the side of the tongue. Finally there are the *submandibular glands* which have single openings each side under the front of the tongue.

The saliva is a watery secretion containing a slippery substance called *mucus*, salts and, as we have seen, the enzyme ptyalin.

FIG. 11.2. The use of iodine in the enzyme experiment. When the first drop of enzyme-starch solution is placed on the first 'blob' of iodine the latter changes to a blue-black colour. Successive drops of enzyme-starch solution give a less dark colour until finally there is no change, showing that all the starch has been digested.

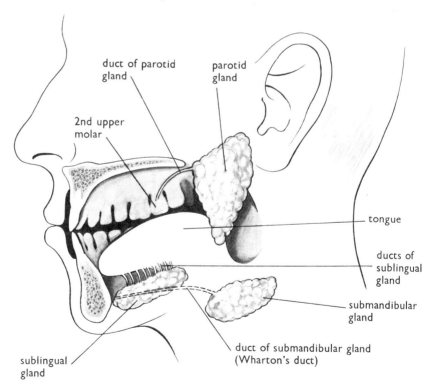

FIG. 11.3.
THE SALIVARY
GLANDS.

The Liver and Gall Bladder

These structures are shown in Figs. 11.1 and 11.4 as well as in Plate 44. The liver lies below the diaphragm, to the right of, and overlapping, the stomach. It is held in place by several ligaments of which the *falciform ligament* is the largest. The liver is the largest organ in the body, weighing about 1·4 kilograms, consisting of *right* and *left lobes*. There are also smaller *quadrate* and *caudate* lobes. The liver is a dark red colour.

The gall bladder is a pear-shaped structure attached to the underside of the liver and its function is to store a greenish-coloured liquid called *bile*. At appropriate times the gall bladder discharges the bile down the bile duct.

In the liver arise a number of ducts called *bile ducts* which join together to form a large duct which receives a branch from the gall bladder known as the *cystic duct*. The main bile duct thus formed from the junction of the cystic duct with the ducts from the liver

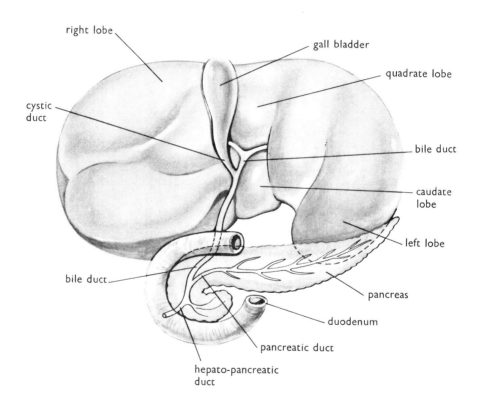

FIG. 11.4 The relationship between the liver, the gall bladder, the pancreas and the duodenum. The liver has been turned back so that it is viewed from beneath.

opens into part of the intestine called the *duodenum*. Just before it joins the duodenum the bile duct merges with the *pancreatic duct* to form a short *hepato-pancreatic duct* (Figs. 11.1 and 11.4).

The functions of the liver are numerous and include the following:

1. *The storage of glycogen.* Glycogen is formed from glucose in the liver by the action of specific enzymes when there is an excess of glucose in the blood. When more glucose is required in the blood the glycogen is turned back to glucose and transported away from the liver in the blood stream. These reactions are controlled by the hormone insulin (page 227).

2. Vitamins A, B and D are stored in the liver.

3. Iron molecules released during the breakdown of the haemoglobin of red blood

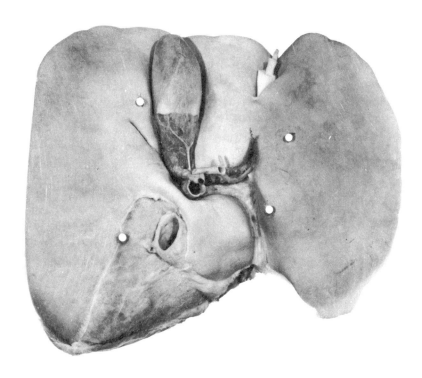

PLATE 44. The liver and gall bladder.

135

cells can be stored in the liver for use in making new haemoglobin when required.

4. Production of bile. This is produced by the liver and stored in the gall bladder. It consists of *bile salts* and *bile pigments*. The use of the salts will be considered later: the pigments—*bilirubin* and *biliverdin*—are waste products formed from the remains of red blood cells which have been destroyed in the spleen.

5. The production of *heparin* (see also page 96).

6. The production of *antitoxins* (see also page 300).

7. *Deamination*. Excess amino-acids cannot be stored as such in the liver. The liver may convert part of the excess to fats and carbohydrates but much of it is *deaminated*.

During deamination the amino (NH_2) group is removed from the amino-acids with the formation of ammonia. Enzymes of the liver bring about a reaction between the poisonous ammonia and the carbon dioxide leading to the formation of the less toxic substance urea. The urea is taken in the blood to the kidneys for excretion. The liver is thus to be viewed as a very important organ with a major role in homeostasis. (See page 114.)

The Pancreas

The pancreas is shown in Figs. 11.1 and 11.4. It lies in the loop of the part of the intestine called the duodenum and is behind the stomach. The functions of the pancreas are to secrete the *pancreatic juice* into the duodenum down the pancreatic duct and to secrete the hormone *insulin* directly into the blood stream. The insulin, the function of which has just been described under the account of the liver is produced by glands within the pancreas known as *Islets of Langerhans*.

The pancreatic juice contains enzymes, water and alkaline salts. Details of the enzymes—*lipase* and *amylase*—will be given in the next chapter where we shall also meet with a substance (trypsinogen) which forms an enzyme when it reaches the intestine.

The Spleen

The spleen, as has been mentioned, lies close to the stomach on the left side of the abdominal cavity. In adults it is about 12 cm. long and is red in colour. Its functions are to destroy used-up erythrocytes and to manufacture some of the white blood cells. It acts as a reservoir for both types of corpuscle. In the foetus within the mother it produces red blood cells.

PRACTICAL WORK ON 11

Perform the experiments described in this chapter.

136

12. Digesting and Utilising our Food

Introduction

We have already learnt quite a lot about the subject of this chapter: here we shall make use of the knowledge acquired so far and draw together numerous facts into a study of the digestive process as a whole.

Digestion is the process whereby food substances—which are frequently insoluble and non-diffusible—are changed into simpler compounds which can pass through the gut wall into the blood. *Mechanical digestion* is the breakdown of large pieces of food into smaller pieces by the action of the teeth and the stomach. A given volume of food has a smaller surface area than the same volume broken into a number of small pieces: breaking the food up by mechanical action gives a larger surface area for enzymes to act on. *Chemical digestion* is the breakdown of large, frequently insoluble molecules of food substances into smaller molecules by the process we have described on page 119—*hydrolysis*.

The process of nutrition comprises not only digestion: we have also to consider *ingestion* or the taking in of food by the mouth; *absorption*—the diffusion of food substances into the blood stream; *assimilation*—the conversion of nutrients into materials used for repair and growth; and *egestion*—the removal of waste substances from the gut through the anus.

The Histology of the Alimentary Canal

The alimentary canal is composed throughout its length of four layers of tissue. These may be seen in Fig. 12.6 and in Plates 45 and 46. The outer layer of tissue is thin but strong and is known as the *serous coat*. It forms a membrane by means of which the alimentary canal is suspended inside the abdominal cavity. The next layer—the *muscular coat*—consists of an outer layer of *longitudinal muscle* and an inner layer of *circular muscles*. Within the muscular coat lies the *sub-mucous coat* and finally, next to the cavity of the gut is the *mucous coat*. This mucous coat is glandular and contains cells which secrete different substances into different parts of the alimentary canal.

The Structure of the Alimentary Canal

The *alimentary canal or gut*—different parts of which vary in nature, function and size—stretches from the *mouth* to the *anus*. It is a long tube whose function is to ingest and digest food and to absorb the end products of digestion by means of its blood vessels, and to separate and remove the waste and harmful substances taken in with the food.

The *mouth* consists of two lips and opens into the *buccal cavity*. The layman loosely includes in the 'mouth' the buccal cavity which has the *tongue* for its floor and a *palate* for its roof. The sides of the buccal cavity are the *cheeks*, and the *lips* close the cavity—or open it—at the front. The cavity is supported by the bones of the jaws and contains the *teeth* which have been described on pages 76 and 78.

The *pharynx* (Figs. 12.1 and 12.2) has two parts—the *oro-pharynx* at the back of the mouth and the *naso-pharynx* at the back of the nose. The *tonsils* are large patches of lymph tissue which lie at the side of the pharynx. Also at the side of the pharynx near the inner edge of the palate are two openings. These are the openings of the *Eustachian tubes* which connect the pharynx with the ear (see also page 188). The *nasal cavity* contains *turbinate bones* over which the air passes as it enters the nose on its way to the oro-pharynx. The palate itself is made of both hard and soft parts, the inner end of the soft palate being called the *uvula*. The *adenoids* lie at the back of the nasal cavity.

The *gullet* or *oesophagus* is a straight tube which runs downwards from the pharynx to the stomach. It has strong muscular walls which are folded longitudinally to allow it to stretch when swallowing occurs. The oeso-phagus runs near the *trachea* which is a tube leading to the lungs. Above the opening of the trachea lies the *epiglottis*.

The *stomach* is an extremely muscular organ lying below the diaphragm and to the left of the liver. Its shape, of course, varies depending upon the amount of food in it. The opening of the oesophagus into the stomach is guarded by the *cardiac sphincter*—a circular muscle which can open and shut. The exit at the other end of the stomach into the duo-denum is similarly guarded by a sphincter muscle—the *pyloric sphincter*.

The stomach opens into the *small intestine*, the first part of which is called, as we have seen, the *duodenum*. This part is nearly 30 cm

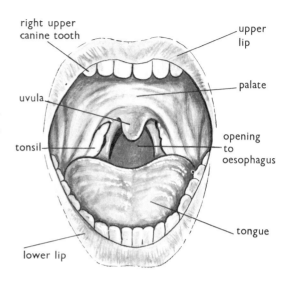

FIG. 12.1. View looking into human mouth.

in length and the bile and pancreatic ducts run into it. The rest of the small intestine com-prises firstly the *jejunum* and secondly the *ileum*, the former being about 2·4 m in length and the latter about 4·3 m. The small intestine has its surface area vastly increased by millions of tiny projections called villi, each of which contains numerous capillaries and a small lymph vessel known as a lacteal. The purpose of the villi is to give a large surface for the absorption of food.

The *large intestine* into which the small intestine leads is about 1·5 m long and is formed by the *caecum*, the *appendix*, the *colon* and the *rectum*. In the human being the caecum and the appendix are small but in animals which feed largely upon grass—sheep, horses and cows for example—they are long. The reason for this is that mammals do not produce enzymes capable of digesting the cellulose walls of plant cells: animals which feed entirely on grass have special bacteria in the caecum and appendix for digesting the cellulose for them. This is not necessary in Man for he eats much animal matter.

The *colon* is a wide tube separated by scientists for convenience of reference into the *ascending colon*, the *transverse colon* and the *descending colon*. This last portion of the colon leads straight into the *rectum*, a tube some 13 cm in length, which opens at the *anus*.

The Functions of the Alimentary Canal

Food is ingested at the mouth and is chewed or *masticated* by the teeth. Water is added with the saliva together with *mucin* and *ptyalin*. Mucin helps to lubricate the food while ptyalin commences the digestion of starch by hydrolysing it to maltose—a sugar which partly dissolves in the water. The food is swallowed as a rounded lump known as a *bolus* and passes to the stomach along a tube known as the oesophagus. It is moved by waves of contraction of the oesophageal wall:

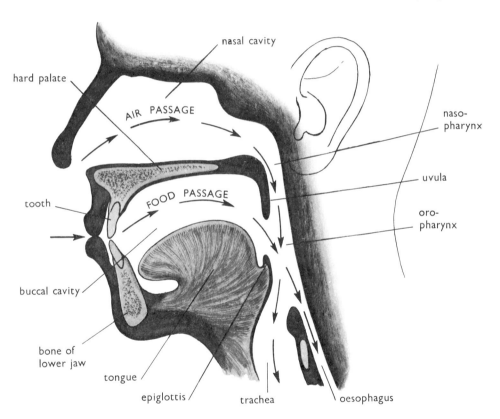

FIG. 12.2. Diagrammatic vertical section through the head to show the relationship between the food and air passages.

139

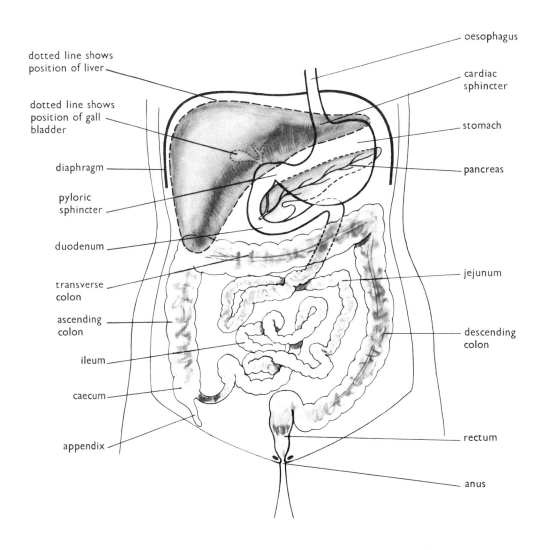

oesophagus

dotted line shows
position of liver

cardiac
sphincter

dotted line shows
position of gall
bladder

stomach

diaphragm

pancreas

pyloric
sphincter

duodenum

transverse
colon

jejunum

ascending
colon

descending
colon

ileum

caecum

appendix

rectum

anus

FIG. 12.3. THE ALIMENTARY CANAL.

140

these contractions occur throughout the length of the gut and are referred to as *peristalsis* (Fig. 12.8).

The food is churned in the stomach for three or four hours. Gradually it is broken down into smaller pieces; water is added together with hydrochloric acid and three enzymes. The water is for the food substances to dissolve in and the hydrochloric acid neutralises the alkaline nature of the food arriving from the mouth, thereby stopping the action of ptyalin, which acts only in an alkaline medium, and providing an acid medium for the stomach enzymes.

The three enzymes found in the stomach are: *pepsin* which coagulates milk proteins and splits them into proteoses and peptones —substances intermediate in molecular complexity between proteins and amino-acids; *rennin* which curdles milk and which is particularly important to young children; and lastly *gastric lipase* which commences the breakdown of fats into fatty acids and glycerol.

The stomach also secretes from its cells a lubricating *mucus* and a hormone called *gastrin* which stimulates the *gastric glands* to activity when there is food in the stomach.

Alcohol is absorbed in the stomach and hence, as it needs no digestion, its effects are frequently very rapid.

The name given to the contents of the stomach by the time they leave it is *chyme*. From the stomach the food passes into the duodenum where it receives the bile and the pancreatic juice. The bile breaks up fats and oils into an emulsion—small drops upon which enzymes can act. The pancreatic juice contains the enzymes *lipase* and *amylase*. Lipase splits fats into fatty acids and glycerol while amylase breaks starch down to maltose. Pancreatic juice also contains *trypsinogen* which is converted to *trypsin* when it is acted

upon by *enterokinase*, a substance produced by the walls of the small intestine.

From the duodenum the food passes first into the jejunum and then to the ileum.

While in the small intestine the food not only receives the bile and the pancreatic juice but also a liquid formed from the cells lining the intestine itself. This fluid is known as the *succus entericus* and it contains several enzymes as follows: *maltase* which reduces maltose to glucose; *sucrase* which turns sucrose to glucose and fructose; *lactase* which breaks lactose into glucose and galactose; *peptidases* which split *proteoses* and *peptones* into amino-acids; and *enterokinase* which converts trypsinogen to trypsin.

The small intestine secretes also the hormone *secretin* which stimulates the pancreas to secrete pancreatic juice.

It is in the small intestine that the products of digestion, glucose, amino-acids and fatty acids and glycerol, are absorbed into the blood stream. Absorption takes place through special structures called villi. The structure of a villus is shown in Figs. 12.5 and 12.6 while the position of the villi is seen in Fig. 12.4 and Plate 45. The villi, which are very numerous, greatly increase the area over which food substances in the small intestine may be absorbed into the blood stream. Each villus contains a network of capillaries into which glucose and amino-acids pass and a small lacteal which absorbs the fatty acids and glycerol. Much of the fat is absorbed into the villi without first being broken down. The lacteals join with the main lymph system. The amino-acids and the glucose are taken to the liver in the hepatic portal vein (page 110).

After the end products of digestion have been absorbed into the blood the remains of the food ingested—now waste substances and roughage—pass into the colon. The function of the large intestine is to absorb small

141

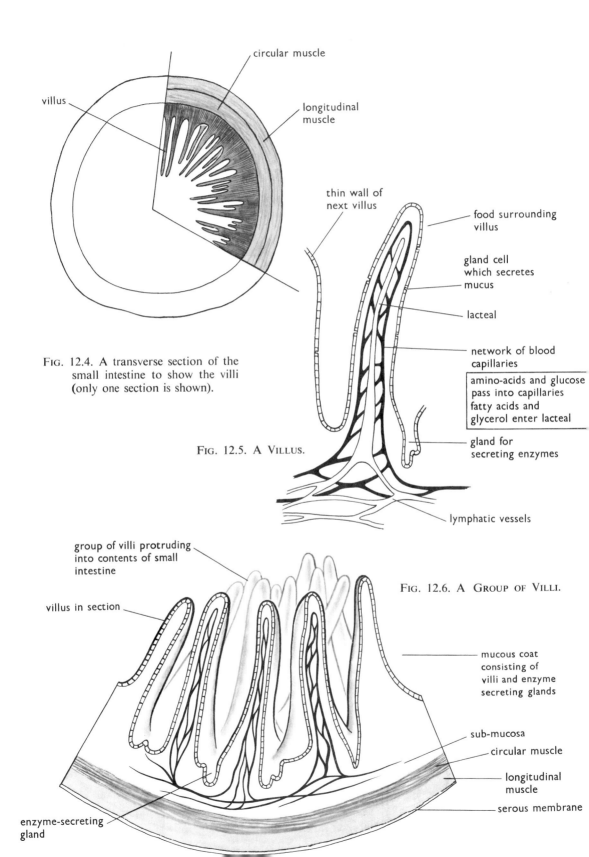

circular muscle

longitudinal muscle

villus

FIG. 12.4. A transverse section of the small intestine to show the villi (only one section is shown).

thin wall of next villus

food surrounding villus

gland cell which secretes mucus

lacteal

network of blood capillaries

amino-acids and glucose pass into capillaries fatty acids and glycerol enter lacteal

gland for secreting enzymes

FIG. 12.5. A VILLUS.

lymphatic vessels

group of villi protruding into contents of small intestine

FIG. 12.6. A GROUP OF VILLI.

villus in section

mucous coat consisting of villi and enzyme secreting glands

sub-mucosa

circular muscle

longitudinal muscle

serous membrane

enzyme-secreting gland

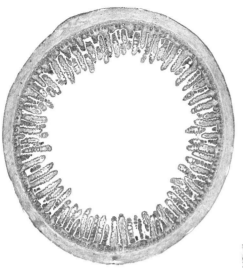

PLATE 45. A transverse
section of the small
intestine.

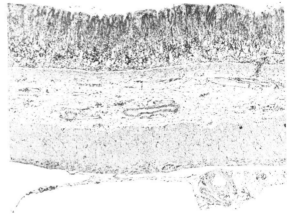

PLATE 46. A transverse
section of the stomach
wall.

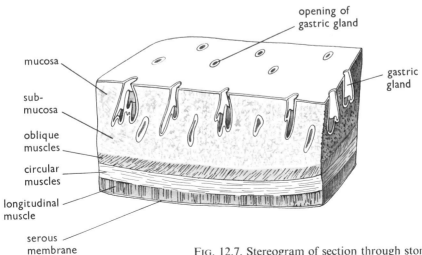

opening of
gastric gland

mucosa

gastric
gland

sub-
mucosa

oblique
muscles

circular
muscles

longitudinal
muscle

serous
membrane

FIG. 12.7. Stereogram of section through stomach wall.

amounts of valuable substances which are still mixed with the waste, to produce mucus to lubricate the waste matter and to absorb water from it, hence preventing unnecessary loss of moisture. The waste matter at this stage is known as the *faeces* and as such is passed at intervals from the anus.

Table 8 summarises the work of enzymes on the food during its passage down the alimentary canal while Table 10 shows what happens to the food, apart from enzyme action, in different parts of the alimentary canal. You may find it difficult to remember the details of all the enzymes: it is more important to know the main functions of each part of the gut. Table 9 will help you to learn them.

Assimilation and the Fate of Food Substances

After the food substances have passed through the thin walls of the villi into the blood of the portal vein, and into the lacteals, they are conveyed to the cells of the body for various purposes—some are, as we have seen, temporarily stored in the liver. Some of the substances—proteins in particular—become incorporated in the material of the cells themselves and it is this which is known as *assimilation*. The use to which the end products of digestion are put is shown in Table 10.

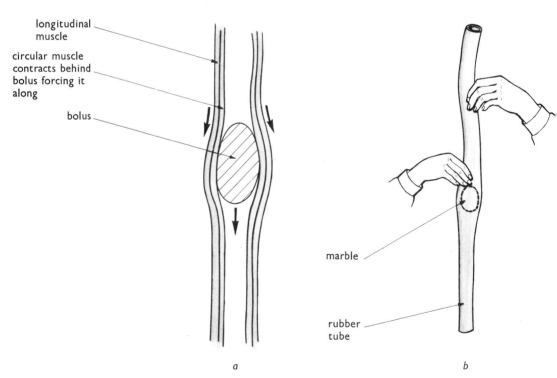

longitudinal muscle

circular muscle contracts behind bolus forcing it along

bolus

marble

rubber tube

a

b

FIG. 12.8. a. The action of the circular muscles of the gut in pushing the food along—Peristalsis. b. Demonstration of peristaltic movement: the marble is pushed along the rubber tube by the hand.

144

Region of Alimentary Canal	Enzyme	Food Substance Acted Upon	Product
Mouth (saliva)	Ptyalin	Starch	Maltose
Stomach (gastric juice)	Pepsin	Proteins	Proteoses and Peptones
	Rennin	Curdles milk	Coagulated proteins
	Gastric lipase	Fats and oils	*Fatty acids* and *glycerol*
Duodenum (Pancreatic juice)	Lipase	Fats and oils	*Fatty acids* and *glycerol*
	Amylase	Starch	Maltose
	Trypsinogen	Has to be acted on by enterokinase	
(Succus entericus)	Maltase	Maltose	*Glucose*
	Sucrase	Sucrose	*Glucose* and fructose
	Lactase	Lactose	*Glucose* and galactose
	Peptidases	Proteoses and peptones	*Amino-acids*
	Enterokinase	Activates trypsinogen to form trypsin	
	Trypsin	Proteins and peptones	*Amino-acids*

TABLE 8. THE ENZYMES OF THE ALIMENTARY CANAL—
THE END PRODUCTS OF DIGESTION
ARE ITALICISED.

Region of Alimentary Canal	Function of Parts of the Alimentary Canal—Excluding Details of Enzyme Action

Buccal Cavity and Pharynx	1. Ingestion
	2. Mastication by teeth, food moved by tongue and cheek muscles
	3. Saliva added—containing:
	  (a) Water
	  (b) Mucin
	  (c) Ptyalin
	4. Food tasted by tongue and other regions

Oesophagus	Carries food to stomach
Stomach	1. Churns food 2. Adds water 3. Adds hydrochloric acid 4. Adds enzymes 5. Secretes gastrin 6. Absorbs alcohol
Ileum	1. Receives bile 2. Receives pancreatic juice 3. Secretes the succus entericus and its enzymes 4. Secretes secretin 5. Absorbs the end products of digestion, water, etc.
Colon	1. Absorbs water 2. Absorbs a little food which has not been absorbed by the ileum
Rectum	Carries faeces to anus for removal—egestion

TABLE 9. SUMMARY OF THE MAIN FUNCTIONS OF THE DIFFERENT REGIONS OF THE ALIMENTARY CANAL.

End Product of Digestion	Destination	Fate of End Product
Glucose	Taken to the liver by the portal vein	(a) Sent on from the liver for use by cells in tissue respiration to give energy (b) Converted to glycogen under the influence of insulin and stored in the liver
Amino-acids	Taken to the liver by the portal vein	(a) Used to manufacture new protoplasm and other substances (b) Repair of worn out tissues (c) Much of the protein is deaminated and this results in the formation of urea
Fats, fatty acids and glycerol	Absorbed by lacteals and taken in main lymph vessels to veins	(a) Fatty acids and glycerol are reformed into fats needed by human beings (b) Fats are used to give energy (c) Storage under skin, etc. (d) Heat insulation

TABLE 10. THE FATE OF THE END PRODUCTS OF DIGESTION.

1. Dissect—or ask your teacher to dissect for you—a rabbit. Identify as many of the organs as possible, paying special attention to the alimentary canal.

2. Investigate sections of the alimentary canal under the microscope. Draw transverse sections of the oesophagus, stomach and small intestine.

THINKING POINT

In view of what has been said in regard to a balanced diet consider carefully (a) whether you are eating a balanced diet and (b) how far it is possible for peoples living in under-developed countries to consume a balanced diet.

QUESTIONS ON 10, 11 AND 12

1. Name *three* carbohydrates and describe a distinguishing test for each. Explain the importance of these carbohydrates in human nutrition. (C)

2. Many people eat large quantities of sweets and biscuits between meals. Why is this an undesirable habit? (C)

3. Follow the changes that may take place in food in the small intestine, showing how that organ is suited to bring them about. (C)

4. Why are proteins important in our diet? Explain how a piece of lean meat is converted to simple substances, and how these are used in the body. (O)

5. What is an enzyme? Name *three* different organs in which enzyme action takes place in man. In each case, state the source of the enzyme and describe its action. (O)

6. What is a balanced diet, and why is it important? Describe in general terms suitable diets for (a) a miner, (b) an office worker, (c) a school child, explaining which foods are most important in each case. (O)

7. Draw a diagram of the digestive system in Man. Explain how a portion of fat is digested and utilised by the body. (O)

8. Describe the structure of the stomach wall and its action in digestion. (L)

9. Give an account of the form and position of the large intestine. What are its functions? (L)

10. What part does the pancreas play in carbohydrate metabolism? Give a diagram of its position in the body. (L)

11. Give a labelled diagram showing the position of the liver. Enumerate its main functions and describe the circulation of blood through it. (L)

12. Describe the digestion of lean meat. Briefly state how you would add to a steak to make a balanced meal for an adult, giving reasons for your choice. (L)

13. Describe the digestion by a man of a cup of tea and a bun. Comment on the suitability of this as a regular mid-day meal for a housewife. (L)

14. State the constituents of a balanced diet and describe their respective functions. How should a balanced diet for a normal adult be adapted to meet the special needs of (a) a three-month-old baby, (b) a teenager, (c) an expectant mother? (L)

15. Describe how and where a meat sandwich is digested. (L)

16. Give an account of the digestion, absorption and utilisation of carbohydrates in Man. (W) (A detailed drawing of the entire alimentary canal is *not* required.)

17. Make a large, fully labelled drawing of the alimentary canal and associated glands of a *named* mammal. Give a detailed account of the structure and functions of the stomach. (W)

18. What is an enzyme? Describe an experiment you have seen carried out to demonstrate the action of *one* named enzyme. (W)

19. Explain fully what you understand by a balanced diet. Outline the special dietary requirements of each of the following, giving reasons for their particular needs: (a) an infant, (b) a pregnant woman, (c) a manual worker, (d) a sedentary worker. (W)

20. The tongue, the teeth and the tonsils are all found in the mouth. Give a description of the position, structure and functions of each. (RSA)

21. The food we eat is broken down into other forms by enzymes and then built up into new substances in the cells of the body. State briefly why these two processes are necessary. Describe the digestion of proteins and starches in the alimentary canal and the use made of the digested products in the cells of the body. (RSA)

22. What is meant by a *balanced diet*? Give the requirements of such a diet and explain why each is necessary. In what way should the daily diet of a 12-year-old child differ from that of a 50-year-old office worker? (RSA)

23. Mention *six* important protein-containing foods that you might eat during the course of a week. By what steps is this protein converted to human protein, and what happens to any parts of it not used for this purpose? (C)

24. Name the properties that enzymes possess in common, and describe experiments you have yourself carried out to demonstrate some of the points you mention. (C)

25. What are the general characteristics of enzymes? Describe the occurrence and work of these enzymes concerned with carbohydrates in the human food tract. (C)

26. Explain the necessity for protein foods in the diet. What are the chief sources of protein in your own diet in an average day? Give an account of the changes undergone by proteins until their digestion is complete. (J)

27. For what purposes is energy required in the body? Explain the units in which we measure energy values, and indicate the extent to which the main classes of foodstuffs serve as energy sources. What are the special energy needs of (a) a five-year-old child, (b) a sedentary worker, (c) a miner? (J)

28. Write on each of the following: (a) peristalsis, (b) sphincters, (c) pepsin, (d) enterokinase. (J)

Summary of 10 to 12

1. All living organisms require a supply of *food* to enable them to *grow*, to have *energy* and to prevent *disease*.

2. There are six basic food substances—*carbohydrates, fats, proteins, mineral salts, vitamins* and *water*. Carbohydrates and fats provide us with energy; fats form a useful food store in the body; proteins are used in the manufacture of new protoplasm; mineral salts are required for healthy growth; vitamins prevent disease and water forms a medium in which chemical actions take place.

3. Milk is an ideal food produced in mammary glands. It contains all the food substances necessary for the growth of a baby.

4. The amount of energy given by one gram of food is its *Calorific Value*.

5. The *metabolic rate* expresses the rate at which the tissues 'burn' sugar and oxygen.

6. A *balanced diet* is necessary for health. The diet required depends on the age, sex and work of the individual concerned.

7. *Enzymes* break down food substances—they are formed by *living tissues* such as those found in the *salivary glands*, the *pancreas* and the lining of the *intestine*.

8. The *liver* is a large organ which *stores glycogen, iron* and vitamins A, B and D; produces *bile, heparin, heat* and *antitoxins. Deamination* of proteins occurs in the liver.

9. *Digestion* is the process by which food substances are broken down into simpler compounds which can pass through the gut wall into the blood.

10. The *alimentary canal* consists of a number of clearly defined regions all of which, however, have basically four layers of tissue—the *serous coat*, the *muscular coat*, the *sub-mucous coat* and the *mucous coat*. Food which has been rendered soluble is absorbed in the small intestine by *villi* and passes into the blood. Waste material passes through the gut to be expelled at the anus: water and other useful substances are absorbed by the colon.

13. Respiration and the Release of Energy

Introduction

The importance of energy production in living things has already been mentioned, for example under the characteristics of living things (page 22) and under the physiology of muscle contraction on page 66. The time has now come to study this vital topic a little more deeply—as it is of such fundamental importance.

On page 22 *respiration* was defined as 'the process by which energy is liberated in living things' and the distinction between *breathing* or *external respiration*, and *tissue* or *internal respiration* was drawn. We shall be concerned with tissue respiration in this chapter; breathing will be the subject of Chapter 14.

Tissue respiration is the complex series of chemical changes which occur in the living substance itself and which result in the release of energy. It is usual to consider with it the way in which the chemicals required get to the cells and how the waste substance, carbon dioxide, is removed from them.

Tissue or Internal Respiration

The metabolic processes by which energy is released in the protoplasm of the living cells themselves is one of great complexity and its details are far beyond the scope of this book. It is possible to represent the

beginning and end of the processes simply, however, but we must remember that it *is* a very simplified representation of a complex matter. You will remember that in Chapter 10 we saw that food substances, and fats and carbohydrates in particular, are sources of energy for our bodies. These substances are oxidised, that is they combine with oxygen and in doing so they produce water and carbon dioxide as waste substances and the energy of the foods is released for use by the protoplasm. The carbohydrate, glucose, is the substance usually oxidised and is known as the *respiratory substrate*. Thus we have:

$$\text{Glucose} + \text{Oxygen}$$
$$\text{(potential energy)}$$
$$= \text{Carbon dioxide} + \text{Water} + ENERGY$$

or expressed chemically:

$$C_6H_{12}O_6 + 6O_2 = 6CO_2 + 6H_2O + ENERGY$$

It is this energy which is used for bringing about other metabolic processes concerned with such important and vital activities as the heart beat, breathing movements, walking, digestion, etc.

Passage of Glucose and Oxygen to the Cells and of Carbon Dioxide and Water from them

We already know that glucose, oxygen, water and carbon dioxide are carried in the

a. Diffusion of substances across a
   cell membrane from regions of
   high concentration to regions of
   lower concentration. Tissue fluid
   is rich in glucose and oxygen;
   cytoplasm has high carbon
   dioxide concentration.

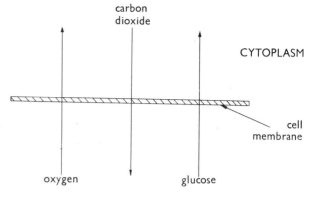

high carbon dioxide concentration
low oxygen concentration
low glucose concentration

carbon
dioxide

CYTOPLASM

cell
membrane

oxygen   glucose

TISSUE FLUID

low carbon dioxide concentration
high oxygen concentration
high glucose concentration

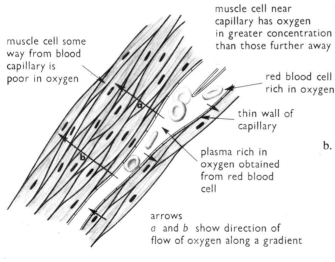

muscle cell some
way from blood
capillary is
poor in oxygen

muscle cell near
capillary has oxygen
in greater concentration
than those further away

red blood cell
rich in oxygen

thin wall of
capillary

plasma rich in
oxygen obtained
from red blood
cell

arrows
a and b show direction of
flow of oxygen along a gradient

b. Diagram to show flow of oxygen
   along a gradient from capillary
   to muscle cells.

c. Graphic representation of
   oxygen gradient.

FIG. 13.1 DIFFUSION AND
DIFFUSION GRADIENT.

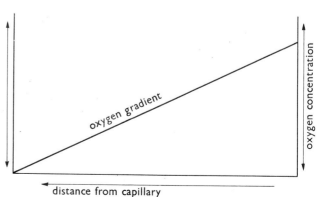

oxygen gradient

oxygen concentration

distance from capillary

blood. To understand the process by which they enter or leave the blood and enter or leave the tissues it is necessary to understand the term *diffusion gradient*. Living cells can allow substances to pass into or out of them in solution, i.e. they can pass through the cell membrane in either direction. This is *diffusion*. The rate at which a substance diffuses depends on the size of its molecules—large molecules passing through more slowly than small molecules. Thus water and carbon dioxide, both of which have small molecules, diffuse through the cell membrane faster than, for example, glucose molecules which are relatively large.

The direction of flow of the molecules is from a region of high concentration to a region of lower concentration and a *diffusion gradient* exists between the two regions. Diffusion and diffusion gradient are shown diagramatically in Fig. 13.1.

Fig. 13.2 shows the passage of substances into and out of a capillary and into and out of muscle cells: the importance of tissue fluid is now seen, for it bathes the cells and forms a liquid through which dissolved substances pass to the cells from the blood, which, it will

be remembered, never leaves the capillaries (except when wounding occurs). Excess tissue fluid drains into the lymphatic system (page 99).

The oxygen is brought to the tissues in the blood combined with haemoglobin. This is a loose combination and in regions of low oxygen concentration the association breaks down, the oxygen being readily given up by the haemoglobin and diffusing through the tissue fluid into the cells where it is needed. By the use of red blood cells about twenty times the volume of oxygen can be carried as it could be if it were dissolved in the plasma alone.

The carbon dioxide produced as a waste product of respiration is more soluble than oxygen and more is carried dissolved in the plasma. Most of it, however, is carried as potassium bicarbonate as is mentioned on page 95.

It may be interesting to recall here the general principle of integration of the body systems mentioned on page 34. We have just seen how the digestive system and the blood system work together to provide the muscle system with the necessary requirements.

FIG. 13.2. Diagram to show the passage of substances between cells, capillaries and lymphatic vessels. The tissue fluid bathes the muscle cells enabling substances to diffuse to and from the capillaries. Excess tissue fluid drains into the lymphatic vessels.

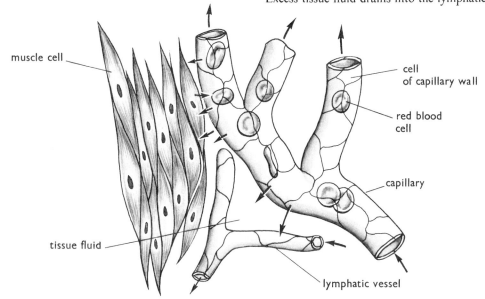

muscle cell

cell
of capillary wall

red blood
cell

capillary

tissue fluid

lymphatic vessel

14. Our Breathing Mechanism

The Structure of the Respiratory System

The respiratory system consists of the *lungs*, the *air passage* to them and the *ribs*—together with the *muscles* which move them—and the *diaphragm*. Fig. 14.1 shows these and other parts. The function of the respiratory system is to make possible a gaseous exchange between the atmosphere and the blood so that oxygen can be available for the cells and carbon dioxide can be removed from them.

The *nostrils* are the openings to the exterior of the *nasal passages*. The passages are separated from the mouth by the *palate* and from one another by a *septum* which is usually a little nearer one side than the other. The surface area of the nasal passages or cavities is vastly increased by the presence of scroll-like bones over whose surfaces the air has to pass on its way to the lungs. The passages are lined with cells which secrete mucus. Some of the cells are ciliated (see also Fig. 2.7). This lining to the nose, which besides having ciliated and mucus-producing cells is rich in blood capillaries, is known as the *nasal mucosa*. The nasal cavities open into the naso-pharynx at the back which leads to the oro-pharynx. The passage can be closed by the *uvula*.

The *wind-pipe* leads from the oro-pharynx to the lungs and its upper portion is modified to form the *larynx* or *voice-box*. The opening of the larynx into the pharynx is known as the *glottis* and it is protected by the *epiglottis.* The larynx is strengthened by a number of cartilages between which the *vocal folds* or *vocal cords* are stretched. It is the vibration of these folds which produces sounds when air is breathed out over them. The quality of the sound produced depends on the tension in the cords, which can be varied by the *vocal muscles*, and also on the size of the glottis. This opening is wide when no sound is produced, as in normal breathing, but is narrow when sounds are produced.

The rest of the wind-pipe, or *trachea* as it is called, is about 13 cm long and leads directly to the lungs via the right and left *bronchi*. Both the trachea and the bronchi are supported by incomplete loops of cartilage which hold the tube open.

The bronchi branch into numerous small tubes known as *bronchioles* which in turn divide again and again until the tubes are very small—not much larger than blood capillaries—and these finally end in small lobed sacs. Each *end-sac* or *alveolar-sac* as it is called, is lobed into numerous *alveoli*. Numerous tiny capillaries form a network of blood vessels over each alveolus. The alveoli are extremely thin so that diffusion through their surface is easy. They are also vast in number, thus giving a tremendous surface area over which gaseous exchange can take place. It has been estimated that the respiratory surface afforded by the lungs is nearly

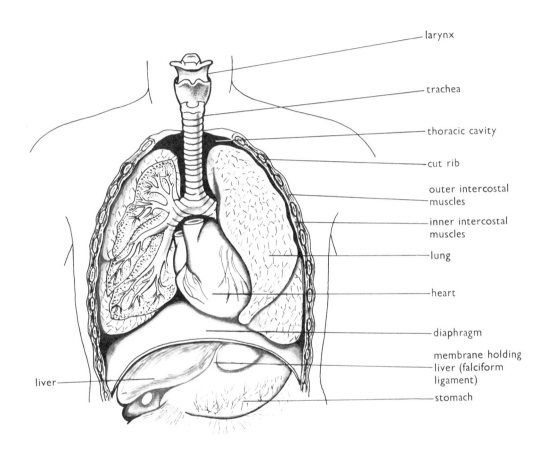

larynx

trachea

thoracic cavity

cut rib

outer intercostal muscles

inner intercostal muscles

lung

heart

diaphragm

membrane holding liver (falciform ligament)

stomach

liver

Fig. 14.1. The respiratory system, lower part. This figure should be studied in conjunction with Fig. 12.1 which shows the upper part of the respiratory system.

155

as large as the area of a tennis court. Fig. 14.2 shows the arrangement of the alveoli and their blood network.

The lungs themselves lie in the thoracic cavity and are enclosed in a double membrane known as the pleurae, the space between the inner and outer pleural membrane being called the pleural cavity. The right lung has three lobes and the left lung two lobes, and the heart, of course, lies between the two lungs.

Gaseous Exchange in the Lungs

The respiratory surface provided by the lungs of human beings fulfils three fundamental requirements. These are, firstly, that the surface area must be large; secondly, that the surface must be moist; and thirdly, that there must be a rich supply of blood in thin-walled capillaries.

Oxygen taken into the lungs can diffuse, along a diffusion gradient, through the walls of the alveoli and blood capillaries both of which are very thin. Once in the blood plasma the oxygen diffuses into the red blood cells and joins with the haemoglobin to form oxyhaemoglobin and is rapidly conveyed away from the lungs in the pulmonary veins. Similarly the carbon dioxide arriving in the pulmonary arteries passes out from the capillaries, being immediately yielded up by the potassium bicarbonate, into the alveoli and is breathed out.

Water, which is a waste product of respiration, is also given off from the surface of the lungs.

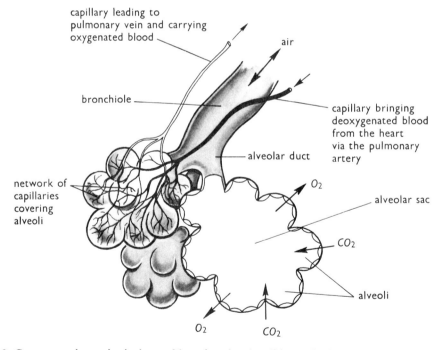

capillary leading to pulmonary vein and carrying oxygenated blood

air

bronchiole

capillary bringing deoxygenated blood from the heart via the pulmonary artery

alveolar duct

network of capillaries covering alveoli

O_2

alveolar sac

CO_2

alveoli

O_2 CO_2

FIG. 14.2. Gaseous exchange in the lungs. Note that the alveoli have elastic tissue which allows them to distend during inspiration and which squeezes air out during expiration.

Functions of the Parts of the Respiratory System

Air enters the body through the nostrils. This air may be cold and dirty. As it passes through the nasal cavity and over the nasal mucosa it is warmed to body temperature in order that it may not chill the lungs when it arrives there. The air is also saturated with moisture as it passes through the nose. Lastly dirt and germs are filtered out of the air partly by hairs near the entrance to the nasal passages and partly by becoming caught on the slimy mucus which is produced by the glands of the mucosa. This mucus is produced in greater quantity when we have a cold and it and the germs it traps are then removed by blowing the nose. Hence the importance of using a handkerchief at such times and not just sneezing into the air, which would only spread the infection to other people. It will be obvious that breathing through the nose is better than breathing through the mouth because it not only avoids chilling the lungs but also prevents the taking in of dirt and germs.

The nose is also able to detect different smells—an important point, for not only does this allow man to enjoy pleasant scents but also provides him with a warning system of such dangers as food which has become bad owing to bacterial decay.

The use of the larynx and vocal cords has already been described: the sounds made by the vocal cords are converted into speech by the lips, tongue and teeth which may be used to control the amount of air expelled. We can see here the difficulty experienced by people who have suffered from loss of teeth, at the front of the mouth in particular, or who have some malformation such as *cleft palate*—a condition where the roof of the mouth is incomplete.

The function of the trachea, bronchi and bronchioles is simply to convey air in and out of the lungs during breathing. The function of the lungs was described in the last section: it is, of course, to effect gaseous exchange between the atmosphere and the body.

Respiratory Movements

Breathing is the series of movements which leads to the intake of fresh air and the removal of stale air. It is often called external respiration but we shall include the gaseous exchange at the lungs in that term as only the initial and end products—i.e., the oxygen, carbon dioxide and water—are concerned.

The intake of air is called *inspiration* and the discharge is *expiration*. The rate of inspiration and expiration depends on the age, sex and activity of the individual concerned but it is faster in children and women than in men. For everyone it is increased with activity. Normally the respiration rate is about 15 times per minute.

The respiratory movements are brought about by muscles which move the ribs and the diaphragm. Fig. 14.3 will help you to follow these movements.

The lungs lie in an air-tight thoracic cavity (Fig. 4.2, page 47) and are enclosed, of course, by the pleural membranes and protected by the thoracic cage (Fig. 7.9, page 82). *Inspiration* is brought about by the contraction of the *external intercostal muscles* which swing the ribs outwards and upwards, thus increasing the diameter of the thorax and hence its volume. At the same time the volume is further increased by contraction of the *diaphragm muscles* which pull the diaphragm downwards thus increasing the depth of the thorax. As the volume of the thorax increases, the pressure of the air inside the lungs decreases and hence, to keep the air pressure in the lungs the same as the pressure outside the body, fresh air flows in. It is at this stage—when the lungs contain fresh air—that gaseous exchange takes place. *Expiration* takes place largely passively, the ribs being lowered by the pull of gravity, although there are another set of intercostal muscles which enable us to force air from the lungs if we desire to do so; and the natural elasticity of the lung tissue also contributes to force out the air.

Normally, when we are breathing quietly, about 500 cm³ of air is taken into the lungs and then, after a pause of about two seconds, the stale air is breathed out. This gentle flow of air in and out of the lungs is known as *tidal air*. Another 1500 cm³ of air can be taken in by making an effort and this is called *complemental air*. Additional air may be forced out of the lungs by a great effort to the extent of about another 1500 cm³—this is *supplemental air*. However much we try we cannot force all the air from our lungs and

A and B. Expiration: size of thoracic cavity reduced; air forced out.

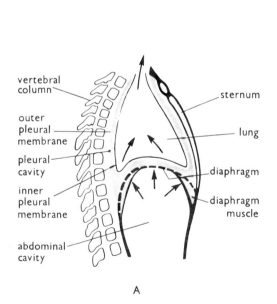

vertebral column

outer pleural membrane

pleural cavity

inner pleural membrane

abdominal cavity

sternum

lung

diaphragm

diaphragm muscle

A

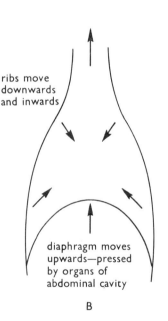

ribs move downwards and inwards

diaphragm moves upwards—pressed by organs of abdominal cavity

B

FIG. 14.3. THE MECHANISM OF RESPIRATION.

Note: The size of the pleural cavity is exaggerated.

158

that which remains after the supplemental air has been forced out is called *residual air*. The total volume of air that can be exchanged—that is the sum of the tidal air, the complemental air and the supplemental air—is known as the *vital capacity*. Thus we have:

Tidal air	.	.	500 cm³
Complemental air	.	.	1500 cm³
Supplemental air	.	.	1500 cm³
Residual air	.	.	1000 cm³
Total	.	.	4500 cm³

Composition of Air. The average composition of inspired and expired air is as follows:

	Inspired	Expired
Nitrogen	78%	78%
Oxygen	21%	17%
Carbon dioxide	0·03%	4%
Water vapour	variable	saturated

C and D. Inspiration: size of thoracic cavity increased; air drawn in.

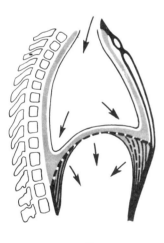

C

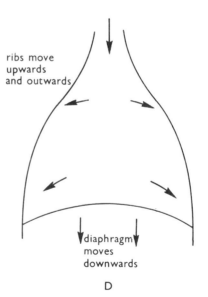

ribs move upwards and outwards

diaphragm moves downwards

D

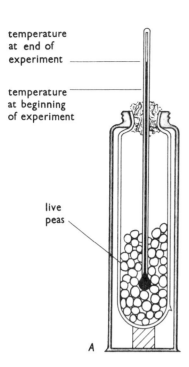

temperature
at end of
experiment

temperature
at beginning
of experiment

live
peas

A

FIG. 14.4. Experiment to show that energy—
in the form of heat—is produced
during respiration. After a few
days the temperature in flask A
is several degrees above that of
flask B.

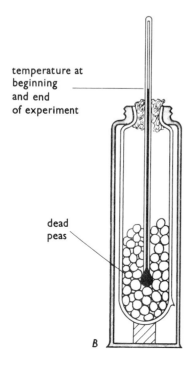

temperature at
beginning
and end
of experiment

dead
peas

B

1. The fact that energy is given off in respiration may be demonstrated using peas. Take two groups of peas of approximately equal numbers and boil one group to kill them and then rinse both groups in antiseptic solution to discourage the growth of micro-organisms. Place each group in a thermos flask whose entrance is lightly plugged with cotton wool—lightly so that the air can diffuse in slowly but heat cannot quickly escape. A thermometer should then be placed in each flask with its lower end resting in the peas. After several hours it is found that the temperature of the flask containing live peas is higher than that of the flask containing dead peas (Fig. 14.4). Heat energy has been given off by the live respiring peas.

Try to answer these points: Why are two flasks necessary? And why does contamination by spores have to be guarded against?

2. To show that carbon dioxide is given off during respiration one simply has to breathe out through a glass tube which has one end in lime water. This liquid is used to test for the presence of carbon dioxide; it turns cloudy if that gas is present. This happens to the lime water in the tube through which you breathe out thus proving its presence in the air we expire.

3. It is interesting to show that the air we expire contains *more* carbon dioxide than that which we inhale. This can be done by using the simple apparatus shown in Fig. 14.5. By breathing in slowly at *A* air is drawn in at *X* passing through the lime water in flask *B*. The air is then expired slowly through flask *C*. This is repeated several times. The lime water in flask *C* turns much more cloudy than does that in flask *B*, thereby proving that the air exhaled contains more carbon dioxide than the air inspired.

160

4. Set up the apparatus shown in Fig. 14.6. Experiment by pulling the rubber sheet up and down. This sheet represents the diaphragm and the balloons represent the lungs. Try to explain carefully the changes in size of the balloons in terms of air pressure and relate the experiment to the breathing movements of Man.

5. Show the relationship between breathing rate and pulse rate by using a stop watch. Take both rates at the same time, before exercise, then after exercise of gradually increasing duration: say one minute's exercise; two minutes' exercise; three minutes' exercise and so on. Time for rest must be allowed before each period of exercise. Plot a graph of pulse rate along one vertical axis and breathing rate along the other vertical axis against time along the horizontal axis.

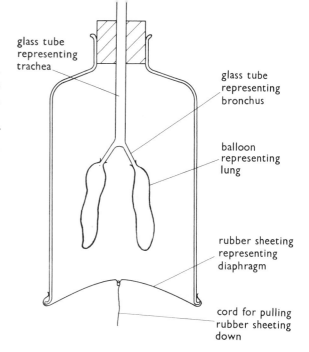

FIG. 14.6. Apparatus used to demonstrate changes of air pressure and air flow in lungs.

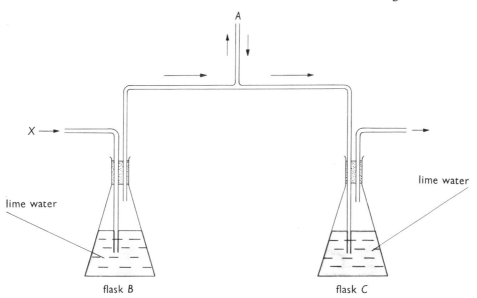

FIG. 14.5. To demonstrate that expired air contains more carbon dioxide than inspired air.

161

6. Examine the respiratory system of a freshly killed rabbit. With bone forceps cut through the ribs and lift off the ventral half of the thorax, revealing the heart and lungs. Cut a hole in the trachea and insert a glass tube. Tie the trachea tightly on to the glass tube with strong thread. Blow down the tube and notice how the lungs inflate. When you remove your mouth from the tube notice how the lungs deflate under their natural elasticity.

Then cut down the trachea towards the lungs and into a bronchus to observe how it joins the lung tissue. Cut open some of the lung tissue and note its soft spongy nature. (Note: Rabbits are expensive and at this point it is therefore advisable to use the rabbit to revise the structure of the blood system, digestive system, etc. If rabbits are too expensive, try the investigation on a rat.) Make drawings of the different structures from the dissection.

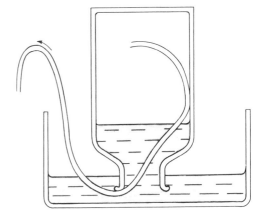

a. Apparatus to find tidal air volume.

7. Fig. 14.7 shows two pieces of apparatus which may be used to find (a) the tidal air volume and (b) the vital capacity volume. In (a) the apparatus is simply a large bottle, containing a rubber tube as shown, inverted over water. As air is drawn out by means of your mouth placed on the end of the rubber tube, water rises in the bottle. When you breathe out, the water is forced out of the bottle. Breathe in normally and invert the bottle and measure the volume of water in it: this represents the volume of tidal air. In (b) the simple apparatus is used as follows: breathe in as deeply as possible thus filling the lungs with the tidal *and* complemental air, place the mouth at X and breathe out as deeply as possible—including, of course, the supplemental air. Collect the water forced out of the bottle and measure it. This volume will be your vital capacity.

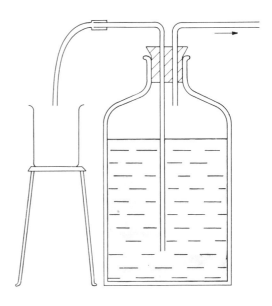

b. Apparatus to find vital capacity.

FIG. 14.7.

162

1. Give a description of the respiratory muscles and their movements. What changes take place in their action when the body is exercised? State briefly how this is brought about. (L)

2. Describe the muscular actions involved in breathing. How do these muscles get the energy to perform their actions? (O)

3. With the aid of labelled diagrams show how gases are interchanged in the lung alveoli. Explain how the blood transports these gases to and from cells. (L)

4. Describe the structure and function of the lung alveoli. Explain what changes take place in the composition of the blood when the breath is held, and state the subsequent responses. (L)

5. Describe an experiment to show that animals breathe out carbon dioxide. Draw a diagram of the apparatus used. What differences would you expect to find in the composition and temperature of inspired and expired air? (W)

6. Give a large, labelled diagram to show the structure of the lungs and of the chest cavity. Explain how air is moved in and out of the lungs and state the use that is made of the oxygen by the cells of the body. (RSA)

7. Describe the nature of the path along which air travels when we breathe in, stating what happens to the air in each region. Explain how the oxygen travels from the air sacs of the lungs to the cells of the body and the use made of it by these cells. (RSA)

8. State clearly why the cells of the body need oxygen and explain the mechanism by which air enters the lungs. Describe simple experiments (a) to demonstrate the action of the diaphragm in breathing, and (b) to find how much air is exchanged by your own lungs in normal breathing. (RSA)

9. Describe the structures and movements involved in breathing and show how these lead to a renewal of air in the lungs. (J)

Summary of 13 and 14

1. Respiration produces energy for living things.

2. *Tissue respiration* is the complex series of chemical reactions which occur in protoplasm and result in the release of energy. *External respiration* refers to the obtaining of oxygen—used in tissue respiration—and the removal of carbon dioxide. The essential *process* of respiration is the combining of oxygen and glucose to release energy: this process takes place in a complicated series of reactions. Chemical substances concerned with respiration enter or leave the cells along a *diffusion gradient* which exists between the cells and the blood capillaries. Food and oxygen are brought to the cells in the blood, the oxygen being combined with *haemoglobin*. Carbon dioxide is removed chiefly in the blood plasma.

3. The *respiratory system* comprises the *nasal passages, lungs, trachea* and *bronchioles, ribs, intercostal muscles* and *diaphragm*. The *larynx* contains the *vocal cords*: its opening into the *pharynx* is guarded by the *epiglottis*. The surface area of the lungs is greatly increased by the presence of *alveoli*. Gaseous exchange occurs in the lungs between the air and the blood, oxygen being absorbed and carbon dioxide given off.

4. Breathing movements are brought about by the intercostal muscles and the diaphragm. *Inspiration* is the taking in of air while *expiration* is the discharge of air.

15. Our Skin

The Structure of the Skin

The skin covers the whole of the outside of the body. It is formed of two layers of tissue: the *epidermis* and the *dermis* (Fig. 15.1 and Plate 46a).

The *epidermis* is the outer layer and itself comprises a number of layers which are, starting from the outer surface, the *cornified layer*, the *granular layer* and the *germinative layer*. The cornified layer is composed of dead cells which have become horny in nature: this layer may be very thick, especially in places where the skin meets with much friction, as on the soles of the feet and the palms of the hand. The cells of the granular layer are granular in appearance as the name implies while those of the germinative layer have darkly staining nuclei.

The *dermis* is formed largely of connective tissue together with blood vessels and nerves and has beneath it a layer of fat deposited in *adipose* cells. The dermis contains also the *hair follicles* which hold the hairs. The hairs themselves are dead and not able to grow as protoplasm grows. They lengthen by the deposition of more hair material (keratin) at their bases. The necessary materials are brought to the hair papilla by blood capillaries.

Each hair is equipped with an *erector muscle*. Near the point where the hair follicle enters the epidermis is a *sebaceous gland*.

Also in the dermis are found the *sweat glands* whose ducts pass through the epidermis on their way to the exterior where they open on the surface by a *sweat pore*.

The Functions of the Skin

Protection. The cornified layer protects the body against *bacterial infection*, *water loss* and *mechanical injury*. Its cells are dead and tough and form an excellent protection especially against friction, for example, on the soles and heels of the feet. As cells are worn away from the surface they are replaced by new cells produced by the germinative layer. The skin may become very thick on the palms of the hands, especially when they are used for heavy manual work such as sawing logs or digging heavy soil with a hand spade. The use of the skin as a protection against bacteria has been already mentioned—when we considered how blood clots.

Sensitivity. The skin is sensitive to touch and to changes in temperature. This is very important because its sensitivity is one of the fundamental properties of living things (see page 23). It is sensitivity which tells us about changes in our environment which may be beneficial or harmful to us. It is interesting to note the sensory function of hairs in animals such as rabbits and rats where they are enlarged to form whiskers: the hair itself is not sensory, of course, being dead, but when touched it moves at the base against sensory nerve endings in the skin. Thus also it hurts when we have our hair pulled.

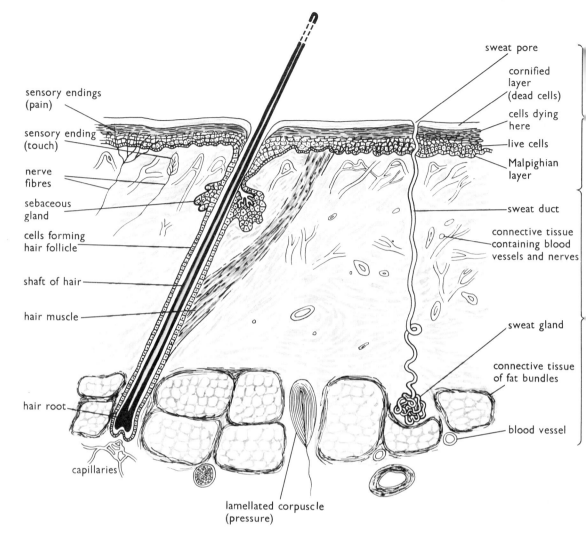

sensory endings (pain)

sensory ending (touch)

nerve fibres

sebaceous gland

cells forming hair follicle

shaft of hair

hair muscle

hair root

capillaries

sweat pore

cornified layer (dead cells)

cells dying here

live cells

Malpighian layer

sweat duct

connective tissue containing blood vessels and nerves

sweat gland

connective tissue of fat bundles

blood vessel

lamellated corpuscle (pressure)

FIG. 15.1 and PLATE 46a. VERTICAL SECTION OF SKIN.

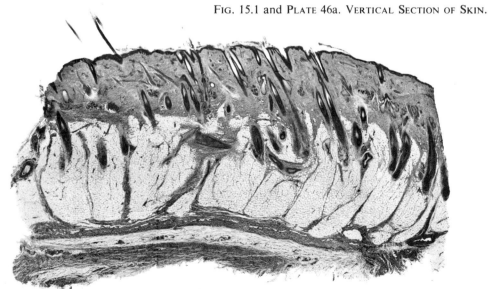

Temperature Control. Both birds and mammals are frequently described as warm-blooded, while fish, amphibians, reptiles and insects are cold-blooded. It is, perhaps, better to refer to the two types as 'constant temperature' animals and 'variable temperature' animals respectively for both contain some amount of heat. The temperature of the 'variable' group changes with that of the surroundings while that of the 'constant' group remains the same irrespective of changes in the temperature of the air around them. This is an advantage, for metabolic processes can occur at a faster rate at a higher temperature than at a low one. Thus it is possible for mammals (and birds) to remain active for the whole year; whereas reptiles, fish and amphibia become less active as the weather becomes colder. How are mammals able to maintain a constant temperature—a temperature of about 38°C in cats and dogs, for example, and 36·9°C in Man?

The constant temperature is maintained by mammals by the exercise of a degree of control over the amount of heat lost from the body and, to some extent, over the amount of heat produced in the body. The amount of heat produced in the body depends on such factors as the type and amount of food ingested and upon the amount of muscular activity. Absorption of heat from the sun, especially in the tropics, can lead to overheating. These factors are fairly easily controlled: if the sun is too hot for comfort then we sit in the shade; in hot weather we can eat foods of low energy content and drink cooling beverages; in very hot weather we can rest during the hottest part of the day—hence the habit of having a siesta, that is, a midday rest, in hot countries.

The heat formed in the body comes from the metabolic processes going on in the living tissues: muscular activity and deamination

for example. The oxidation of glucose during respiration, which occurs in all cells, has already been shown to produce heat (page 160). Now this heat must be removed from the body, for protoplasm can live only up to a certain temperature after which it is killed by the heat. It is by controlling the amount of heat lost from the body that mammals chiefly maintain a constant temperature.

The rate at which heat is lost from the body depends partly on the difference in temperature between the body and the surroundings and partly upon the surface area of the body. Thus we tend to lose heat faster on cold days than when the weather is hot and small animals lose heat more rapidly than large ones: it is interesting to note that small mammals are not found inside the Arctic circle.

Similarly it is small mammals only which hibernate—the dormouse and the bats, for example, because they have a large surface area relative to their volume, and hence lose heat easily. They are unable to obtain and digest and oxidise sufficient food to keep up their temperature in very cold weather.

Heat is lost from the body in several ways: about three-quarters of the heat lost is from the skin by radiation and convection; some is lost by the evaporation of sweat: some by warming the air coming into the lungs; some by evaporation at the surface of the lungs; and a little passes from the body with the waste matter.

When heat-loss from the skin becomes too great it is reduced in several ways. Firstly, the erector muscles at the base of the hairs contract pulling the hair into a more upright position: this makes deeper the layer of air trapped in the hair and, since air is a good insulator, less heat is lost (Fig. 15.2). This is not very effective in such a hairless animal as Man but is of great importance to furry animals. Man can produce the same effect by putting on clothes: each additional layer trapping air between it and the layer below it. Thus, it is often warmer to wear two thin garments than one thick one, because a layer of air is trapped between them.

Secondly, heat-loss is reduced by preventing internal heat from reaching the skin. This is achieved by constricting the blood capillaries near the surface of the skin so that less blood —and hence less heat—reaches the surface. This process is known as *vaso-constriction* (Fig. 15.2). Thirdly, sweat production is reduced and lastly shivering takes place. Shivering is due to involuntary muscle contraction, and muscle contraction, as we have seen, produces heat.

If over-heating occurs, as for example during vigorous exercises, two factors come into play which exert a cooling effect on the body. Firstly, sweat is produced on the surface of the skin and this evaporates; evaporation causes cooling as it takes heat from the skin. Secondly, the reverse of vaso-constriction occurs, i.e. *vaso-dilation*—the blood capillaries dilate so that more blood is brought near the surface and the heat from it is used to evaporate the sweat. The heat is also lost from the skin by radiation. The fact that radiation from a cooling surface is quicker when it is black than when it is white explains why it is better to wear white clothing in hot weather. More will be said about clothing in a later chapter.

To summarise: over-heating is prevented by reducing the intake of high energy foods,

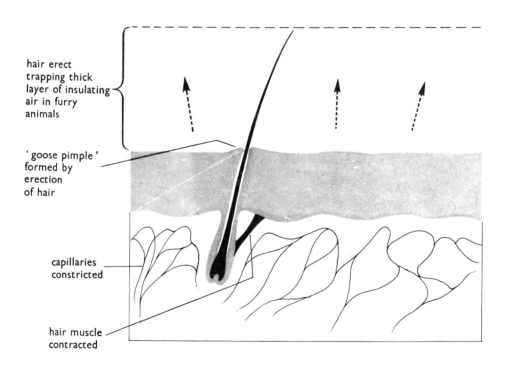

hair erect
trapping thick
layer of insulating
air in furry
animals

'goose pimple'
formed by
erection
of hair

capillaries
constricted

hair muscle
contracted

a. Heat being conserved: hairs erect; capillaries constricted; not much sweat produced.

by reducing the amount of muscular activity, by sweating, by vaso-dilation and by wearing light suitable clothing. Over-cooling is prevented by eating foods of high energy value, by vigorous exercise, by shivering, by reducing sweat production, by vaso-constriction and by wearing clothing which traps layers of air.

In conditions of high air temperature and humidity sufficient heat may not be lost from the body and 'heat-stroke' may result. The patient appears flushed, his temperature rises and he develops severe headache.

The skin as a regulatory mechanism for temperature control provides yet another example of homeostasis. (See page 114.)

Excretion. This is a function of the skin which might easily be overlooked. A small, but not insignificant, amount of nitrogenous waste, as well as salt, is lost with the sweat. This fact emphasises the need for frequent washing of the skin, especially in hot weather, for once the waste is on the skin it soon gives rise to unpleasant odours if it is not quickly removed.

Production of other Structures. We have already seen how the skin produces *hair*. Also formed by the skin are the *teeth*—these become firmly embedded in the bones of the jaws; the *nails* of hands and feet; and the *mammary glands* which are formed from sebaceous glands. It will be remembered that the action of sunlight on the skin produces Vitamin D.

FIG. 15.2. TEMPERATURE CONTROL BY THE SKIN.

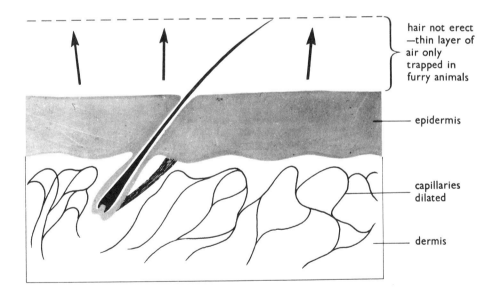

b. Animal losing heat rapidly: much blood passing through capillaries to skin; much sweat produced; hairs lying flat.

169

16. Removal of Waste

Introduction

The removal of waste substances from the human body takes place in various ways. Broadly speaking there are two main classes of waste material: waste substances which have been produced as a result of the metabolic processes going on within the protoplasm itself; and waste materials which, although taken into the alimentary canal, have never formed part of the living matter and which have not been produced by its activity directly. This latter type of waste is solid matter, which is removed from the alimentary canal through the anus and is called *egestion* (page 22) or *defaecation*. The solid waste materials are referred to as the *faeces*. The removal of waste substances which have been produced by the living cells themselves is known as *excretion* (page 22).

A careful distinction, then, must be drawn between egestion or defaecation on the one hand and true excretion on the other.

Ways of Excreting

Three of the body systems are closely concerned with excretion. They are firstly the lungs, secondly the skin and thirdly the kidneys, these last being the main excretory organs.

We have already dealt with the excretion of *carbon dioxide* from the lungs in Chapters 13 and 14, and with the excretion of *nitrogenous* waste and *salts* from the skin in the last chapter. We must now turn our attention to the main organs of nitrogenous excretion—the kidneys. At the same time we will consider the other functions of the kidneys.

The Structure of the Renal System

The excretory system consists of two *kidneys*, two *ureters*, the *bladder* and the *urethra* (Fig. 16.1).

The kidneys (Plates 47 and 48) lie in the abdominal cavity against the posterior wall and are surrounded by a variable amount of fat. They are not seen immediately the abdominal cavity is opened in a dissection because they are covered by the liver and part of the alimentary canal. Each kidney is, in the human being, a bean-shaped structure about $11\frac{1}{2}$ cm in length and 5 cm broad. It is dark red in colour.

From the middle of each kidney a tube arises on the median side and passes downwards to join the urinary bladder on the posterior surface. This tube is the ureter.

The urinary bladder is a sac which acts as a reservoir for the urine. Its size, of course, varies with the amount of fluid in it, ranging in an adult man from 120 cm^3 to 320 cm^3. Its walls are elastic and allow the size of the bladder to increase as fluid accumulates in it.

The urethra is a tube leading from the bladder to the exterior and through which the urine passes when it is excreted.

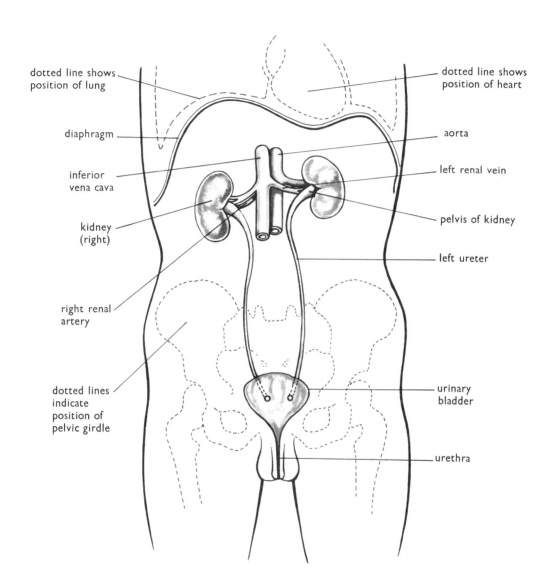

dotted line shows position of lung

dotted line shows position of heart

diaphragm

aorta

inferior vena cava

left renal vein

pelvis of kidney

kidney (right)

left ureter

right renal artery

dotted lines indicate position of pelvic girdle

urinary bladder

urethra

FIG. 16.1. THE KIDNEYS AND ASSOCIATED STRUCTURES (DIAGRAMMATIC).

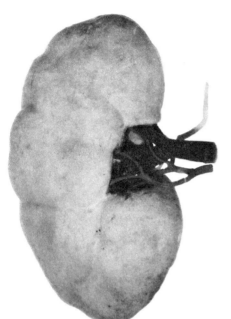

PLATE 47. The kidneys.

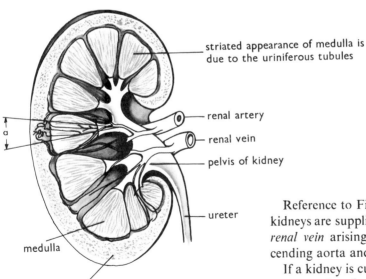

striated appearance of medulla is
due to the uriniferous tubules

renal artery

renal vein

pelvis of kidney

ureter

a

medulla

cortex

FIG. 16.2. Longitudinal section of a kidney.
a. is the segment enlarged in FIG. 16.4.

Reference to Fig. 16.1. will show that both
kidneys are supplied with a *renal artery* and a
renal vein arising respectively from the descending aorta and the inferior vena cava.

If a kidney is cut longitudinally it is at once
apparent that there are two regions: an outer
cortex and an inner *medulla* (Fig. 16.2). The
outer region is darker in colour and denser
in structure than the inner. The medulla

172

PLATE 48. The blood supply
to the kidneys.

PLATE 49. Malpighi.

consists of a number of cone-shaped pieces
called the *pyramids*. The pointed end of each
pyramid opens into a space known as the
pelvis.

The cortex contains very many microscopic
malpighian bodies—named after the seven-
teenth-century anatomist Malpighi (Plate 49).
Each consists of a *Bowman's capsule* which
contains a knot of blood vessels known as a

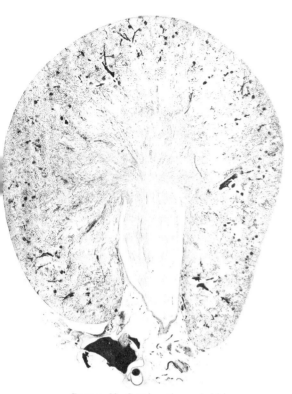

PLATE 50. Section through kidney.

FIG. 16.3. Diagram to help interpret Plate 50.

Malpighian body

uriniferous
tubule

tubules
joining
together at
the pelvis

glomerulus (Figs. 16.2 and 16.3 and Plate 50). Fig. 16.4 shows a Bowman's capsule together with the *kidney tubule* which arises from it. This tubule consists of four parts: immediately upon leaving the Bowman's capsule the tubule is wavy or *convoluted*; this region is known as the *first convoluted tubule*. Following the first convoluted tubule is the *loop of Henle*, next comes the *second convoluted tubule* and finally is the *collecting duct* which opens at the tip of the pyramid. Both capsule and tubules are richly supplied with blood capillaries.

The Functions of the Kidney

The function of the kidney is to *regulate the composition of the body fluids*, especially the blood plasma, and this it does by *determining the amount of water retained in the body*, by *regulating the salt content of the blood* and by *removing harmful substances*. It is sometimes stated that the function of the kidney is to excrete *urea*, and this, of course, is true, but it is, perhaps, better to look on the kidney as a regulatory organ with a multiple function.

The blood entering the glomerulus is at a higher pressure than the blood leaving it and hence some of the water is forced from the blood capillaries of the glomerulus into the Bowman's capsule: this water takes with it most substances in the plasma but not the blood cells or blood proteins. Urea of course passes into the tubule. Now many of the substances which pass into the tubule are not waste substances, as is the urea, and those which are valuable—sugar and some of the salts—are re-absorbed into the plasma as the fluid passes through the first convoluted tubule. Only the necessary amount of salt is re-absorbed to keep the blood at its correct salt concentration and here we see one of the functions of the kidney — namely salt regulation.

As the fluid passes on from the first convoluted tubule, through the loop of Henle and into the collecting duct water is re-absorbed thus keeping the amount of water in the body fluid constant. The fluid passes on through the second convoluted tubule and down the collecting duct to the pyramids and out into the pelvis and thence to the ureter. It is now called urine and contains the waste substances—here is the third function of the kidney, namely removal of nitrogenous waste. The urine collects in the bladder and is discharged at intervals through the urethra—a process called *micturation*.

The composition of urine is variable but is approximately 96% water, 2% salts and 2% urea and other nitrogenous substances. The composition varies, of course, with the food eaten, the amount of fluid drunk and the temperature of the surroundings—this last causing a variation in the amount of water lost by the skin.

The tremendous work done each day may be gauged from the fact that something like $230 \, dm^3$ of fluid pass through the renal tubules in 24 hours, while only about $1 \, dm^3$ of this is passed out during micturation. All the rest is re-absorbed and this process requires energy. Hence the blood leaving the kidney in the renal vein contains less glucose and oxygen, and more carbon dioxide, than does the blood entering by the renal artery. It also, of course, contains less water, mineral salts and urea.

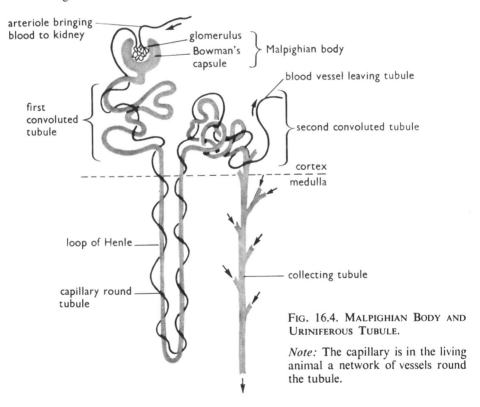

FIG. 16.4. MALPIGHIAN BODY AND URINIFEROUS TUBULE.

Note: The capillary is in the living animal a network of vessels round the tubule.

175

1. Look at the surface of the skin of your hand with a hand lens. Notice the pores and the hairs.

2. Examine a prepared slide of human skin in vertical section, under a microscope. Draw.

3. Demonstrate the cooling effect of evaporation by placing a few drops of ether on the back of your hand. (Ether is inflammable so extinguish all flames before trying this demonstration.)

4. Observe the position of the kidneys, ureters, renal arteries and veins, and the bladder on a dissected rabbit or on a museum specimen.

5. Obtain a sheep's kidney from the butcher. Remove the surrounding fat and notice the renal artery and vein, and the ureter. Draw. Cut the kidney in halves on the flat and observe the cortex and the medulla. Notice how the renal arteries and vein, and the ureter join the kidney.

6. (a) Test the reaction of a sample of urine with litmus. The reaction should show that urine is acidic.

(b) To half a test-tube of urine add a few drops of nitric acid and a little silver nitrate solution. The presence of chlorides is shown by the formation of a white precipitate of silver chloride.

(c) Perform Fehling's Test on some urine (see page 129). The absence of brick-red precipitate shows that sugar is absent from urine.

1. What is excretion and why is it necessary? Describe the part played by the blood in excretion in Man. (O)

2. Make a labelled diagram to show the structure of the human skin. How does Man maintain a constant body temperature? (O)

3. Discuss the uses of water to the body. How is the amount present in the body regulated by the kidney? (L)

4. Describe the position and structure of the kidneys. How does the blood from the heart reach them and how is the composition of the blood kept relatively constant by them? (S)

5. What is the origin of urea in the human body? Where is it formed, and how is it eliminated? (L)

6. Make a large, fully labelled diagram of the skin. Why is it important to keep the skin clean? How does the skin help in the regulation of body temperature? (W)

7. Give an account of the work of the kidney in maintaining the constant composition of the blood. Name the chief substances concerned in this control. (C)

8. Give a clear, well-labelled diagram of *either* the male or the female urinary system. In this diagram, one of the kidneys should be drawn in section (cut in half) to show the main regions of the kidney. Give a clear account of the part played by the kidney in (a) maintaining the water balance of the body, and (b) removing waste products. (RSA)

9. What are the functions of the kidneys? Give a description of a kidney sufficient to show how these functions are carried out. (J)

Summary of 15 and 16

1. The skin is composed of two layers—the *epidermis* and the *dermis*. The dermis, lying below the *cornified, granular* and *germinative* layers of the epidermis, contains *hairs, hair follicles, hair muscles, sebaceous* and *sweat glands, blood vessels, nerves* and *fat cells*.

2. The *skin protects* against bacteria, water loss and mechanical injury. The skin is *sensitive* to touch and to changes in temperature. It helps in the regulation of *body temperature* both by the loss of sweat and by varying the thickness of air trapped in the hair. A small amount of *waste matter is lost* through the skin. *Hair, teeth* and *mammary glands* are derived from the skin.

3. *True excretion* must be distinguished from *egestion*: in the former the waste products are formed by metabolic activity; in the latter the waste has never been taken into the cells. *Excretion* takes place from the *skin*, the *lungs* and the *kidneys*. The *renal system* comprises the *kidneys*, the *ureters*, the *bladder* and the *urethra*. Each kidney has a *cortex* containing *Bowman's capsules*, and a *medulla* comprised of *tubules*.

4. The functions of the kidney are to *excrete urea*, to *control the salt content* of the blood and to *regulate the amount of water* in the body.

17. Reaction to Environment and Co-ordination—1

Introduction

The close relationship between an animal and its environment has already been pointed out in Chapter 3. Animals need to be able to detect changes in the environment if they are to survive. Changes which may occur are, of course, innumerable but they fall broadly into three categories as far as the animals—including human beings—are concerned. They are changes connected with obtaining food, changes concerned with reproducing the species and changes requiring some defensive action (Fig. 17.1). The first and third of these changes are concerned with the *preservation of the individual* while the second is concerned with the *preservation* of the race or species. Preservation of the individual and preservation of the species are sometimes referred to as '*Laws of Nature*' because they are so fundamental.

It is obvious that should an animal fail to maintain these two laws it will either be destroyed itself or endanger the species. The strength of the two laws is seen by the determined way in which almost any animal will fight to preserve itself and its young. The authors have seen parent blackbirds attack a cat which had caught one of their young.

The survival of an animal may depend, for example, on the speed with which it can detect the sudden appearance of another animal upon which it could feed or which is about

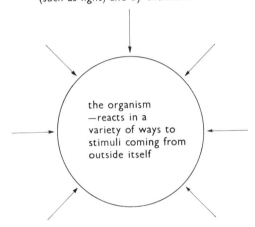

the external environment— stimulates the organism by vibrations (such as sound waves), by radiations (such as light) and by chemicals.

the organism —reacts in a variety of ways to stimuli coming from outside itself

FIG. 17.1. The relationship between an organism and its environment. Arrows represent the stimuli which come to the organism from all directions. Reactions of the organism are such as to be of value to it in connection with self-preservation and preservation of the species.

to attack it or its young. Some system for rapidly detecting environmental changes is therefore found in all animals. In the multicellular animals it is the *nervous system* which carries out this function and in fact special parts of the nervous system are highly specialised for this purpose. They are known as the *sense organs*—the *skin*, the *nose*, the *tongue*, the *eye* and the *ear* in the mammals.

Not only does an animal need to be aware of changes in the world around it but also, if it is to make use of the information obtained, it needs to have a method of sensible reaction to the changes: its different parts must be co-ordinated so that the organism acts as a whole. This working together of the different parts of the body for the good of the whole animal is brought about by two of the body systems. Firstly, the *nervous system* plays its part by transmitting messages from one part of the body to another with great rapidity so that quick reactions to danger, etc., are possible. Secondly, messages are taken round the body in the blood stream by chemicals known as hormones: these substances are produced in ductless glands which together constitute the *endocrine system*: we have met with hormones already on page 120 and page 141 and the whole subject will receive further treatment in Chapter 19.

We saw in Chapter 1 that even the simplest animals such as Amoeba are sensitive to environmental changes and that this feature was indeed a fundamental property of protoplasm. It is interesting to find that the nervous system becomes more and more complex as we study the larger and more complex animals. Fig. 17.2 shows this fact. The *Hydra* has a simple *nerve-net* made up of cells spread fairly evenly over the whole body: they are actually situated between the two layers of cells known as the ectoderm and endoderm. This diffuse nature of the nervous system is possibly due to *Hydra's* mode of life: it is sedentary; that is, it remains in one place most of the time, waiting for food to come to it rather than going about hunting for it. The food, which consists largely of fast-moving water fleas, may approach from any direction, and hence the *Hydra* needs to be able to detect their presence on all sides. The animal, which is symmetrical about its long axis, is

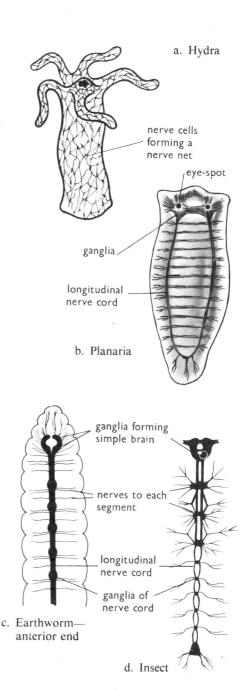

a. Hydra

nerve cells forming a nerve net

eye-spot

ganglia

longitudinal nerve cord

b. Planaria

ganglia forming simple brain

nerves to each segment

longitudinal nerve cord

ganglia of nerve cord

c. Earthworm—anterior end

d. Insect

FIG. 17.2. Nerve systems of increasing complexity from a to d.

179

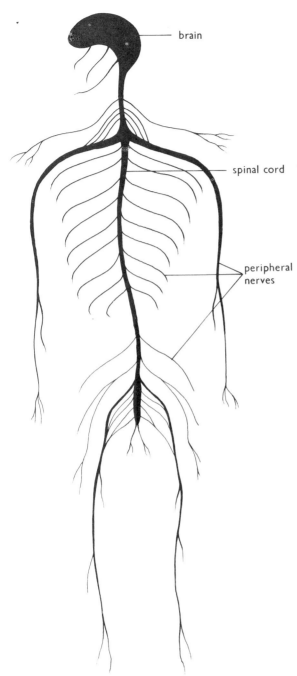

brain

spinal cord

peripheral
nerves

FIG. 17.3 The central nervous system and the
peripheral nerves of Man. Sense organs
and autonomic nervous system are not
shown.

said to be *radially symmetrical* and this shape is typical of sedentary animals. It contrasts with the shape of the *Planaria* as does its type of nervous system. *Planaria* has a certain amount of specialisation of the nervous system and this becomes increasingly obvious as we proceed to the higher animals. *Planaria* shows the beginning of a head in that its sense organs are slightly concentrated there as is part of the nervous system, which forms a simple 'brain' in that region. The concentration of sense organs and of the brain at the end which moves first when the animal is in motion is typical of *bilaterally symmetrical* animals, most of which move about a great deal. The end which goes forward first obviously is more likely to meet with either food or danger before the posterior end and hence it is not surprising to find the sense organs and brain in the head.

In the *earthworm* the nervous system is even more centralised for instead of two longitudinal nerve cords there is only one and the 'brain' is more complex than is that of *Planaria*. Certain nerve cells are gathered together in groups to form the 'brain' in these simple animals and these groups are referred to as *ganglia* (Fig. 17.2). The nervous system of the *insects* is again more centralised and efficient than that of the worms: we would expect to find this to be so for the insects are an efficient and fast-moving group of animals —perhaps the most successful group that has so far evolved as far as numbers of species and types of habitat exploited are concerned.

Finally we come to the vertebrate animals and here the nervous system is very complex and efficient reaching its highest degree of development, in regard to both structure and function, in the mammals and especially in Man himself.

The *nervous system* of Man (Fig. 17.3) is composed of the *sense organs*, the *brain* and *spinal cord*, and the *peripheral nerves*. These parts of the nervous system are concerned mainly with external stimuli but there is another important part whose function is to deal with internal stimuli. This part of the nervous system is called the *autonomic nervous system* and it serves the cardiac muscles of the heart and the involuntary muscles such as those of the blood vessels and glands.

The Histology of the Nervous System

The cells which make up the nervous system are specially sensitive and are called *neurones*. They are supported in some parts of the nervous system by cells known as *neuroglia*. The neurones are unusual in shape: they may be seen in Plate 51 and Figs. 17.4 and 17.6. They are of three types: firstly

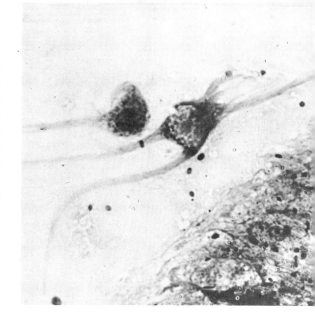

PLATE 51. Neurones (approximately × 225).

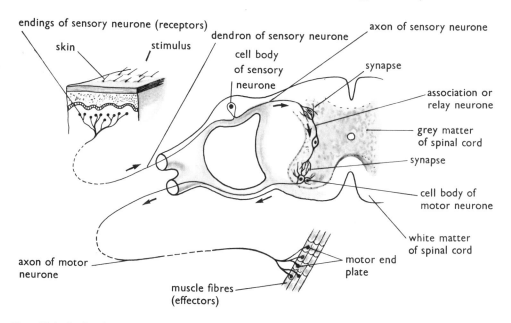

FIG. 17.4. A simple arrangement of three neurones linking the skin with a muscle. The nerve impulse passes from the receptors in the skin along the sensory neurone, across a synapse to a relay neurone and on across another synapse to the motor neurone and hence to the muscle. The direction of the impulse is shown by the small arrows.

181

there are *sensory neurones* which receive messages and pass them to the spinal cord and brain; secondly there are *association neurones* which pass messages on from one neurone to another; and thirdly there are *motor neurones* which pass messages from the brain and the spinal cord to muscles or glands. The simplest arrangement of neurones is theoretically three as is shown in Fig. 17.4 but in fact usually many neurones are concerned with taking even the simplest message. The cell or organ which receives the stimulus is called the *receptor* while the cell or tissue which reacts is the *effector*. Muscles and glands are effectors. The ends of sensory neurones are of three types: *exteroceptors* (sense stimuli from outside the body), *enteroceptors* (sense stimuli in the intestine and other internal organs), and *proprioceptors* which can detect tension in muscles and tendons.

Thus exteroceptors are concerned with factors in the environment—sound vibrations, light waves, chemicals, etc.—and tell us about our surroundings while enteroceptors inform us about our internal state—information leading to sensations such as hunger, stomach ache and thirst. Proprioceptors are concerned with balance and posture and the position of our body in space. Stimulation of the proprioceptors helps to co-ordinate the action of our muscles. Fig. 17.5 shows sensory endings of neurones of the proprioceptor and exteroceptor type.

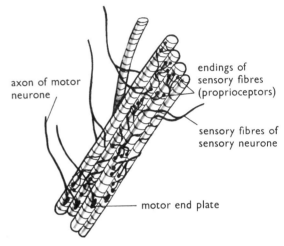

axon of motor neurone

endings of sensory fibres (proprioceptors)

sensory fibres of sensory neurone

motor end plate

a. Proprioceptors are stimulated by tension in the muscle. Motor end plates are also shown, the impulses arriving to the muscle along the motor neurone.

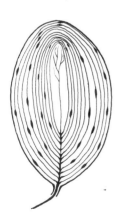

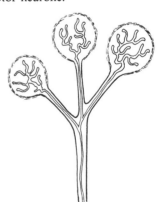

b. Lamellated corpuscle (pressure)

c. Oval corpuscles (warmth)

d. Bulbous corpuscles (cold)

FIG. 17.5. RECEPTORS. a. Proprioceptors. b–d. Exteroceptors.

Fig. 17.6 shows in more detail the structure of motor and sensory neurones. The portion of the cell which contains the nucleus is known as the *cell body* or *cyton*; the threads of protoplasm which bring the nerve message towards the cell body are called *dendrons* while that which takes the message away from the cell body is the *axon*. Notice that the cell body of the sensory neurone lies slightly to one side of the dendron and axon. The cell bodies of both motor and sensory neurones contain *Nissl's granules* whose function is possibly that of protein synthesis. The axons and dendrites are frequently referred to as *nerve fibres* and they may be individually covered by a sheath of fatty substance— *myelin*.

The myelin sheath insulates one fibre from another, when they are said to be *myelinated* or *medullated*. This myelin sheath is not continuous but is interrupted at intervals by *nodes of Ranvier*. External to the sheath is a thin membrane called the *neurilemma* secreted by *Schwann cells* whose nuclei lie just below it. *Non-myelinated* or *non-medullated* neurones possess a neurilemma but are not covered by myelin.

Myelinated fibres form the *white matter* of the *central nervous system*, as the brain and spinal cord together are called. Non-myelin-ated fibres form the *grey matter* (Fig. 17.4 and Plate 52). The neurilemma is not found in the brain and spinal cord. Instead, the nerve cells of the central nervous system are supported by the neuroglia cells.

When the nerve message, or *nerve impulse* as it is called, reaches the end of a nerve fibre it must be passed on to the next fibre: the place where the impulse is passed on is known as a *synapse*. The space between the ends of the two fibres at a synapse is less than two millionths of a centimetre in width.

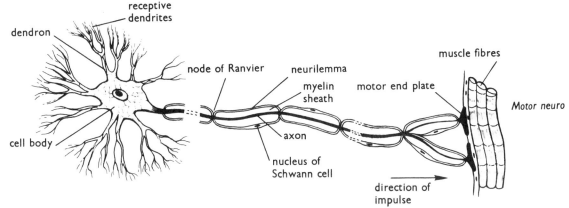

FIG. 17.6. NEURONES.

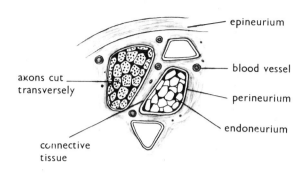

epineurium

blood vessel

axons cut
transversely

perineurium

endoneurium

connective
tissue

FIG. 17.7. A large nerve cut transversely to
show the way in which the fibres are
grouped in bundles.

Nerves are collections of axons or dendrons running parallel to each other: many hundreds or even thousands may be found in a single nerve. The larger nerves are easily visible to the naked eye and may be observed as white strands during dissections. A transverse section of a nerve reveals the axons cut through and this is shown in Plate 53 and Fig. 17.7. In a large nerve the bundles of fibres are grouped together and bounded by connective tissue which forms a sheath called the *perineurium*. The *endoneurium* holds the fibres of individual bundles together. A really large nerve, such as the sciatic nerve of the leg, contains a large number of bundles, each surrounded by their perineurium, bound together by the *epineurium*.

PLATE 52. Transverse section of the spinal cord.

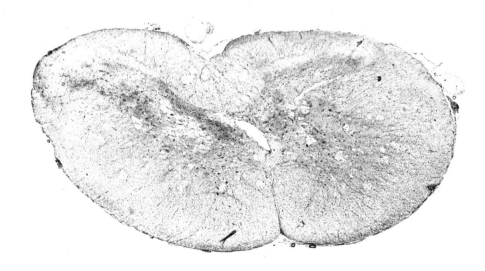

The Nerve Impulse

Fig. 17.4 shows the simplest possible arrangement of neurones. How does the nerve impulse travel along the neurones and how does it cross the synapses? The exact details are beyond the scope of this book and are indeed not yet fully understood. However, it may be briefly stated that the conduction of the nerve impulse is partly chemical and partly electrical. The surface of the nerve fibre is positively charged electrically and stimulating the surface by mechanical or electrical means causes the positive charge to disappear. This is called *depolarisation* and a wave of depolarisation sweeps over the surface along the whole length of the fibre as a *nerve impulse*. The small portion of a fibre which has been depolarised becomes re-polarised very quickly so that in less than one thousandth of a second the nerve fibre is ready to conduct another impulse. Depolarisation and repolarisation are brought about by the passage of potassium and sodium ions through the membrane of the axon.

Both the speed and strength of a nerve impulse are constant—the nerve works on the 'all-or-nothing' principle—and variations in the strength of messages depend on the *frequency* at which impulses are sent along a fibre. A strong message, such as that resulting from someone stamping on your toe, has many impulses in a given time, while a weak message would have far fewer. Human nerve fibres can transmit over 300 impulses a second. After each impulse there is a short period of recovery known as the *refractory period*. The speed at which a nerve impulse travels may be as much as 50 m/s in some animals.

The synapse, as has been mentioned, may be only two millionths of a centimetre across. It is believed that the nerve impulse is passed across the tiny space by a chemical transmitter substance which is produced at the end of the fibre on the arrival of an impulse. It is also thought that the contraction of a muscle fibre is initiated by a substance—*acetyl choline*—released at the end of an axon when a nerve impulse arrives there. The end of the axon is known as a *motor end plate* (Figs. 17.4 and 17.6).

Sensations and Sense Organs

Under another section of this chapter we saw that messages arrive from the outside environment and stimulate sensory neurones known as receptors. We now have to consider the kinds of sensations which arise from stimulation of these sensory neurone endings and their arrangement in the body.

We are conscious of eight types of sensation and we will study each in turn. The eight types are:

1. Pressure and touch	5. Taste
2. Temperature	6. Hearing
3. Pain	7. Balance
4. Smell	8. Sight

Pressure and Touch. These sensations arise from stimulation of nerve endings known as *lamellated corpuscles* which are found in the skin. Their distribution is not even, some parts of the skin being more sensitive than others. The tips of the fingers contain many touch receptors and hence their sensitive nature (Fig. 17.5).

Temperature. *Bulbous* and *oval corpuscles* (Fig. 17.5) can detect cold and heat respectively. Here again we find an uneven distribution of the receptors: the skin over the elbows and the backs of the hands is particularly sensitive to temperature.

Pain. The sensation of *pain* arises when any of the pressure, touch or temperature receptors are over-stimulated. This, of course, is biologically valuable for it enables us quickly to become aware of danger—for example if we pick up an object which is likely to burn the skin if not quickly dropped. In such a case the nerve impulses—all of equal speed and strength—would be sent in large numbers along the neurones and give rise to strong sensations. In a pleasant sensation of warmth, such as might be experienced in sun-bathing, the impulses would be far fewer in number. Again over-stimulation of the pressure receptors might serve as a warning that we were being crushed.

Smell. Fig. 17.8 shows the *olfactory nerve plexus*: a group of nerves serving to take the impulses from the *olfactory mucous membrane* to the brain where they are interpreted as *smell*. The mucous membrane itself contains sense cells which are sensitive to chemicals in solution. The chemicals arrive in the air breathed in through the nose and dissolve in the liquid covering the mucous membrane: they must be in solution before they can stimulate the sense cells. This is why our sense of smell seems to disappear on a very hot dry summer day—the heat dries the lining of the nose. It also explains why we cannot detect smells when we have a cold for the excessive amount of mucus produced on such occasions prevents the chemicals reaching the sense cells.

The arrows in Fig. 17.8 indicate that chemicals may be given off from the food we eat into the air in the buccal cavity: this

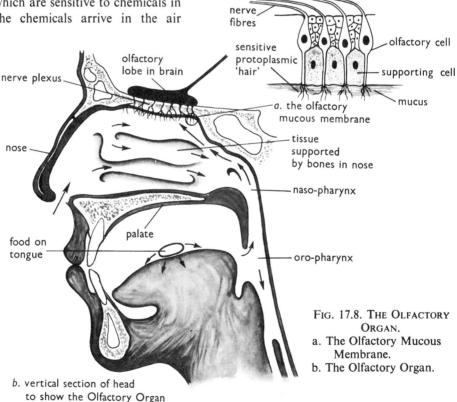

FIG. 17.8. THE OLFACTORY ORGAN.
a. The Olfactory Mucous Membrane.
b. The Olfactory Organ.

186

mixes with the air in the nose and hence the sensations of smell and taste are not always easily separated

Like pain, the sensation of smell is biologically useful, for it enables us to detect the presence of harmful substances—such as bad food. In other animals the sense of smell is frequently better developed than it is in Man and they rely upon it to a much greater extent, for their very life may depend upon detecting the presence of enemies or of food by means of the smell given off from them.

The dogfish hunts almost entirely by smell. Some animals rely on smell to direct them towards a mate: certain moths, for example, are able to detect the smell arising from a potential mate from a very considerable distance away. And we are all familiar with the use of scents and perfumes by human females to make themselves attractive to the opposite sex.

Taste. The sensation of *taste* arises from receptors in the mouth and in particular on the tongue. The receptors are situated on projections on the upper surface of the tongue known as *papillae* and are known as *taste buds* (Fig. 17.9).

The papillae are of three main shapes—*filiform, fungiform* and *foliate* (see also in Fig. 17.9). This figure shows that different areas of the tongue can detect different flavours. These are *sweet* and *salt* at the front of the tongue, *sour* at the sides and *bitter* at the back.

As was the case with the sensation known as smell the chemicals giving rise to the sensation of taste must be in solution: they then stimulate the receptors which send nerve impulses to the taste centres of the brain.

Biologically, taste enables animals to determine whether or not they are eating materials suitable for food. In Man different flavours give rise to different pleasant sensations.

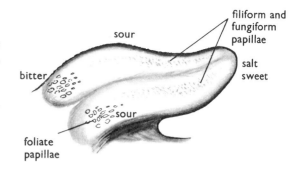

a. The areas of the tongue sensitive to different tastes

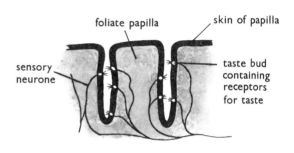

b. A taste papilla from the back of the tongue

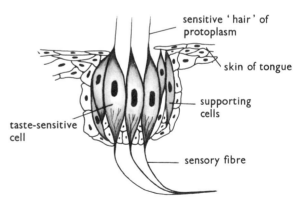

c. An enlarged diagram of a taste bud

FIG. 17.9. THE ORGAN OF TASTE.

Hearing and Balance. These two sensations are dealt with together here because the same sense organ—the *ear*—is involved. The structure of the ear is very complex compared with that of the sense organs already considered: reference to Figs. 17.10, 17.11 and 17.12 will help you to understand the following description.

The ear is composed of three regions—an *outer ear* or *pinna*, a *middle ear* and an *inner ear*.

The *pinna* is relatively unimportant in Man but in many animals it is large and movable and not only acts as a trumpet to pick up sound vibrations but is also a means of ascertaining from which direction the sound is coming. This is important in animals such as the zebra whose life may depend on detecting the direction from which a lion is approaching to attack it. It is worth noting the size of the external ears of these animals during your next visit to a zoo. Note also the way in which the ears are constantly moving. In some animals the accuracy with which the position of two sounds can be distinguished is almost unbelievable: for example, cats can distinguish between the position of two sources of sounds when they are only half a metre apart and 18 metres away. Dogs have been shown to be able to distinguish the position of two sounds 15 cm. apart and 5 metres away. From the pinna a tube—the *external auditory meatus*—leads inwards towards the middle ear from which it is separated by the *ear drum* or *tympanic membrane*. The tympanic membrane is made of many fibres of different lengths which allow it to vibrate to sound waves of different frequencies. The walls of the external auditory meatus contain glands which secrete wax. This helps to keep the tympanic membrane pliable and affords it some protection. The meatus is also protected to some extent by hairs which help to keep out dust particles and small insects.

The *middle ear* lies beyond the tympanic membrane and consists of a small chamber containing three tiny bones or *ear ossicles* as they are called. These bones are shown in Fig. 17.11 removed from the ear. The first of these bones is attached to the tympanic membrane and is called the *malleus* or *hammer*. At the opposite end of the middle ear is the ossicle known from its shape as the *stapes* or *stirrup*. The *incus* or *anvil* connects the malleus and stapes. Thus the three bones form a connection across the middle ear by means of which vibrations, which have passed down the external auditory meatus as air vibrations and set the tympanum in motion, can be transmitted to the inner ear. The ear ossicles also act as levers increasing the power of the vibrations. The stapes fits over an *oval window* or *fenestra ovalis* which leads to the inner ear.

Opening into the middle ear from the pharynx (page 138) is a *Eustachian tube* whose purpose is to keep the air pressure in the middle ear the same as that of the atmosphere. If changes in air pressure take place outside the ear drum the pressure is equalised by the Eustachian tube's admitting air to, or releasing air from, the middle ear. This equalising of air pressure may become necessary when one goes up in an aeroplane or ascends a high mountain. The Eustachian tube sometimes becomes blocked—as, for example, when we have a cold and air pressure adjustments are then impossible and our hearing may be affected adversely.

The Eustachian tubes are normally closed but open when we yawn or swallow: at such times a 'popping' sound may sometimes be heard.

The *inner ear* is the most complex part of the whole organ and contains the receptor

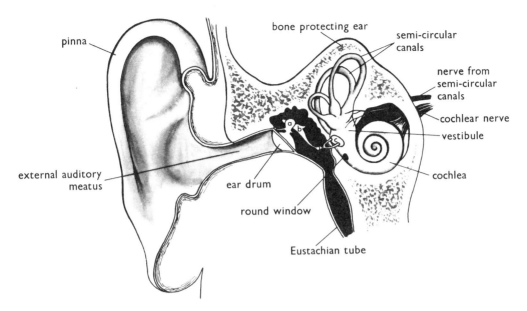

FIG. 17.10. The ear. For the sake of clarity the bone cavity in which the ear lies has been omitted. a, b, and c are the ear ossicles which transmit vibrations across the ear. Should they become fused, as sometimes happens with advancing age, the person will become deaf.

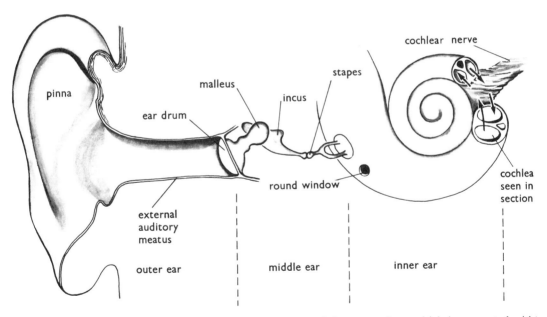

FIG. 17.11. Diagrammatic representation of the structure of that part of ear which is connected with hearing. Parts are not to scale.

cells which are sensitive to vibrations and which send nerve impulses along the *auditory nerve* to the brain. The inner ear consists of a *membranous labyrinth* of complex shape which fits into a bony labyrinth of the same shape. The solid nature of the thick bone in this region of the skull affords good protection to the delicate parts of the ear. Further 'shock absorbing' protection is given by the fact that the space between the bone and the membranous labyrinth is filled with a fluid. This liquid is called the *perilymph*. The membranous labyrinth is itself filled with *endolymph*.

The labyrinth is formed of three main parts—the *vestibule*, the *semi-circular canals* and the *cochlea*. This last structure is a spirally coiled duct and is the organ concerned with hearing. The cochlea arises from the *sacculus* of the vestibule and also has a connection with the middle ear by means of the *fenestra cochlea*. The semi-circular canals arise from the *utriculus* of the vestibule and form the part of the ear concerned with balance. The three canals are at right angles

to one another, one in each plane. Each is hollow and contains endolymph in which float small particles of calcium carbonate. When the head is moved these particles fall on to sensitive cells in the semi-circular canals, stimulating them to send nerve impulses along the auditory nerve to the brain, enabling balance to be maintained. The ends of the semi-circular canals are enlarged to form *ampullae* which also contain sensitive cells which help to maintain balance.

The structure of the cochlea is seen in Figs. 17.10, 17.11 and 17.12. It is seen that a section through it reveals three tubes, the *scala vestibuli* (which is continuous with the vestibule), the *scala media* and the *scala tympani*. This last is in contact with the middle ear at the *fenestra rotunda* but separated from it by a membrane. The scala media contains sensitive hair cells which are stimulated by movements of a *tectorial membrane* which is moved by vibrations of the endolymph. The nerve impulses thus set up pass along the auditory nerve to the brain.

The sequence of events leading to a person

a. A section through the Cochlea

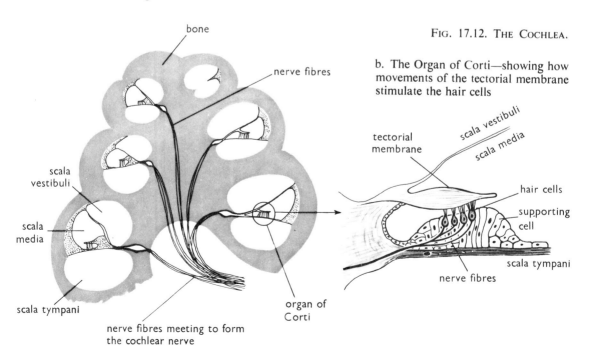

Fig. 17.12. The Cochlea.

b. The Organ of Corti—showing how movements of the tectorial membrane stimulate the hair cells

hearing a sound is as follows: sounds enter the pinna as air vibrations and pass down the external auditory meatus to the tympanic membrane which is thus caused to vibrate. The vibrations are transmitted by the ear ossicles across the middle ear, being much amplified on the way, to the fenestra ovalis which is an opening covered by a membrane which is caused to vibrate. The vibrations of this membrane set the fluids of the cochlea vibrating and this in turn moves a tectorial membrane which stimulates 'hair cells' to send nerve impulses to the brain.

The cochlea enables us to distinguish high notes from low but the exact mechanism involved is beyond the scope of this book. Notes of frequencies ranging from 20 to 20,000 cycles per second can be heard by Man. Some animals have a different range of notes from those which Man can hear. Some of the notes made by bats (and hence those heard by bats) are too high for the human ear to detect: in fact only people with good hearing can hear any of the notes made by bats. The 'soundless' dog whistle depends on the fact that dogs can hear notes which are beyond those which Man can hear.

Sight. The function of sensitivity to light in the mammals is possessed by special cells confined to the eyes. The eye is in fact designed to produce a clear image on a layer of light-sensitive cells. The structure and functioning of the eye is perhaps the most wonderful of all the phenomena found in nature for not only does the eye enable us to see objects clearly but it can focus on objects which are far away and almost instantaneously re-focus on near objects. Eyes can also function in lights of different intensity and can reveal to us the important factor of colour. We must remember, of course, as with the other sense organs, that the organ itself only receives stimuli—in this case light

waves—and relays messages by means of nerves to the brain. It is the brain which interprets what we see as vision.

It must not be imagined that sensitivity to light is confined to the mammals, however. Light-sensitive cells are found in animals as simple as some of *Hydra's* near relatives— the jellyfish for example. *Planaria*, as we have seen, also has cells which are sensitive to light: these are collected together in the 'eye spots'. These light-sensitive cells are not able to form images, as is the vertebrate eye, but they can enable the animals to distinguish the position from which light is coming. *Planaria* will move away from bright light to places of dim light—places such as may be found under damp leaves which are more suitable to its mode of life. Even the lowly *Amoeba* is sensitive to light.

The more complex invertebrates such as the crabs, crayfish, lobsters and insects have more complex eyes. These animals have what are known as *compound eyes* which consist of thousands of simple eyes aggregated together to give a mosaic picture. The increase in complexity of the eye is, of course, accompanied by an increase in the efficiency of the nervous system. This reaches quite a high level in the insects, where the individual facets of the compound eye produce an overlapping pattern which is particularly efficient at detecting movements. This ability to notice movement will be familiar to anyone who has attempted to catch butterflies or moths and it forms an important aspect of the animals' escape mechanism.

It is interesting to note that the squids and octopuses have eyes which are very similar in structure and in functioning to the vertebrate eye although their origin in the embryo is completely different.

When we come to look at the eyes of vertebrates we find that they are all built on a similar plan. This we may call the camera type of eye in contrast to the mosaic type of most invertebrates. (The squids and octopuses, alone amongst the invertebrates, have eyes of the camera type.) The camera type of eye consists essentially of: a light-proof box with a small hole in the front, a hole whose diameter may be altered according to need; a lens for focusing; and a layer of light-sensitive cells corresponding to the film of the camera. There are, of course, differences in detail between vertebrate eyes but they all work on the 'camera plan'. Fishes, amphibians and birds focus by altering the position of the lens while reptiles and mammals focus by changing the shape or curvature of the lens. It is worth noting that the eyes of birds are as efficient, and in some respects more efficient, than those of mammals. For example the bird eye can focus more rapidly than the

mammalian eye—an adaptation which helps them to catch food when flying at high speeds. Vision is very acute in birds as is shown by the ease with which swifts catch tiny insects in flight; the kestrels, buzzards, kites and other birds of prey, when they are flying very high, spot small animals on the ground and swoop upon them with unerring aim. Some birds such as owls have especially acute vision at night: their eyes are large and adapted to make the best use of the little light available at dawn and dusk.

Fig. 17.13 shows the parts of the eye and the surrounding tissues viewed from in front. The eyebrows and eyelashes help to prevent particles of dust from falling on to the eye itself. The upper lid is movable and each time we blink it washes the surface of the eye free of any particles which may have fallen on it.

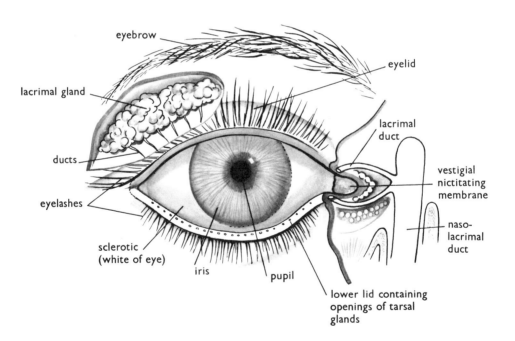

FIG. 17.13. The eye and associated structures viewed from in front.

192

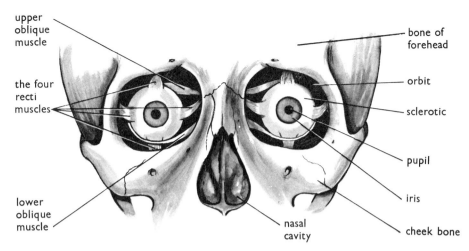

upper oblique muscle

the four recti muscles

lower oblique muscle

bone of forehead

orbit

sclerotic

pupil

iris

nasal cavity

cheek bone

FIG. 17.14. THE EYES AND THE EYE MUSCLES.

The lower lid moves only slightly in human beings. In the inner corner of the eye is a small triangular prominence which represents a third eyelid found in amphibians and called the *nictitating membrane*. The edges of the eyelids contain the openings of tiny *tarsal glands* whose function is to secrete fluid which prevents the lids from sticking together. These glands should not be confused with the *lacrimal glands* which continuously secrete *tears* over the surface of the eye to wash it and lubricate it. The liquid secreted contains an enzyme (lysozyme) which destroys bacteria. Normally the tears produced are sufficient only to wash the eye so that we do not really notice them, but emotional stress, or the presence of a foreign particle on the surface of the eye, stimulates the lacrimal glands to such great activity that the fluid may form as drops normally known as *tears*. The lacrimal glands are to be found above the eye and towards the outside of it. At the inner corners of the eye two small ducts— the *lacrimal ducts*—drain the tears away from the eye and into the nose (Fig. 17.13).

The parts of the eye itself which can be seen from the front, while the eye is still in place, are the *pupil*, the *iris* and the *white of the eye.*

The pupil is a hole in the iris the size of which can be altered according to the light intensity. The iris is the coloured part of the eye. Over the surface of the eye is the protective *conjunctiva.*

The eyes lie in bony sockets in the skull known as *orbits*. In Man they face the front in contrast to some mammals such as the rabbit. Each eye is held in its socket by the *optic nerve* and by muscles. The eye muscles are shown in Figs. 17.14 and 17.15. They are responsible for moving the eye in all directions—

FIG. 17.15. The eye muscles of the left eye seen from the side.

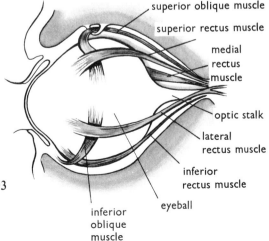

superior oblique muscle

superior rectus muscle

medial rectus muscle

optic stalk

lateral rectus muscle

inferior rectus muscle

eyeball

inferior oblique muscle

193

the eye is a very mobile organ. There are three pairs of eye muscles. The *superior* and *inferior rectus muscles* oppose one another in turning the eyeball upwards and downwards respectively. The *exterior* and *interior rectus muscles* turn the eye outwards and inwards respectively. Lastly the *superior* and *inferior oblique muscles* enable oblique movements to be made. By a combination of contractions of these muscles the eye can be moved accurately in any direction over a wide field of vision.

The internal structure of the eye is best seen in a vertical section (Fig. 17.16). The light-proof box of the camera is represented here by the *sclerotic*—a tough layer of fibrous nature whose anterior face is modified as a slight bulge of transparent material known as the *cornea*. This cornea is protected by the *conjunctiva* already mentioned. Next to the sclerotic and internal to it is a nutritive layer rich in blood vessels called the *choroid*. This layer supplies the innermost layer—the *retina*—with food and oxygen. This is important as the retina is a very active tissue. The retina itself is composed of light-sensitive cells and, as has already been mentioned, corresponds to the film of the camera. Its detailed structure will be considered later.

At the front of the eye the choroid gives

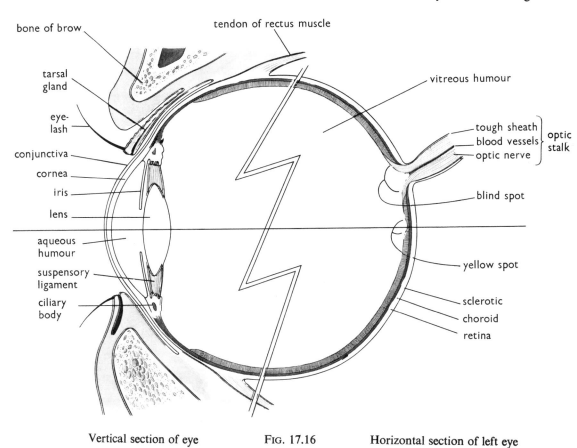

Vertical section of eye   Fig. 17.16   Horizontal section of left eye

194

way to the *iris diaphragm* which functions in a manner similar to the diaphragm of a camera (Fig. 17.17). It consists of a circle of tissue with a hole in the centre, called the *pupil*, the size of which can be varied according to the light intensity. In bright light the pupil becomes small but in poor light it increases in size to make the most of whatever light is available. The iris contains coloured pigments which make it opaque.

Behind the iris and supported by *suspensory ligaments* is the lens (Fig. 17.17). It is made of transparent cells which are surrounded by an elastic capsule. This gives to the lens an elasticity which enables its shape to be altered by variations in the tension of the suspensory ligament, thus allowing the focal length of the lens to be changed. The purpose of this will be described later. The suspensory ligaments are attached at the edge of the eye to the *ciliary bodies* which contain circular muscles whose contraction and relaxation can alter the tension on the suspensory ligaments. Another function of the ciliary bodies is to produce the *aqueous humour*—the liquid which fills the *anterior chamber* which lies in front of the lens. Behind the lens is the *posterior chamber* containing the *vitreous humour*.

From the posterior edge of the eye the *optic nerve* leaves the eye and passes towards the brain. It is enclosed in a tough material with which it forms the *optic stalk*.

The structure of the light-sensitive layer, the retina, deserves more detailed consideration. On its posterior surface are two areas: one which is particularly sensitive to light stimulation and the other which is completely insensitive because it does not contain any receptor cells. This latter area is called the *blind spot* and it is at this point that the blood vessels serving the retina enter and leave the eyeball. It is also the place where the nerve fibres from all parts of the retina leave the eye.

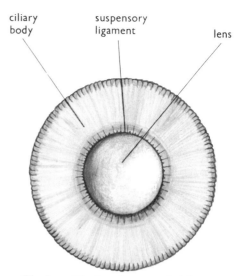

a. The lens. The lens is suspended from the ciliary body by the suspensory ligaments

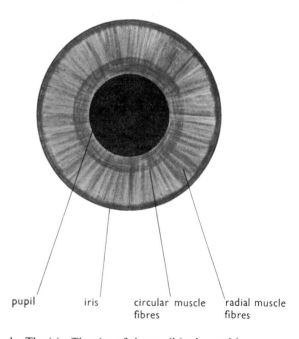

b. The iris. The size of the pupil is changed by contraction and relaxation of the iris muscles

FIG. 17.17. THE LENS AND THE IRIS.

195

Owing to the mode of development of the eye the nerve fibres are on the outer surface of the retina, and light which is going to stimulate the receptor cells has to pass through a layer of fibres before it can do so.

The very sensitive area is called the *yellow spot* and its central portion—the area of most acute vision—is known as the *fovea centralis*. Both the blind spot and the yellow spot are shown in Fig. 17.18 which is of the part of the retina seen when the eye is looked at through a special instrument—the *ophthalmoscope*—which shines a beam of light through the pupil on to the retina.

Note that the light rays must pass through a number of layers of cells *before* they can stimulate the rods and cones.

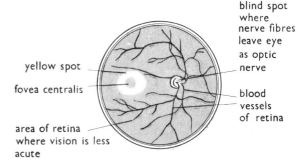

FIG. 17.18. View of retina of right eye as seen through an ophthalmoscope.

Fig. 17.19 gives an idea of the histology of the retina. It will be seen that the receptor cells of the retina are of two types—the *rods* and the *cones*. Rods are sensitive to intensity of light while cones are concerned with colour vision. The fovea centralis contains cones only. When the pupil is wide open, as it is in dim light, a large part of the retina undergoes stimulation and since this part contains mainly rods we see no bright colours—at dawn and dusk we tend to see everything in terms of grey. In bright light, however, the pupil is small and the light falls largely on the fovea with the result that the cones are strongly stimulated and we see bright colours.

As the light intensity decreases the cones cease to respond and the rods take over. Conversely as the light intensity increases the rods appear to lose their sensitivity and the cones become more important.

The actual stimulus to the receptors is chemical, for the receptors contain pigments which break down in the presence of light to form chemicals which trigger off impulses which proceed along nerve fibres to the brain. The pigment concerned is known as *visual purple* and is closely related to Vitamin A—this is one reason why Vitamin A should be included in the diet.

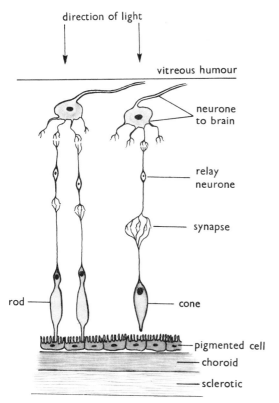

FIG. 17.19. Histology of the retina. The choroid and sclerotic layers are not to the same scale as the retina but are shown to help understand the position of the retina.

The formation of an image on the retina is shown in Fig. 17.20. It is upside down and reversed from side to side but the brain, soon after the birth of the baby, learns to interpret the image the correct way up and the right way round. The lens is biconvex but the posterior surface is more strongly curved than is the anterior. As light enters the eye it is bent to some extent by the lens but mostly by the cornea and aqueous humour. In the diagrams only the bending effect of the lens is shown.

Rays of light coming from distant objects —that is those which are more than 6 m away—are parallel (Fig. 17.20), but those coming from nearer objects radiate. Thus for near objects a more convex lens is required. This is obtained by a *contraction* of the *ciliary muscles*, which releases the tension on the suspensory ligaments and thus allows the lens to bulge under its own natural elasticity.

It may seem strange that a release of tension on the suspensory ligaments is obtained by a *contraction* of a muscle but this will be understood when it is remembered that the ciliary muscles are circular muscles. Similarly a relaxing of the ciliary muscles leads to an increase on the tension of the suspensory ligaments which then pull the lens into *a less biconvex* shape which is necessary for looking at an object which is far away. This wonderful ability of the lens to alter its shape and thus to focus both near and far objects accurately on the retina is called *accommodation*.

It has already been mentioned that the function of the *iris* is to control the amount of light coming into the eye. It contains both circular and radial muscle fibres. The muscles are, of course, involuntary muscles and are not under the control of the will. We do not have to think every time there is a change in light intensity: the iris muscles work automatically. The circular muscles contract to make the pupil smaller in bright light and the radial muscles contract to make it larger in light of low intensity.

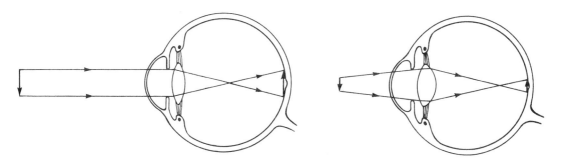

a. Object at a distance. When the object is more than 6 m away the rays may be regarded as parallel coming from it: they are brought to a focus on the retina by the lens.

b. Object near, i.e. less than 6 m away. Rays of light radiate from the object so that the lens is more strongly convex than in a. This stronger lens shape brings the rays in focus on the retina.

FIG. 17.20. Formation of an image on the retina and accommodation.

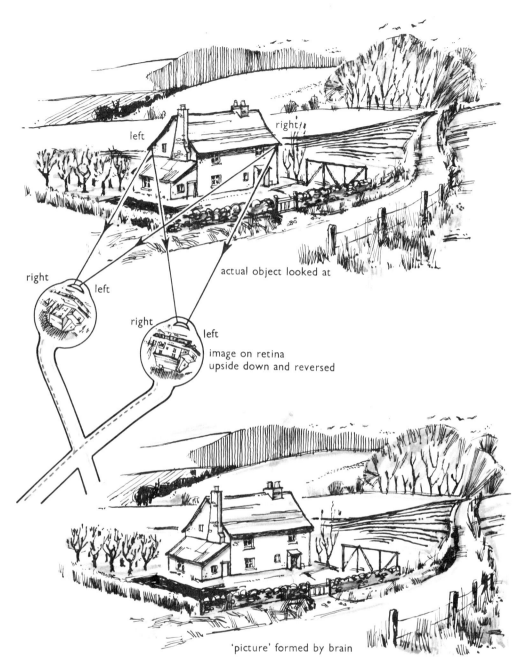

left

right

right

left

actual object looked at

right

left

image on retina
upside down and reversed

'picture' formed by brain

FIG. 17.21. Stereoscopic Vision. The view seen by the left eye is not quite the same as that seen by the right eye. The two images formed on the retina enable the brain to give a three-dimensional picture. Note that the image formed on the retina is upside down and reversed from side to side: the brain is able to reverse the picture again so that we see it the 'correct' way up and correct from side to side.

When we look at something—be it near or far—the view seen by the left eye is slightly different from that seen by the right eye (Fig. 17.21). Thus there are two slightly different images formed on the retina: these are fused in the *visual centres* of the brain to give a three-dimensional picture, that is, one which enables us to appreciate depth, distance, height and width. This is known as *stereoscopic vision*. Our recognition of distance and solidity is also helped by such factors as perspective—the way in which straight parallel lines appear to converge with distance, by light and shade on the surface of an object and by the fact that colours appear to fade as distance from the eye increases. Also distant objects are less distinct than those near at hand.

There are several common defects and diseases of the eye about which it is interesting to know a little. One of the commonest defects is known as *long sight* or *hypermetropia*. In this condition—which is particularly common in people of forty years of age whose ciliary muscles are beginning to tire and whose lenses are losing some of their elasticity—the focal point is behind the retina and the image is therefore blurred (Fig. 17.22). This defect may be corrected by fitting spectacles with a convex lens.

Short sight or *myopia* is a defect in which the focal point of the lens lies in front of the retina and hence a blurred image is formed. This may be corrected by use of a concave lens as is shown in Fig. 17.22.

Short sight and long sight may also be

FIG. 17.22. SHORT AND LONG SIGHTEDNESS.

a. Long sight and its correction. The lens does not bend the light sufficiently and the image is formed *behind* the retina. Correction is by means of a biconvex lens which bends the rays more sharply than the natural lens.

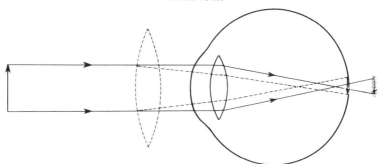

b. Short sight and its correction. The natural lens is too convex and brings the image into focus *in front* of the retina. Correction is by means of spectacles with concave lenses. These bend the light as shown thus enabling an image to be formed on the retina.

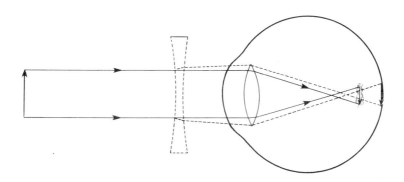

caused by a change in shape of the eyeball: in the former case the eyeball is too long while in the latter case it is too short.

The hardening of the lens which sometimes occurs in older people and which leads to a loss in the power of accommodation, with the consequence that near objects, such as the page of a book, cannot be clearly seen, is frequently called *presbyopia*.

Astigmatism is a defect in which horizontal and vertical lines are not seen with equal clarity and hence print, for example, cannot be clearly seen. Astigmatism was first described by an Englishman named Thomas Young in 1793. The defect usually occurs together with short or long sight. It is usually due to a defect in the cornea and only rarely in the lens.

Colour blindness is a defect which is frequently inherited and which is linked with sex (see also Chapter 23), for it is more common in men than in women, there being between 4 and 8% of men affected and only about ·4% of women. Few people are completely colour blind but some are unable to distinguish the various shades of reds and greens while others find difficulty in distinguishing shades of yellows and blues.

Blindness is a condition where vision is lacking in one or both eyes to a marked degree and is due to a variety of causes the most common of which, in the western countries, is *venereal disease*. In other countries the major eye disease may be different: for example, *trachoma*—a disease in which the conjunctiva and later the cornea is affected by a virus—is the commonest cause of blindness in Egypt and is very common in Russia and China. It is a disease associated with squalid and unhygienic conditions. Blindness is commoner in countries possessing poor medical services and sanitary facilities, the condition being commonest in Tunisia

(400 per 100,000 of population) and least common in New Zealand (32 per 100,000).

Conjunctivitis in this country is common amongst young people and is often associated with eyestrain sometimes due to too much study! It is a condition in which the conjunctiva becomes red and is accompanied by an intense itching which leads to a large flow of tears.

Good habits in connection with eyesight will be considered in Chapter 30.

No account of human biology would be complete without reference to the work done by great men down the ages in their attempts to better the living conditions and happiness of their fellow men. One such man who brought a measure of happiness and interest into the lives of thousands of blind men and women was *Louis Braille*, 1809–1852, a Frenchman born in the village of Coupvray near Paris. He was himself blind. At the age of three Louis was playing in the workshop of his father who was a saddlemaker. An awl slipped and went into his eye; he soon became totally blind. When he was a man, Louis went to teach at the National Institute for the Young Blind in Paris and worked on endless ideas to try to help those unfortunate children to learn to read. All his efforts were to no avail until one night in a cafe he met a captain of the French Army who told him about 'night-writing'. This was a system used in the army at night when it was too dangerous to use a light. It consisted of coded marks punched in a thick paper.

Braille thought about what the army captain had told him and he soon devised a system consisting of forty-three symbols by means of which the entire alphabet, pronunciation marks and numerals could be expressed by punched holes. Music too can be read in Braille as Louis' system is now called; indeed it can be read faster that way than by the ordinary visual method. There now exist large libraries of books and of music in Braille in almost all major languages. Braille is 'read' by passing the tips of the fingers over raised dots on the paper. As is often the case with inventors of wonderful benefits to mankind, Braille gained little for himself for his trouble. Braille died from tuberculosis at the age of forty-three, alone and penniless. During his lifetime he met only with scorn and it was not until after his death that his system was adopted.

History records that many people have been helped by the system of reading invented by Louis Braille but few have achieved more fame than the American Helen Keller whose life is an inspiring example of courage and determination in the face of great difficulty. Helen Keller was born in America in 1880 and as a result of illness at the age of only eighteen months became deaf and blind. She soon forgot the few words which she knew and her parents were left with the problem of helping a deaf, blind and mute child.

Although education of the blind had begun in Scotland as early as 1793, both blind and deaf people were still classed as idiots in the 1880's but in spite of this Helen's parents consulted a doctor who thought that it might be possible to develop her intelligence and on his advice a teacher was obtained from the Perkins Institute for the Deaf and Blind in Boston. This teacher was Anne Sullivan and her task was to overcome the barrier of darkness and silence which surrounded the child. The barrier was broken by Anne Sullivan's tapping 'words' into Helen's hand and it was not long before this remarkably gifted teacher had taught her pupil to read and write in Braille. Miss Keller learnt to type and took a degree at Radcliffe College. She herself became a teacher of the blind and through her books and lectures did much to make others aware of their responsibility towards the afflicted.

Thus the sense organs are seen as important, indeed vital, parts of our bodies and of those of other animals. Not all the receptors are equally important: the eye and the ear are, of course, of great use to Man as is the sense of touch; taste and smell are to mankind of less importance although they are associated with pleasures upon which whole industries are founded—the confectionery, brewing and cosmetics trades for example. In certain of these trades men and women may develop one sense particularly well; for example, the sense of taste in tea- and wine-tasters and the sense of smell in perfume-testers. It is interesting to note that blind people develop by constant use the senses of touch, smell and hearing. Some towns have special gardens for blind people which contain only scented plants. Deaf folk develop keen senses of touch and sight and can, indeed, 'hear' the music of an organ by means of the vibrations of the floor.

PRACTICAL WORK AND QUESTIONS
See end of Chapter 18.

18. Reaction to Environment and Co-ordination—2

Introduction

We have dealt with the histology of nervous tissue, the structure of nerves, the physiology of the nerve impulse and the structure and functions of the sense organs and are now in a position to study more fully the structure and functions of the central nervous system and the peripheral nerves. It will be remembered that the central nervous system consists of the brain and spinal cord and that the peripheral nerves are the cranial nerves, the spinal nerves and the autonomic nerves.

The Spinal Cord, Spinal Nerves and Reflex Action

The *brain* will be given fuller treatment in a later section of this chapter. Here it will suffice to say that the brain is the largest mass of nervous tissue in the body and that it acts as the centre of nervous activity and control. In Man and the more complex animals the largest part of the brain is formed by the *cerebral hemispheres* (Figs. 18.8 and 18.9 and Plate 55). This part is the centre of intellectual activity. The whole surface of the brain is made of grey matter and is known as the cortex. The brain is continuous with the *spinal cord* and tracts of axons run from one to the other. Both the brain and the spinal cord are hollow and contain a liquid known as the *cerebrospinal fluid*.

The spinal cord is a soft white tissue extending from the brain to the second lumbar vertebra and is connected with the lower end of the vertebral column by a non-nervous tissue called the *filum terminale*. The spinal cord is about 46 cm long and 2 cm thick but is wider in two regions—the places where the nerves from the upper and lower limbs join it. In contrast to the brain the grey matter of the spinal cord does not lie on the outside but forms an H-shaped central area when the cord is seen in transverse section (Fig. 18.1 and Plate 52). The grey matter contains the relay neurones and the cell bodies of the motor neurones together with a short part of the axon which is non-myelinated in this region. The white matter is formed from myelinated fibres, the myelin giving this area its white colour. The neurones of the white matter are of both sensory and motor types, the former taking impulses from the sense organs to the brain and the latter conducting the impulses from the brain down the cord to the effector organs. It will be seen from Fig. 18.2 that each *spinal nerve* has two roots, a *dorsal* or *sensory* root and a *ventral* or *motor root*. The two roots join where the nerves leave the spinal column—the cord being housed, of course, under the neural arches of the vertebrae and above the centra (Fig. 18.5). Because of the shortness of the

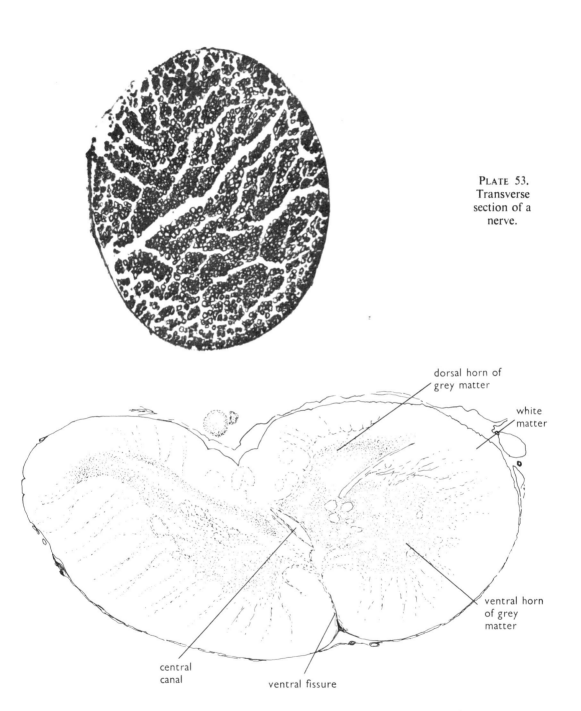

dorsal horn of
grey matter

white
matter

ventral horn
of grey
matter

central
canal

ventral fissure

FIG. 18.1. Transverse section of the spinal cord—compare with Plate 52.

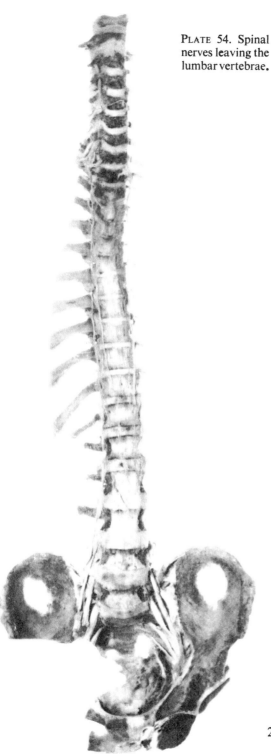

PLATE 54. Spinal nerves leaving the lumbar vertebrae.

cord the lumbar and sacral spinal nerves have to pass some way down the spinal column before leaving it; this can be seen in Plate 54. There are thirty-one pairs of spinal nerves in the human being.

Both the brain and the spinal cord are covered by three membranes known as the *meninges* (Figs. 18.2 and 18.5). The outer, tough, protective *dura mater* is lined by a delicate *arachnoid mater* which in turn is lined by the *pia mater*. The pia mater is a very delicate membrane closely investing the brain and supporting a fine network of blood vessels. The spaces between the meninges are filled with fluid.

The arrangement of neurones in the spinal nerves has already been shown in Fig. 17.4 and is given in more detail in Fig. 18.2. Notice that the cell bodies of the sensory neurones lie outside the spinal cord. The cell bodies are, of course, thicker than the axons and dendrons so that where a large number of cell bodies are aggregated together a swelling is present on the dorsal root of the spinal nerve. This swelling is called a *ganglion*. The arrangement of neurones as shown in the figure is known as the *reflex arc*. Consider a nervous reaction to pricking one's finger on a pin: the pin prick is the stimulus which activates a receptor cell (or cells) to initiate a nerve impulse away from the skin and along the sensory neurone to the spinal cord. Here the impulse is passed by the relay neurone to the motor neurone and finally arrives at a muscle fibre (or fibres) which contracts, and moves the hand from the painful pin.

This reaction is called a *reflex action*; it is rapid and takes place automatically: we do not need to think beforehand and, indeed, in many cases we are not aware that any reaction is taking place. The brain is not normally involved in reflex actions, at least in the more simple ones. We become conscious of some

204

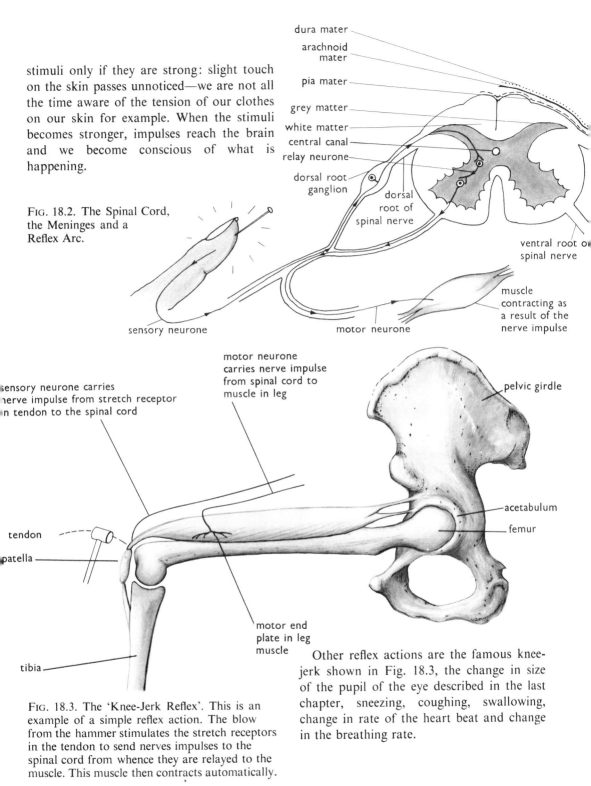

stimuli only if they are strong: slight touch on the skin passes unnoticed—we are not all the time aware of the tension of our clothes on our skin for example. When the stimuli becomes stronger, impulses reach the brain and we become conscious of what is happening.

dura mater
arachnoid mater
pia mater
grey matter
white matter
central canal
relay neurone
dorsal root ganglion
dorsal root of spinal nerve
ventral root of spinal nerve
muscle contracting as a result of the nerve impulse

FIG. 18.2. The Spinal Cord, the Meninges and a Reflex Arc.

sensory neurone
motor neurone

motor neurone carries nerve impulse from spinal cord to muscle in leg

sensory neurone carries nerve impulse from stretch receptor in tendon to the spinal cord

pelvic girdle

acetabulum
femur

tendon
patella

motor end plate in leg muscle

tibia

FIG. 18.3. The 'Knee-Jerk Reflex'. This is an example of a simple reflex action. The blow from the hammer stimulates the stretch receptors in the tendon to send nerves impulses to the spinal cord from whence they are relayed to the muscle. This muscle then contracts automatically.

Other reflex actions are the famous knee-jerk shown in Fig. 18.3, the change in size of the pupil of the eye described in the last chapter, sneezing, coughing, swallowing, change in rate of the heart beat and change in the breathing rate.

Much of our understanding of the functioning of the nervous system is due to the work of the great Russian physiologist Ivan Pavlov, 1849–1936. Pavlov was the first Russian to receive the Nobel Prize. This great honour was given him in 1904 for work in connection with the regulation of the digestive glands by reflex action. Pavlov, however, introduced a new idea—the conception of the *conditioned reflex*. The production of saliva by dogs upon their eating food was an ordinary reflex

action just as our salivary glands function quickly, without our thinking about them, when we eat a juicy steak. Pavlov discovered that if, when the dog was given food, a bell was sounded at the same time, after a number of trials the bell became sufficient alone to produce saliva. The dog had learned to associate the sound of the bell with the receiving of food. This type of reflex is known as a conditioned reflex (Fig. 18.4).

Conditioned reflexes play an important part

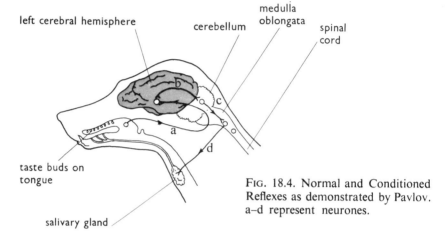

Fig. 18.4. Normal and Conditioned Reflexes as demonstrated by Pavlov. a–d represent neurones.

1. Normal Reflex. The taste buds are stimulated by food in the mouth and nerve impulses sent along 'a' to sensory area of the brain, from whence they pass along 'b' to the motor area. Impulses are then sent from the motor area along 'c' to the medulla and finally along 'd' to the salivary duct causing it to secrete.

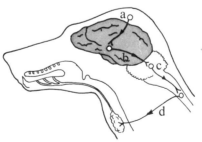

2. Conditioned Reflex. The sound of a bell stimulates sense cells in the ear which initiate nerve impulses along 'a' to the association centre of the brain from whence impulses pass along 'b' to the motor area. From the motor area impulses pass along 'c' and 'd' to the salivary gland causing the secretion of saliva.

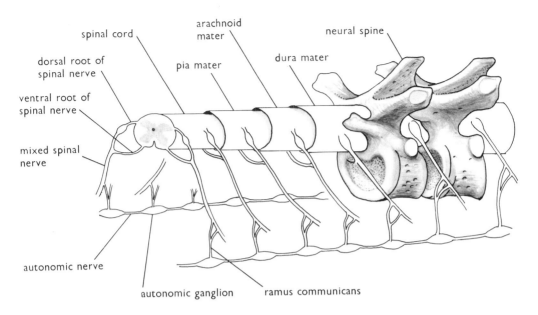

spinal cord

arachnoid mater

neural spine

dorsal root of spinal nerve

pia mater

dura mater

ventral root of spinal nerve

mixed spinal nerve

autonomic nerve

autonomic ganglion

ramus communicans

FIG. 18.5. The relationship between the spinal cord and the autonomic nervous system.

in our lives and indeed some physiologists attempt to explain all our actions in terms of reflex action. Many of the reactions of a newly born baby are simple reflex actions: he cries when hungry, sucks the nipple automatically and passes urine when his bladder is full. As the baby becomes older he learns from experience that it 'pays' to control some of these urges. A polite request for food is likely to get a more satisfactory response than a howling demand, a visit to the toilet will earn mother's praise whereas a wet floor will not please her, and so on. In other words the simple reflexes are becoming conditioned. More will be said about conditioned reflexes in the chapter on habits.

The Autonomic Nervous System

The autonomic system, part of which is shown in Fig. 18.5, consists of two longitudinally running cords, with ganglia at intervals along them, one on each side of the spinal column. The cords are linked through the ganglia by short branches to the spinal nerves and hence to the spinal cord. These linking nerves are called *rami communicantes*. Functionally, the autonomic system is made of two parts, the *sympathetic system* and the *parasympathetic system*. The effects of the two systems are antagonistic; for example, while the sympathetic autonomic system causes dilation of the pupil the parasympathetic causes its contraction. The two systems therefore help to maintain a balance of activity which is to the best advantage of the organism as a whole. Generally speaking the sympathetic system prepares the animal for defence or for flight and the parasympathetic helps to create the internal conditions found during rest, sleep and digestion. Table 11 shows the effect of the two systems on various parts of the body. The autonomic system serves involuntary muscles and glands.

Organ Stimulated	Parasympathetic	Sympathetic	Result
Iris	Contracted	Dilated	Controls amount of light entering eye
Ciliary muscles	Contracted	Relaxed	Controls accommodation
Blood vessels	Arterioles of viscera and glands dilated giving good blood supply for digestion	Arterioles of viscera and skin constricted: arterioles of voluntary muscles dilated	Adjusts blood flow and distribution for digestion or for 'fight or flight'
Digestive glands	Increased activity	Decreased activity	Flow of juices adjusted to suit demands
Peristalsis	Increased	Decreased	Controls rate of passage of food
Sphincters	Relaxed	Contracted	Food allowed to pass through the intestine at the most suitable time
Heart beat	Slowed	Speeded up	Adjusts rate of heart beat according to muscular activity
Tear glands	Inhibits action	Increases action	Controls amount of tears — increased, for example, when dust gets in eyes

TABLE 11. SOME PARTS OF THE BODY UNDER THE CONTROL OF THE AUTONOMIC SYSTEM

The Brain and Cranial Nerves

The reflex actions just described enable rapid responses to given stimuli in certain situations to be made without conscious thought: no reasoning takes place and a given stimulus always results in the same response. Among the lower animals most of the movements are of the reflex type and the total behaviour of such animals is based on instinct rather than reason. In the vertebrate animals the development of sense organs of a complex type has necessitated a corresponding development of the central nervous system and in particular the front or head end has become enlarged to form the *brain*. The brain increases in size and importance in higher animals and becomes the central exchange of nerve impulses. It correlates messages, sends out instructions, stores impressions for future use and forms the seat of intelligence.

In the simpler vertebrates the brain is less complex and Fig. 18.6 shows how closely the dogfish brain follows the generalised plan of vertebrate brains shown in the same figure. The figure also shows how during development the mammalian brain grows very large *cerebral hemispheres*. It is this enormous development of the cerebral hemispheres which gives to mammals their superior intelligence. The surface of the hemispheres is known as the *cerebral cortex* and it is this region of the brain in particular which serves to combine all incoming impulses.

The brain is divided into three areas easily distinguished in the embryo: they are the *fore-brain*, *mid-brain* and the *hind-brain*. The fore-brain receives impulses from the olfactory organ, the mid-brain receives impulses from the eyes and the hind-brain receives them from the ears including the semicircular canals. Impulses from the skin also enter the hind-brain.

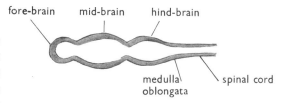

a. The early brain in section to show the main areas.

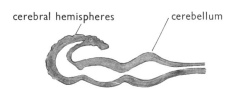

b. The cerebral hemispheres are beginning to enlarge and grow over the rest of the brain. This does not occur in animals such as fish and amphibia.

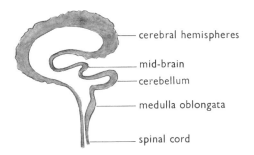

c. The cerebral hemispheres have greatly enlarged and have grown backwards to cover the rest of the brain. Compare this figure with the fully developed brain shown in Fig. 18.8.

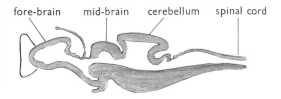

d. A section through the brain of a dogfish.

FIG. 18.6. The development of the mammalian brain in the embryo to show the enormous development of the cerebral hemispheres. The dogfish brain illustrated is fully developed—the fish never have large cerebral hemispheres.

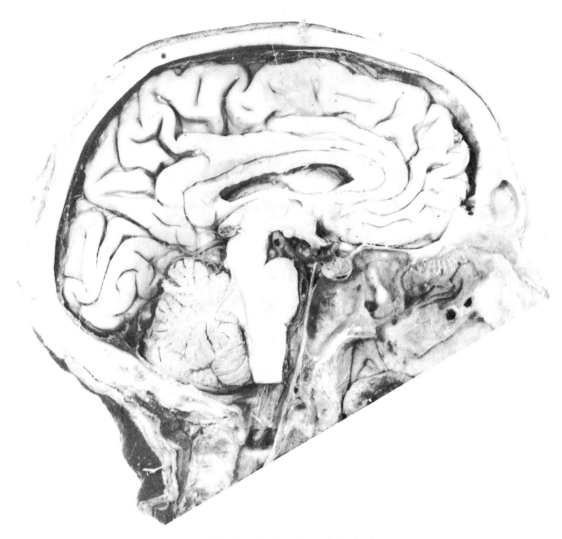

PLATE 55. A vertical section of the brain.

The *brain-stem* (Fig. 18.7 and Plate 55) in human anatomy consists of four regions— the *medulla oblongata*, the *pons*, the *mid-brain* and the *thalamus*. The medulla is the part of the brain which is continuous with the spinal cord and it deals with reflexes to the chest and to the tongue, the pons deals with sensa-

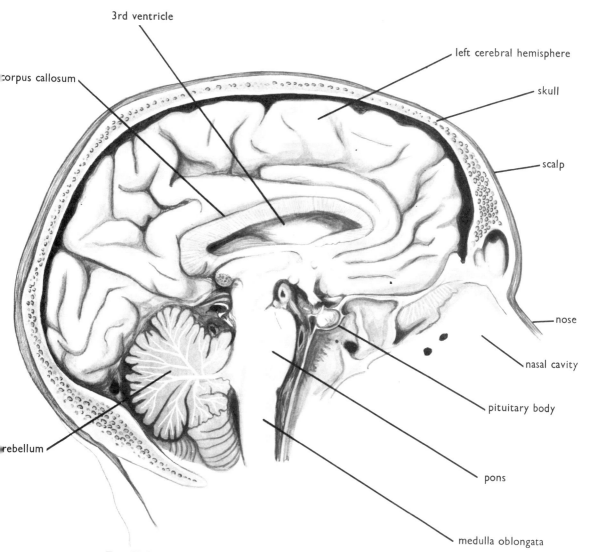

3rd ventricle

corpus callosum

left cerebral hemisphere

skull

scalp

nose

nasal cavity

pituitary body

rebellum

pons

medulla oblongata

FIG. 18.7. A drawing of Plate 55 to show the main parts of the brain.

tions from the face, the mid-brain receives impulses from the eyes, and lastly, the thalamus is an important relay centre for impulses on their way to the cerebral cortex. The thalamus also receives the optic nerves which cross sides at the *optic chiasma*.

The *cerebrum* or *cerebral hemispheres* (Fig. 18.8) forms in the human by far the greatest bulk of the brain; it is extremely convoluted to provide maximum surface area for the cerebral cortex which, as has been mentioned, is the centre for intellectual activity.

The *cerebellum* lies between the brain-stem and the hind part of the cerebrum and its function is to regulate and co-ordinate muscular activity including the important factor of balance. The cortex is made of astronomical numbers of neurones—estimated at about 10,000 million. These neurones do not have long axons and are inter-connected by synapses. The cortex is therefore incredibly complicated and the study of the brain correspondingly difficult.

As well as receiving impulses from the sense

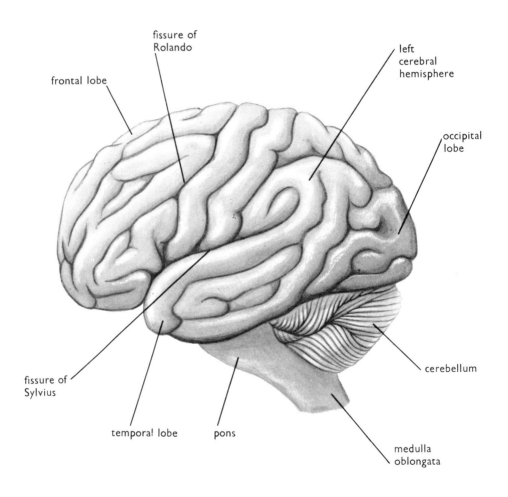

FIG. 18.8. The brain seen from the left side.

212

organs the brain can send impulses to initiate activity: the areas of the brain which do this are called *motor areas*. These 'instructions' may be in response to external stimuli and sometimes to internal ones such as those associated with sensations of hunger and thirst.

Certain areas of the brain are supplied with fibres from the main sense centres of the fore-, mid- and hind-brains and their purpose is to correlate them so that information gained from several sense organs may be used to gain a true picture of a given situation. These areas are called *association centres*. Some of the important areas of the brain dealing with different aspects of life are shown in Fig. 18.9.

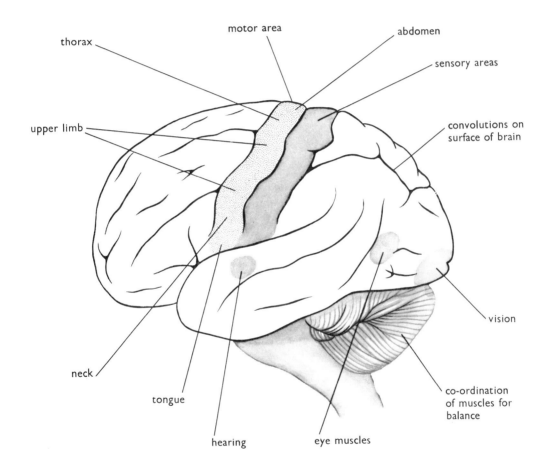

FIG. 18.9. Some of the association areas in the brain.

213

The *cranial nerves* (Fig. 18.10) are those nerves which enter or leave the brain to serve the sense organs, glands and muscles of the anterior end of the body and the viscera. A detailed study of the cranial nerves is not usually required at an elementary level but they are shown in Table 12 for the use of readers who wish to know more about them.

TABLE 12. THE CRANIAL NERVES

No.	Names and Nature	Origin of Impulse	Destination of Impulse	Result
1.	Olfactory (sensory)	Olfactory organs	Olfactory lobes	Sensation of smell
2.	Optic (sensory)	Retina	Optic lobes	Sensation of sight
3.	Oculomotor (motor)	Mid-brain	Eye muscles	Movement of eye
4.	Pathetic (motor)	Medulla	Eye muscle	Movement of eye
5.	Trigeminal	Sensory branch from skin of face Motor branch from medulla	Medulla Jaw muscles	Sensation of touch Movement of jaws
6.	Abducens (motor)	Medulla	Eye muscle	Movement of eye

No.	Names and Nature	Origin of Impulse	Destination of Impulse	Result
7.	Facial	Sensory branch from nose, lips and tongue Motor branch from medulla	Medulla Salivary glands, tongue, lower jaw	Sensation of touch and taste Secretion of saliva Movement of jaw and tongue
8.	Auditory (sensory)	Ear—both cochlea and semi-circular canals	Medulla	Sensation of hearing and balance
9.	Glosso-pharyngeal	Sensory branch from tongue Motor branch from medulla	Medulla Salivary glands, muscles of tongue and pharynx	Sensation of taste Secretion of saliva Movement of tongue and pharynx
10.	Vagus	Sensory from heart, lungs, pharynx, gut Medulla	Medulla Motor to heart, lungs, pharynx, gut	Regulation of heart-beat, breathing and peristalsis Regulation of heart-beat, breathing and peristalsis
11.	Spinal accessory (motor)	Medulla	To muscles of neck, pharynx and larynx	Movement of head, pharynx and larynx
12.	Hypoglossal (motor)	Medulla	Tongue and neck muscles	Movement of tongue and head

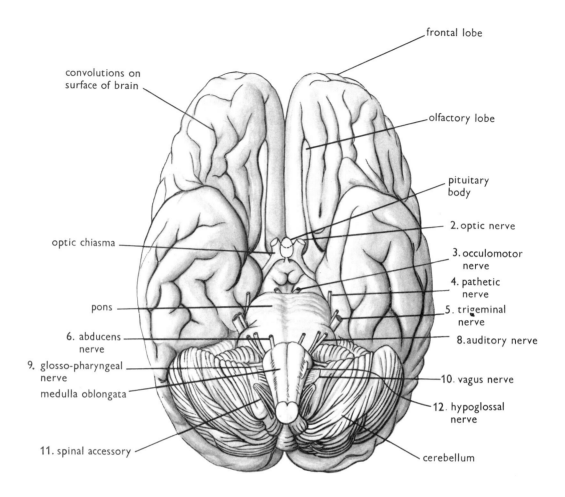

convolutions on
surface of brain

frontal lobe

olfactory lobe

pituitary
body

2. optic nerve

3. occulomotor
nerve

optic chiasma

4. pathetic
nerve

5. trigeminal
nerve

pons

6. abducens
nerve

8. auditory nerve

9. glosso-pharyngeal
nerve

medulla oblongata

10. vagus nerve

12. hypoglossal
nerve

11. spinal accessory

cerebellum

FIG. 18.10. The brain from below showing the cranial nerves.

Final Note on the Nervous System

From the last two chapters it will have become clear once again that the systems of the human body are not to be thought of as independent, self-functioning units. They are closely linked together by the nervous system whose activities ensure that all parts of the body work together for the good of the whole animal. This co-ordination is a very complex matter—think for example of the number of systems which need to be co-ordinated in order that a piece of meat may be purchased, cooked, eaten, digested, assimilated and the waste egested.

216

Practical Work on 17 and 18

1. Examine under the microscope a prepared transverse section of a nerve which has been stained with osmic acid. Observe how the fatty sheath of each axon has stained black. The whole nerve is seen to be composed of many nerve fibres bound together in bundles. Draw.

2. Examine a prepared slide of a transverse section of the spinal cord under the microscope. Notice the relative positions of the white and grey matter and compare your slide with Plate 52 and Fig. 18.1. Draw. What accounts for the difference in appearance of the white and grey matter?

3. Take a piece of cardboard 10 cm by 3 cm in size. Pass two pins through one end of the cardboard, the pins being 6 mm apart. Gently touch the two pin-points on the skin of your finger tips, wrists, lower and upper arms, neck and back. Can you feel two pin-pricks in all the places touched? If you cannot do so, what does this tell you of the distribution of touch receptors in the skin?

4. Take three bowls, the first containing hot water, the second containing warm water and the third containing cold water. Place one hand in the hot water and one in the cold water for about three minutes. Then place both hands in the warm water. Notice the different sensations in each hand. What may we learn from this experiment about the reliability of the skin as a thermometer?

5. Prepare solutions of sugar, salt, 1% acetic acid and 0·1% of quinine sulphate using distilled water and place a little of the four solutions in separate labelled watch glasses. Dip a clean glass rod in the sugar solution and apply a small quantity of it on a small area of the surface of the tongue. Repeat this on the other areas of the tongue until its whole surface has been tested. Draw a diagram of your tongue and indicate on it the areas where sugar is most strongly tasted. Repeat this experiment with each of the other solutions, washing the mouth out between each. Plot on your diagram the areas most sensitive to salt, sugar, acetic acid and quinine.

6. Place some sugar crystals on the tongue after carefully drying the tongue with a piece of clean gauze. Can you taste the sugar immediately? What conclusion can you draw from this experiment?

7. Close one nostril by pressing the side of the nose with a finger. Hold open a bottle of clove oil under the other nostril and gently inhale the vapour; breathe out through the mouth. Record the time it takes before you can no longer detect the smell of cloves—the sense receptors have become insensitive to this smell. Because the nose is no longer sensitive to the smell of cloves does it mean that it is not sensitive to other smells? Test this by sniffing other substances.

8. Blindfold another person and hold a piece of a pear under his nose while he is eating a slice of apple. Ask him to say what he is eating. What does this experiment tell you?

9. Study a large model of the ear to understand the structure. Draw the different parts.

10. Obtain from a butcher a large ox eye. Notice the position of the eye muscles and the optic nerve. Cut the eye open vertically starting at the optic nerve. Observe the lens and other parts of the eye. Remove the lens and look at print through it. What does this tell us about the function of the lens?

11. On a piece of white paper mark a cross and a disc about 8 cm apart. The disc should be about 1 cm in diameter and the cross about the same size. Cover the left eye and keep the right eye focused on the cross. Hold the paper about 12 centimetres from the eye and slowly move the page away until the circle disappears. In this position the

image of the circle is falling on the blind spot which, it will be remembered, is insensitive to light.

12. Cover one eye with your hand and ask a friend to observe the size of the pupil of the other eye which should be directed towards a light. After one minute uncover your eye and allow the friend to observe the difference in the size of your two pupils. How long does it take for the two pupils to become the same size? What part of the eye enables the size of the pupil to vary?

13. Ask a friend to look steadily out of the window at a distant object. Hold a pencil about 25 cm in front of his face and then while you carefully watch his eyes tell him to look at the pencil. You will notice that his eyes roll inwards slightly, and that the pupils change in size as his eyes accommodate to the near object.

14. Take two retort stands about one metre apart and stretch a fine, white string between them. Stand about one and a half metres from the string and ask a friend to drop peas, one at a time, directly above the string so that each falls only just one side or the other of it. With both eyes open try to judge which side of the string the pea falls. The friend must count the number of correct judgements out of twenty falls. Repeat this with one eye covered. What does this experiment tell you about stereoscopic vision?

15. Obtain from a butcher a portion of the spinal cord of a cow. Observe the meninges as you remove the cord from the bone. Cut a thin section of the cord and identify as many structures as you can with the aid of a hand lens.

16. Ask your teacher to dissect the brain, spinal cord, cranial nerves and spinal nerves of a rabbit.

17. Ask your teacher to dissect a frog to show the autonomic nervous system.

18. Perform the knee jerk experiment shown in Fig. 18.3.

19. Examine a model of the brain, carefully observing the different structures.

QUESTIONS ON CHAPTERS 17 AND 18

1. You hear a dinner bell and walk to the dining room. Describe briefly how nervous, muscular and bony structures bring this about. (C)

2. Describe, with the aid of a diagram, the chief features to be seen in a cross-section of the spinal cord at the level of a spinal nerve, and indicate the part they take in bodily activities. (C)

3. With the aid of simple diagrams explain what is meant by:
    (a) central nervous system
    (b) autonomic nervous system
    (c) spinal reflex
    (d) conditioned reflex. (O)

4. With the aid of a labelled diagram of the human eye explain the function and importance of (a) the lens, (b) the retina. (O)

5. Make a labelled diagram to show the main parts of the human central nervous system. Describe (a) a spinal reflex, (b) a voluntary action, explaining the importance of each to Man. (O)

6. Give an illustrated description of the cerebral hemispheres. Describe the functions of the cerebral cortex. (L)

7. Give an account of the structure of the eyeball and indicate the function of its different parts. (L)

8. Describe a neurone and its medullated nerve fibre. What part do nerves play in the movement of the body? (L)

9. Give an account of a spinal reflex, illustrating your answer with a labelled

diagram. How would you demonstrate the pupillary reflex? (L)

10. What parts of the body does the autonomic nervous system control? Describe its action in any one of these parts. How does it differ structurally from the other parts of the nervous system? (L)

11. Briefly describe the structure of a nerve cell and nerve fibre. Explain the importance of the cochlea and show how it is connected to the brain. (L)

12. Make a labelled diagram to show the general anatomy of the brain of a named mammal. Indicate the regions where sight and hearing are localised and those which are concerned with the control of respiration and muscular co-ordination. (S)

13. Explain how we are able to see:
   (a) in colour
   (b) in dim light
   (c) in three dimensions
   (d) near and distant objects clearly. (S)

14. Make a labelled diagram of the ear. State the functions of the ear and explain how they are carried out. (S)

15. Using the knee jerk as an example describe how reflex actions are brought about. What do you understand by conditioned reflexes? Discuss their importance in habit formation. (S)

16. What regions of the nervous system are concerned with:
   (a) answering a written examination paper

(b) dropping a hot dish.
In what ways do these actions differ? (S)

17. Draw and label a diagram of the eye. Explain how accommodation is brought about. What is (a) long sight, (b) short sight? What compensations can be made for these defects? (W)

18. Give an account of the structure of the spinal cord. What is a voluntary action? Describe how such an action is brought about (W).

19. Make a large, fully labelled diagram of the ear. Explain the parts played by the ear and the central nervous system in the recognition of a sound. (W)

20. Give a large, labelled diagram to show the structure of the eye. Explain briefly what happens when one sees an object such as a flower. What changes take place when we come from a darkened room into bright sunshine? (RSA)

21. Describe the position and structure of the spinal cord and medulla oblongata, outlining the chief functions of these regions. Show, by means of a labelled diagram, the nerve path used in a simple reflex action. (Description of the reflex action is *not* required.) (RSA)

22. Write notes on (a) the iris, (b) the taste buds, (c) the semi-circular canals, (d) the cochlea. (J)

23. Give an account of the part played by the nervous system when you see a ball approaching and move to catch it. (J)

219

Summary of 17 and 18

1. The *nervous system* enables animals to detect changes in the environment. Changes are detected by *sense organs*—the *skin, nose, tongue, eye* and *ear*.

2. The nervous system also enables animals to make use of the information given to them by the sense organs: *nerve impulses* are carried to various parts of the body enabling the animal to react in a sensible, co-ordinated way.

3. There is an increasing complexity seen in the nervous systems of animals from Hydra to Man.

4. In Man the nervous system is composed of the *sense organs*; the *brain* and *spinal cord*; the *peripheral nerves*; and the *autonomic system*.

5. *Nerve cells* or *neurones* are of three types—*sensory, motor* and *association*. *Receptor* cells receive stimuli, *effector cells* react. Neurones are separated by *synapses*.

6. *Sensations* are of eight kinds—*pressure* or *touch, temperature, pain, smell, taste, hearing, balance* and *sight*.

7. The brain and spinal cord are protected by bone and by *meninges*—the *dura mater*, the *arachnoid mater* and the *pia mater*. *Spinal nerves* leave the spinal cord by *dorsal* and *ventral roots*. The simplest arrangement of neurones is the *reflex arc*. *Reflex actions* take place automatically without our being conscious of them. Pavlov introduced the term *conditioned reflex*.

8. The *autonomic system* serves involuntary muscles and glands and comprises the *sympathetic* and *parasympathetic* parts.

9. The *brain* is the centre where nerve impulses are correlated, where impressions are stored for future use, where intellectual activity takes place and from whence instructions are sent out. In Man the brain is characterised by very large *cerebral hemispheres*, the surface of these being known as the *cerebral cortex*. Certain areas of the brain are associated with definite activities such as vision or hearing. The *cranial nerves* are those nerves which leave the brain to control sense organs, glands and muscles near the anterior end of the body.

19. Chemical Messengers

Introduction: the Discovery of Hormones

In 1902 the two physiologists Bayliss and Starling, shown in Plates 56 and 57, made an important and exciting discovery. They found that the pancreas continued to produce pancreatic juice *at the correct time* even after the nerves supplying it had been cut. The correct time was, of course, when food from the stomach entered the duodenum. Somehow a message was reaching the pancreas instructing it to secrete its juice without the aid of the nervous system. The researches of Bayliss and Starling showed that the entry of the acid contents of the stomach caused the duodenum to produce a substance which passed into the blood and was thus conveyed to the pancreas which it stimulated to produce its juice. This substance was called *secretin* and was the first of many *hormones* to be discovered. The science of *endocrinology* had been born.

The name *hormone* means accelerator but it later became clear that some hormones could slow down metabolism and the alternative name autocoid was suggested. Either name may be used but 'hormone' is perhaps the more usual. The important point is that hormones are chemicals secreted into the blood by *ductless* or *endocrine glands*, and that they

PLATE 56. Bayliss.

PLATE 57. Starling.

carry messages from one part of the body to another.

The endocrine glands together make up the *endocrine system*: this system is more diffuse than most of the other systems considered, the actual location of the glands in the body being relatively unimportant. The hormones are produced in glands which do not have their products conveyed to some surface by ducts as do, for example, the salivary glands, but instead their secretions are poured directly into the blood stream and are hence carried rapidly round the body.

The endocrine system is a co-ordinating system but in contrast to the nervous system its action is not always fast. For example while the hormone *adrenalin*, from the adrenal glands, produces rapid effects, *thyroxine*, from the thyroid gland, is one which produces slow effects over a long period.

Chemically, hormones differ widely from one another: some are proteins, others are derived from amino-acids and yet others are fat-like in nature.

Most hormones do not carry out their function independently but act in some sort of relationship to other hormones—for example the production of milk in the mammal involves hormones from several endocrine glands. The endocrine system plays a major role in homeostasis.

The Ductless Glands of the Human Body

Fig. 19.1 shows the main endocrine organs found in human beings. Wherever the gland is situated its secretions are poured directly into the blood and, owing to the rapidity with which blood flows through the blood vessels, they are almost immediately passed to their destination where they activate some other gland or effect metabolic processes. The main glands are:

1. The *pituitary*, situated in the head.
2. The *thyroid*, which is found in the neck.
3. The *parathyroids*, which are also found in the neck.
4. The *thymus*, which lies just anterior to the heart.
5. The *adrenals*, situated anterior to the kidneys.
6. The *islets of Langerhans*, which are found in the tissue of the pancreas.
7. The *ovaries* in the female.
8. The *testes* in the male.
9. The part of the *mucous membrane* of the *duodenum* which has already been mentioned in connection with secretin.
10. The *mucous coat* of the stomach.

The last two 'glands' are not compact structures but are diffuse in contrast to the other ductless glands.

The Pituitary. The pituitary gland is found in the head on the underside of the brain. During development of the embryo the pituitary is formed by the fusion of an up-growth from the roof of the mouth with a downgrowth from the floor of the brain. The connection with the roof of the mouth is soon lost during later development of the foetus and the pituitary remains attached to the underside of the brain. The part which arises from the roof of the mouth forms what is known as the *anterior pituitary* and the part arising from the floor of the brain forms the *posterior pituitary*.

The pituitary gland is sometimes called the 'master' gland of the endocrine system as one of its chief functions is to regulate the activity of other ductless glands. It has also a wide influence on all metabolic processes including growth. For example, the anterior pituitary secretes hormones controlling growth and milk secretion, and influencing the adrenal

222

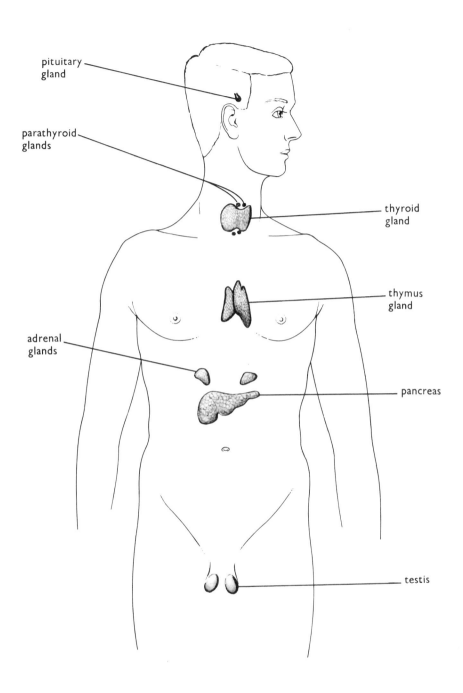

FIG. 19.1. THE ENDOCRINE GLANDS.

223

bodies and the testes and ovaries. The posterior pituitary produces hormones affecting the kidneys and regulating the tone of involuntary muscle: for example, one hormone stimulates the muscles of the womb to contract during birth.

The effects of over- and under-activity of the pituitary are interesting.

Over-activity of the pituitary gland frequently leads to *giantism* in the child. This is due to an excess of the hormone *phyone* which influences protein, carbohydrate and fat metabolism of all cells of the body including those of the skeleton which becomes very large although the child may remain well proportioned. If the over-activity begins in later life, that is when the person is an adult, the condition known as *acromegaly* results. In this case the bones of the face, jaw and nose thicken giving a coarse expression to the face. The bones of the hands and feet also thicken. The skin also becomes thick and coarse.

Under-activity of the pituitary results in a deficiency of phyone and leads to a condition called *infantilism* in which the child may be a dwarf due to a delayed development of the bones. This is often accompanied by a retarded sexual development.

The influence of the pituitary gland on the ovaries and testes and on the reproductive activity of the animal will be considered in the next chapter.

The Thyroid. This gland is two-lobed and lies in front of the trachea at the base of the larynx. The secretion of the thyroid gland is *thyroxine*, an organic compound containing iodine. This indicates the importance of iodine in the diet as has been mentioned in Chapter 10. If there is a lack of iodine in the diet the gland tries to compensate for its reduced output of thyroxine by becoming larger: this may give rise to a swelling on the

PLATE 58. Nagas woman with goitre.

neck, sometimes referred to as '*Derbyshire neck*'. A lack of iodine may be present in districts far from the sea, for a common source of iodine is from seafoods. The Nagas woman (Plate 58) belongs to a tribe which lives far from the sea in India. Manufacturers of salt often add iodine to table salt to ensure an adequate supply.

Thyroxine affects the metabolism of the body and in particular the rate of oxidation processes in the cells which in turn affects the rate of growth.

A lack of thyroxine in the child is serious for it results in stunted mental and physical

224

growth and the child looks an imbecile. The head and hands are disproportionately large. The child in this unfortunate condition is known as a *cretin* (Plate 59). Fortunately, thyroxine can be extracted from animals and the extract given to the cretin. Provided the treatment is continuous great improvement results.

In the adult a lack of thyroid activity results in a slowing down of all metabolic processes and the person appears indolent and even lazy, both mentally and physically. There is a tendency to put on weight and for the skin to thicken: a condition known as *myxoedema*.

Over-activity of the thyroid increases the metabolic rate very greatly and the person concerned becomes energetic and irritable. The food consumed is rapidly oxidised so that there is a tendency to thinness accompanied by a swelling of the neck and protruding eyes—a condition known as *exophthalmic goitre*.

It is interesting to note, then, that the thyroid gland plays a part which is important in the forming of our characters as well as bodily shape and activity. All degrees of over-activity and under-activity of the thyroid exist so that it is difficult to say what is normal: someone with a slightly over-active thyroid may be hard-working, anxious to get to the top of his profession and perhaps irritable, while another individual whose thyroid is slightly under-active may be placid, unworried and amiable. Both types may be perfectly normal.

The Parathyroids. The parathyroids are four small ductless glands situated behind the thyroid, two on each side of the trachea. They secrete *parathormone* which plays an important part in the calcium and phosphorus metabolism of the body. Parathormone acts on the cells of kidneys and bone, thus helping to control the amount of calcium in the blood. The blood calcium level has to be maintained at the correct amount of about 11 mg. per 100 cm^3 and the parathormone ensures that this is done. It is interesting to note how small are these organs despite their importance: hormones need to be present only in minute quantities (compare with the similar case of the vitamins which we considered in Chapter 10) to bring about their important controlling effects. Slight excess or deficiency of a

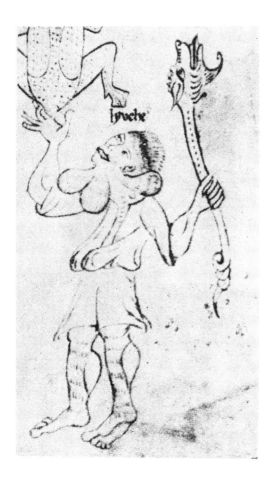

PLATE 59. A drawing of a cretin.

225

hormone may bring about not only bodily changes but mental changes as well. A lack of activity of the parathyroids leads to a fall in the blood calcium level and to increased excitability of nervous and muscular tissue which may lead to convulsive movements. Over-activity of the parathyroids may lead to excessive calcium in the blood and this may be deposited in unusual places such as the kidneys.

The Thymus. This gland is found in the human being behind the breast bone. Although it is usually classed as an endocrine gland, little is known about its function. It is quite large in the child but is virtually absent after puberty. It is possibly connected with the growth of the individual.

The Adrenal Glands or Suprarenals. There are two adrenal bodies, one located at the upper end of each kidney. Each gland is composed of two parts which in fact constitute two glands: the outer part being the *cortex* and the inner forming the *medulla*. The suprarenal cortex, whose activity is essential to life,

No.	Action of Adrenalin	Reason for the Action
1.	Smooth muscle of blood vessels to gut constricted	Less blood to gut means more available for the skeletal muscles
2.	Smooth muscle of blood vessels to skin constricted, resulting in paleness of face	More blood available for skeletal muscles concerned with 'flight or fight'
3.	Inhibits peristalsis	More energy available for 'flight or fight'
4.	Blood vessels of heart and skeletal muscles dilate	Increases supply of oxygen and glucose to muscles responsible for running or fighting
5.	Increases heart rate	Increases supply of oxygen to muscles
6.	Dilates pupil of eye	More light admitted, quick stimulation of the retina
7.	Stimulates respiration	More oxygen available
8.	Improves functioning of skeletal muscle	Muscle then tires less quickly

TABLE 13. SOME EFFECTS OF ADRENALIN

secretes hormones which influence the formation of sugar from proteins (hence leading to increased stores of glycogen in the liver) and which help to control the sodium and potassium content of the blood. The suprarenal cortex also produces sex hormones.

The medulla secretes the important hormone adrenalin which is similar in its effects in many ways to the sympathetic nervous system and which, indeed, reinforces the action of that system. During normal resting conditions there is little adrenalin in the blood but under conditions demanding great effort or when there is much excitement adrenalin is poured into the blood stream from the suprarenal medulla. Its effects are often expressed by saying that it prepares the body for 'flight or fight' and this is not an inaccurate description, for circumstances producing fear, such as being chased by a bull or being called before the headmaster after committing a serious offence, lead to secretion of adrenalin and give characteristic symptoms such as trembling, sweating and a prickly sensation on the skin at the back of the neck. This last sensation is due to the adrenalin causing the hair muscles to contract and make the hair 'stand on end'. Other effects of the secretion of adrenalin into the blood are given in Table 13. Thus we see that adrenalin brings about changes which enable the body to face emergencies to the best possible advantage.

The Islets of Langerhans. The islets of Langerhans are found within the tissue of the pancreas and they produce the hormone *insulin*. This hormone was discovered by two Canadian physiologists—Banting and Best (Plate 60). During the summer of 1921 Banting and Best, working in the laboratory of Professor Macleod at the University of Toronto, produced an extract from the islets of Langerhans which improved the condition of a dog suffering from diabetes—a disease

in which the sugar in the blood cannot be oxidised in the normal way. This is serious. Since the body is not able to utilise its sugar, it draws too heavily on the fats and proteins to obtain its energy, causing a wasting away of the tissues. Sugar accumulates to such a degree in the blood that it is excreted in the urine. In addition, poisonous breakdown substances from the fats and proteins are formed—aceto-acetic acid for example—and these lead to a slowing down of metabolic activity followed by coma and finally death. Normally insulin passes continuously into the blood enabling oxidation of sugar to proceed in the tissues. Insulin also promotes the formation in the liver and muscles of glycogen from the sugar in the blood, i.e., it has an opposite effect to adrenalin. Great activity in the laboratory produced extracts of greater

PLATE 60. Best.

and greater purity and effectiveness until it was safe to try them with human patients. The first patient was a severely diabetic juvenile who received treatment on 11th January, 1922. He improved dramatically thus demonstrating once again the tremendous benefit brought to mankind by the researches of physiologists.

For their work on insulin and diabetes Macleod, Banting and Best received many honours: Banting and Macleod were jointly awarded the Nobel Prize in 1923 while Best received the Charles Mickle Fellowship from the University of Toronto. The University Board of Governors established a Banting and Best Chair of Medical Research and the Parliament of Canada voted a life annuity to Banting.

As a result of the work of Banting and Best, thousands of people now live normal, healthy and happy lives, who would otherwise have been condemned to die, for insulin now is easily obtainable and easily administered.

The Ovaries and Testes. The hormones produced by these sex glands will be considered in the next chapter.

The Mucous Membrane of the Duodenum has already been mentioned as producing secretin. The mucous membrane of the duodenum also produces a hormone called *enterogastrone* which is taken in the blood to the stomach where it inhibits the production of gastric juice near the end of digestion.

The Mucous Membrane of the Stomach secretes the hormone *gastrin* which stimulates the production of gastric juice.

Thus the endocrine system is seen to be essentially a system which co-ordinates and controls the metabolic processes of the body and particularly influences the long-term processes of growth and development.

PRACTICAL WORK ON 19

To demonstrate the effect of thyroxin on the metamorphosis of tadpoles to frogs is a simple but striking experiment. Obtain a number of tadpoles of approximately the same age and divide them into two groups. Place each group in a separate vessel, feeding them on raw meat. The meat should be tied to a string so that it can be pulled out each day and a fresh piece put in its place: if this is not done the meat putrefies and spoils the water. Every week place a thyroid tablet in the water with one group of tadpoles. The second group acts as a control—that is they are kept under normal conditions without extra thyroid. The tadpoles which have thyroid in their water metamorphose—that is they change into tiny frogs—long before those without thyroid.

QUESTIONS ON CHAPTER 19

1. What is meant by an endocrine gland? Describe one such gland, and discuss the importance of its secretion in the normal functioning of the body. (C)

2. Describe the position of the adrenal gland. How does adrenaline affect the body? (L)

3. What is an endocrine gland? Describe the appearance and position of the pituitary gland. Give an account of its functions. (L)

4. Describe the position of the thyroid gland and discuss the effect of its secretion upon the body. (L)

5. What is a hormone? Describe the source and action of any three hormones. (O)

Summary of 19

1. *Hormones* are chemical substances of a complex nature whose function is to help *control metabolism*. Their effect may be fast or it may extend over a period of years.

2. Hormones are produced by *ductless glands* of the *endocrine system*.

3. The ductless glands frequently affect each other by their secretions.

4. The ductless glands include the *pituitary*, the *thyroid, parathyroids, adrenals, islets of Langerhans, ovaries, testes* and *certain regions of the alimentary canal.*

20. Producing the Next Generation

Introduction

Animals are here today because their ancestors reproduced young which were well equipped to survive the dangers of the world in which they found themselves. Furthermore they were so well adapted to their environment that they survived while other species became extinct. Geological studies have shown that there have existed, at one time or another in the past epochs of time, great numbers of animals whose sole remains today are fossils. *Charles Darwin* (Plate 17) showed that there is in nature a *'struggle for existence'* in which only the best adapted animals survive—those, perhaps, whose nervous system is just a little more efficient, thus enabling them to escape from an enemy while an individual whose reaction to danger is a little slower will be caught. Thus we speak of *'the survival of the fittest'*. During the course of time—long-scale time, that is, millions of years—new species have evolved as we saw in Chapter 5. This is because offspring differ from their parents: a new characteristic developed, or a characteristic slightly improved, will enable an animal to survive in the struggle for existence and this characteristic will be passed on to the next generation. Gradually over millions of years new species are thus evolved.

Darwin pointed out the struggle for existence which occurs during the life of blackbirds: two parent birds may produce four or five young in one nest and may have three or even four broods a year. Thus the single pair may produce nearly twenty young each year. The total number of birds which one pair need to produce in their lifetime in order to keep the population of blackbirds constant is only two. If all the eggs laid turned into birds which grew to maturity and mated, the world would soon be over-run by blackbirds! This does not happen, of course, because so many are killed during the 'struggle for existence'.

As far as reproduction goes, animals and plants face the problem of maintaining their species either by producing vast numbers of offspring, a few of which will by chance survive, in spite of terrific losses, or by producing only a few young but taking great care of them until they are old enough to fend for themselves. For example, while the codfish may lay up to thirty million eggs in one season the elephant produces only one offspring in nine years. In the first case the young fish are in no way protected by the parents, and many perish even as eggs; in the second the mother elephant not only cares for the young one but 'employs' another unmated female to help her. Indians refer to this second elephant as the 'auntie', a name which fits her occupation well, for she stands on one side of the youngster while the mother stands on the other side, so that the youngster

230

is protected by several tons of elephant! Even a tiger would be deterred from attacking the baby under such circumstances!

Generally speaking, the more advanced and complex animals tend to lay fewer eggs or give birth to fewer offspring than do the more primitive species. In the invertebrate animals parental care is usually not well developed or is entirely lacking. Some, however, show a remarkable degree of care for the young—earwigs, for example, protect their young. Amongst the fish the stickleback is an interesting case, for the male builds a nest by sticking together pieces of water weed (Fig. 20.1) producing a sticky substance for this purpose. The nest is barrel-shaped and when it is completed the male fish chases a female into it and while she lays her eggs he sheds his sperm over them to fertilise them. During this time the male stickleback guards a part of the stream as his territory and any other fish entering this area does so at his peril.

fish, however, and it is not until we consider the birds that we meet with advanced forms of parental care. In the mammals parental care is most highly developed and the primates in particular show it to a very marked degree. Parental care is perhaps seen in its fullest development in the human being where the young are looked after for a number of years and where they receive intensive education and training to fit them for life as adults capable of filling useful places in the community.

It is interesting to note in passing that parental care is not developed in plants but that these organisms produce large numbers of seeds or spores because the chance of many surviving to adulthood is small. The production of spores in the fungi is astronomical in number—a single mushroom cap, for example, may form as many as 16,000,000,000 spores! Only a tiny fraction of these land in a place where all the conditions are suitable

FIG. 20.1. A female stickleback laying eggs in the nest built by the male.

This interesting reproductive behaviour does not stop here, however, for the male fish remains near the nest after the eggs are laid and drives away intruders. He also fans a current of water over the eggs with his fins in order to give them a good supply of oxygen. This type of behaviour is rather unusual in

for their growth. The flowering plants themselves produce large numbers of seeds, particularly orchids where a single flower may form 10,000 seeds.

Reproduction is of two types: *asexual* and *sexual*. Asexual reproduction is confined to the plants and simpler animals. For example,

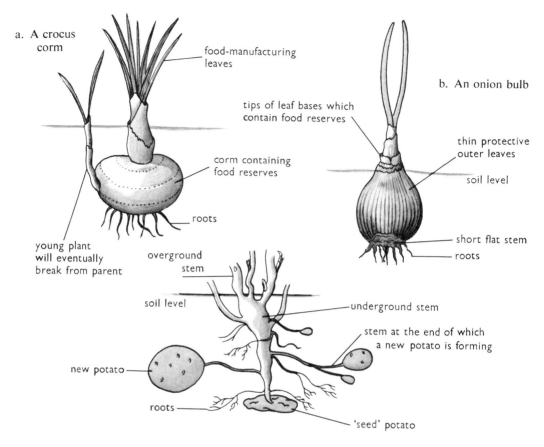

a. A crocus corm

food-manufacturing leaves

tips of leaf bases which contain food reserves

corm containing food reserves

roots

young plant will eventually break from parent

b. An onion bulb

thin protective outer leaves

soil level

short flat stem

roots

overground stem

soil level

underground stem

stem at the end of which a new potato is forming

new potato

roots

'seed' potato

c. Potato tuber. Each of the young potatoes if left in the ground would grow into a new plant

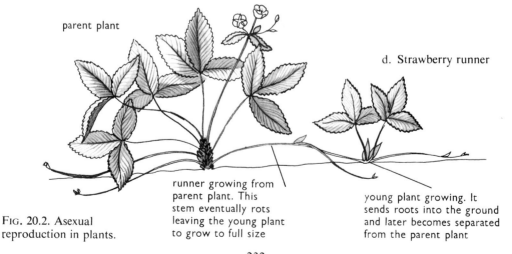

parent plant

d. Strawberry runner

runner growing from parent plant. This stem eventually rots leaving the young plant to grow to full size

young plant growing. It sends roots into the ground and later becomes separated from the parent plant

FIG. 20.2. Asexual reproduction in plants.

232

plants form runners (strawberry), rhizomes (iris) or tubers (potato). These are shown in Fig. 20.2. Part of the parent plant itself breaks off and forms a new plant which then grows to full size. Any gardener will be familiar with such processes as the taking of cuttings and the grafting of buds. These are all asexual methods of reproduction. *Amoeba* reproduces asexually by binary fission to form two new individuals and *Hydra* can bud new individuals asexually (Fig. 20.3).

The higher types of animals, however, only reproduce sexually—all the vertebrates, for example. The essential features of sexual reproduction are the formation of *sex cells* or *gametes*, as they are called, which are of two kinds—one, the *male gamete* or *spermatozoon* (usually abbreviated to *sperm*), fuses with the other, the *female gamete* or *egg*. The fusion of the two gametes, one male and one female, is called *fertilisation* and results in the formation of a single cell called a *zygote*. During fertilisation there is an important fusion of nuclear material from the gametes, the significance of which will be considered in the chapter on genetics. The organs in which the gametes are formed are called *gonads*. The male gonad is the *testis* and the female gonad is the *ovary*.

Fig. 20.4 shows diagrammatically the fusion process.

In the vertebrate animals such as the human being the two sexes are always separate but in some of the invertebrate animals both male and female gonads occur in the same animal when the animal is said to be *hermaphrodite*. Both *Hydra* and the earthworm are hermaphrodite animals.

The sperm and eggs have features which easily enable them to be distinguished. Sperm are motile, microscopic and do not contain a food supply; eggs are non-motile, much larger and contain a supply of food usually

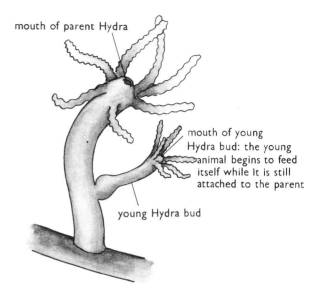

mouth of parent Hydra

mouth of young Hydra bud: the young animal begins to feed itself while it is still attached to the parent

young Hydra bud

FIG. 20.3. Budding of Hydra. An example of asexual reproduction in animals.

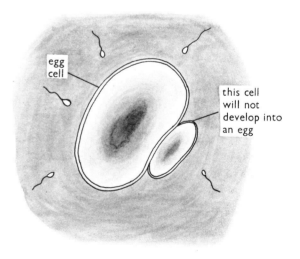

egg cell

this cell will not develop into an egg

FIG. 20.4. Fertilisation. The egg is seen to be surrounded by a number of sperm only one of which will fuse with the egg to form the zygote.

233

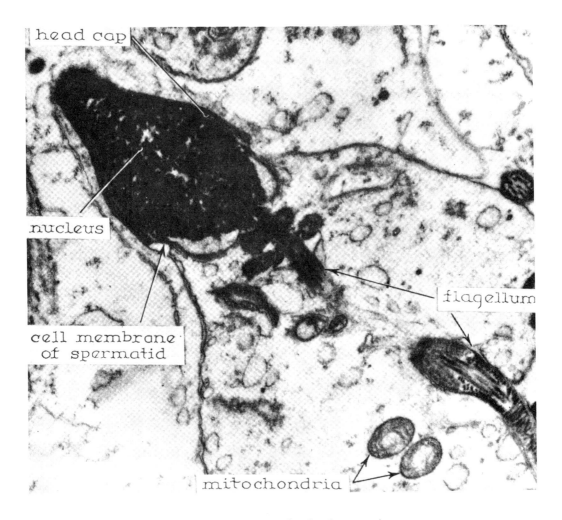

head cap

nucleus

cell membrane of spermatid

flagellum

mitochondria

PLATE 61. A human sperm under the electron microscope.

known as *yolk*. An egg, however large it may be, is a single cell and thus it is sometimes said that the largest living cell known to Man is the egg of the ostrich. The sperm (Fig. 20.5 and Plate 61) are made of a head, which is almost entirely nucleus, a middle-piece and a tail. It is by means of this tail that the sperm can swim, the energy for this activity being provided by substances in the middle-piece.

The sperm must have a liquid in which to swim and this, of course, presents no problems to animals which are aquatic. Here the sperm are just shed by the male into the water and swim towards an egg and fertilise it. Usually the sperm are shed over the eggs as the female lays them. The female salmon lays her eggs in a hollow in the sand at the bottom of a river bed and the male pours the

234

sperm over them; *Hydra* releases the sperm only in the vicinity of another *Hydra*; the male frog makes certain that the sperm are released near the eggs by clinging to the back of the female frog as she lays her eggs and shedding his sperm at the same time, and so on. For land animals the problem is different for there is no medium in which the sperm can swim. We find that land animals provide their own liquid for the sperm to swim in and the male injects it into the body of the female. Once inside the female's body, the sperms have plenty of liquid available. This type of sexual reproduction, where the egg is fertilised within the body of the female, is called *internal fertilisation* and contrasts completely with that just described for aquatic creatures. In their case we speak of *external fertilisation*. Internal fertilisation is more efficient than external fertilisation for there is a greater certainty that the sperm will meet with an egg. Far fewer eggs need, therefore, to be produced.

In all the mammals a special *intromittent organ*, the *penis*, by means of which the sperm are injected into the female, is present in the male.

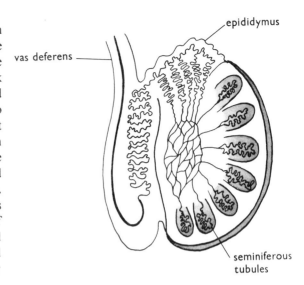

a. Section through a testis to show the internal structure. The seminiferous tubules all finally empty their products into the vas deferens.

FIG. 20.5. The structure of the testis and the formation of spermatozoa.

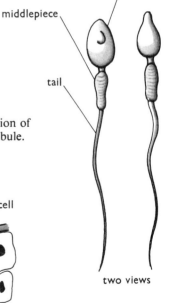

c. An enlarged portion of a seminiferous tubule.

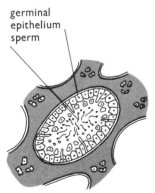

b. Section through a seminiferous tubule.

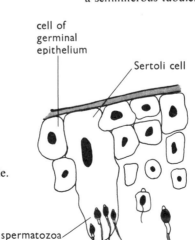

d. Spermatozoa.

Histology of the Testis and Ovary

The testes are composed of a large number of *seminiferous tubules* surrounded by connective tissue in which occur numerous *interstitial cells*. The seminiferous tubules are coiled so that a section cut through a testis shows many cut tubules as in Fig. 20.5. The connective tissue surrounding the tubules is continuous with the outer fibrous covering of the testis which is known as the *tunica albuginea*. The function of the tubules is to produce the spermatozoa from the wall of each tubule—a layer of cells called the *germinal epithelium*. The interstitial cells act as endocrine glands producing, as they do, hormones which are responsible for the appearance in the male of the *secondary sexual characteristics*. These characteristics are in the human being the 'breaking' of the voice, as the boy becomes more adult, and the growth of the beard, for example. The hormones produced by the testes are *testosterone* and *androsterone*. If young mammals are *castrated*, that is if the testes are removed by operation, the secondary sexual characters fail to develop. This practice is employed on domestic animals to render them more passive and manageable and, in the case of pigs, sheep and cattle, to make them grow fatter.

The ovary (Fig. 20.6) is the female gonad and is composed of fibrous connective tissue in which are embedded at various stages of development, numerous *Graafian follicles*, each of which has been formed from the outer layer or *germinal epithelium*. Each Graafian follicle is formed of the *egg* or *oocyte*, as it is called, together with investing cells. The mature follicle has a fluid-filled cavity containing the egg which is surrounded by an envelope of cells attached to one side of the follicle. In mammals the egg is discharged from the surface of the ovary into the body cavity of the abdomen. The follicle cells which remain behind in the ovary after the discharge of the egg multiply to form a solid mass of cells called the *corpus luteum*. This soon disappears if the female mammal does not become pregnant. If the mammal becomes pregnant, however, the corpus luteum persists during the pregnancy, and for some time after birth, and acts as a temporary ductless gland. The functions of the ovaries as endocrine organs will be considered in the next chapter: here we are concerned with them as reproductive organs producing the female gametes or eggs.

FIG. 20.6 The Ovary in section. 1–8 show stages in the development of the Graafian follicle and the corpus luteum.

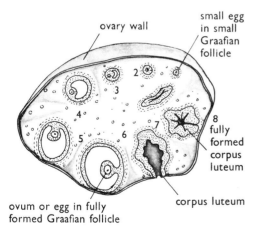

ovary wall

small egg in small Graafian follicle

8 fully formed corpus luteum

corpus luteum

ovum or egg in fully formed Graafian follicle

The Female Reproductive Organs (Fig. 20.7)

The human female reproductive organs consist of the *ovaries*, the *uterus* or *womb*, the *vagina* and the *vulva*.

The ovaries are two glandular structures

Fɪɢ. 20.7. The female reproductive system from the side.

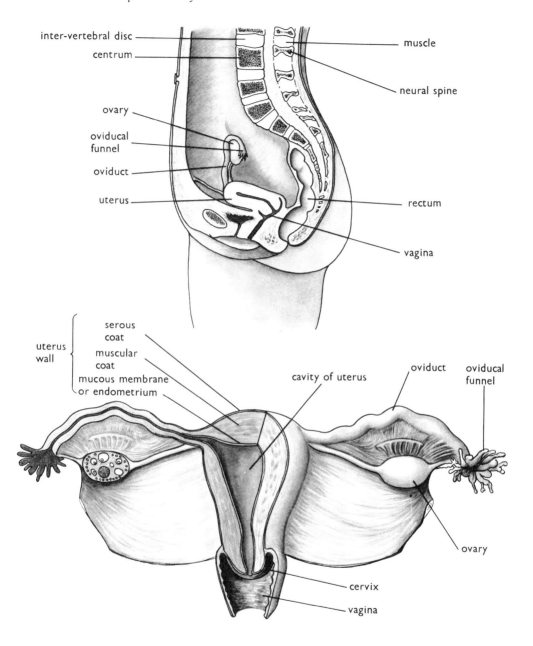

The female reproductive organs from above. The uterus and oviduct have been cut open and the right ovary is shown in section.

237

whose function, as we have just seen, is to produce eggs and hormones. They are present one on each side of the abdominal cavity in the position shown in the figure. The oviducts, or Fallopian tubes, are paired structures which extend from the ovaries to the uterus to which they are attached, one on each side. Each tube is about 8 cm long and about as thick as a pencil. The cavity of each tube is continuous with the cavity of the uterus. The *oviducal funnel* opens at the end of each Fallopian tube and it and the tubes possess cilia whose function is to waft the discharged egg into the tube and along it towards the uterus. The beating of the cilia sets up a flow of liquid in which the egg is passively carried: the egg itself has no power of self-locomotion.

The uterus in the non-pregnant female is a hollow, thick-walled structure lying in the part of the abdomen which is frequently called the pelvic cavity. It measures about 8 cm by 5 cm by 3 cm and its upper end receives the Fallopian tubes while at the lower end it is continuous with the vagina. The lower end of the uterus is the *cervix* and this projects into the vagina which in turn opens to the exterior at the vulva. The vagina is a sheath-like tube about 8 or 9 cm long.

It is usual to consider the *mammary glands* with the reproductive system for they produce the *milk* upon which the young mammals feed when they are born.

The Male Reproductive Organs (Fig. 20.8)

The male human being has reproductive organs consisting of two *testes* and their *ducts*, the *penis* and an accessory organ, the *prostate gland*. The internal structure of the testes has been considered. Externally each testis is an oval structure suspended by a *spermatic cord* in a sac-like structure, the *scrotum*. The seminiferous tubules unite to form a structure

known as the *epididymus* which consists of a coiled tube which leads in turn to the *vas deferens*. This tube leads upwards into the body where it loops round the ureter on the same side at a point near where the latter enters the bladder. As the vas deferens on each side passes downwards towards the penis it is joined by a duct from the *seminal vesicle* and together they open into the *urethra*—the tube which runs through the penis to the exterior. The prostate gland opens directly into the base of the urethra.

The functions of these parts are as follows: the testes produce spermatozoa and hormones; the epididymus and vas deferens convey the sperm in *seminal fluid* to the urethra; the seminal vesicles produce more seminal fluid for the sperm to be carried in; the prostate gland also produces seminal fluid; and the urethra passes the seminal fluid containing the sperm from the body. The urethra, it will be remembered, also passes out urine.

The penis is a structure which serves to pass the sperm into the body of the female during the process of *mating* or *copulation*, as it is called. It contains many large blood vessels which become gorged with blood during copulation. This stiffens the penis in order that it may be passed into the vagina of the female. Friction between the penis and the vagina results in *ejaculation*—the name given to the passing of the seminal fluid from the body of the male. Vast numbers of sperm—about 500 million—are passed out of the male at once. Within about six hours the sperm have swum, by lashing movements of their tails, up into the oviducts where, if an ovum (egg) is present, one of them will have joined with it to form a *zygote*. This fusion of the two gametes is *fertilisation*.

The subsequent development of the fertilised egg forms the subject of the next chapter.

238

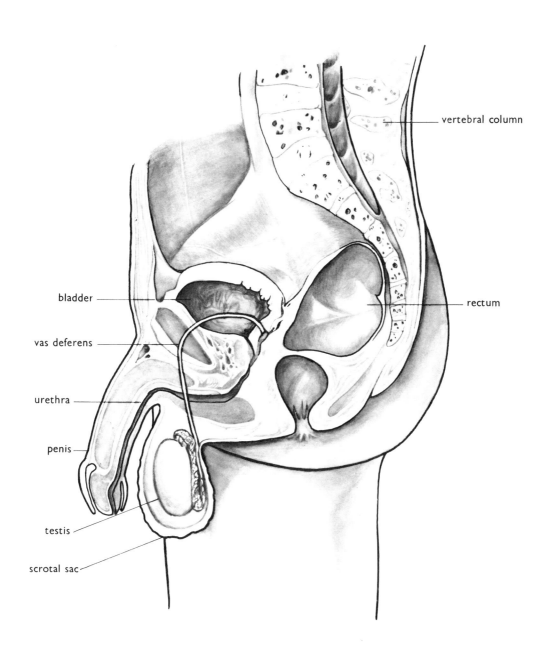

vertebral column

bladder

rectum

vas deferens

urethra

penis

testis

scrotal sac

FIG. 20.8. The male reproductive system.
A section seen from the side.

239

21. Joined Together—Mother and Foetus

The Development of the Fertilised Egg to form an Embryo

Fertilisation of the human egg occurs in the outer third of the oviduct. Once it has taken place all the other sperm—only one, of course, joins with the ovum—die. Entry into the egg by other sperm is prevented by the formation of a membrane round the egg through which they cannot penetrate. Immediately after fertilisation, while the zygote is still in the oviduct, cell division takes place. This process is called *cleavage*. The zygote divides into two cells, then each of these divides into two thus forming four cells in all. Each of the four cells thus formed now divides giving a total of eight—16, 32, 64, 128 cells form by subsequent divisions and the process is repeated until a sphere of cells is formed. This structure becomes hollow, in the centre, by the movement of its cells to the periphery of the sphere and at this stage it is known as a blastocyst. Its formation is shown in Fig. 21.1. Currents in the liquid of the oviduct, as well as contractions of the muscles of its wall, cause the young blastocyst to pass into the uterus where it arrives before the end of the first week after fertilisation has taken place. Here it floats in a secretion of the uterine wall.

The action of cilia keep it near the uterine wall whose innermost layer is the *endometrium*. During all the time the blastocyst is in the oviduct and the uterus it is nourished and supplied with oxygen by the uterine fluid. The blastocyst continues to develop and is called the *embryo*. This embryo sticks to the uterine wall and starts to destroy and to penetrate the endometrium. The surface of the embryo forms *villi*—projections which increase its surface area—which join it to the uterus lining. These villi invade the blood vessels of the endometrium so that they are not only firmly locked to the maternal tissue but are also surrounded by maternal blood from which they obtain, by diffusion, oxygen and food materials and to which they give carbon dioxide and other waste products. This region where the embryo is fixed to the mother is called the *placenta* and it consists of both embryonic and maternal tissues (Fig. 21.2). (It is important to note that there is no mixing of the embryonic and maternal blood, for the two circulations are separated by thin layers of cells. At this early stage the embryonic blood system is not yet developed.) The embryo continues to develop, the nerve cord, brain and blood system forming before the other body structures.

The embryo early becomes surrounded by protective membranes the most important of which is the *amnion* (Fig. 21.3). As the embryo

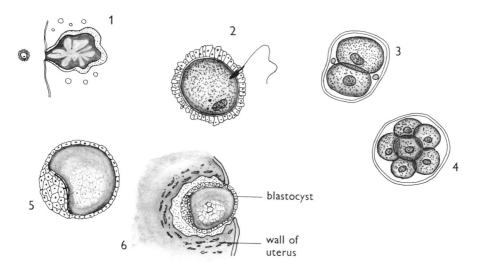

1. Ovulation. The egg has just left the Graafian follicle
2. Fertilization. The head of the sperm has entered the egg
3. The two cell stage
4. The eight cell stage—two of the cells are out of sight
5. The blastocyst. A hollow sphere formed as the result of many cell divisions
6. Implantation. The blastocyst has sunk into the wall of the uterus

FIG. 21.1. Ovulation, fertilisation, cell division and implantation.

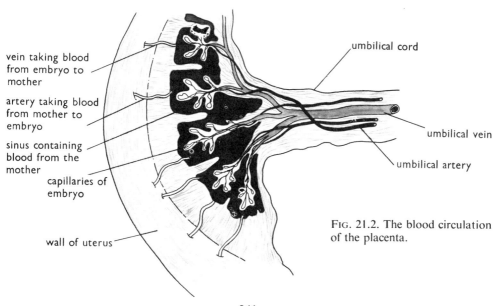

vein taking blood from embryo to mother

artery taking blood from mother to embryo

sinus containing blood from the mother

capillaries of embryo

wall of uterus

umbilical cord

umbilical vein

umbilical artery

FIG. 21.2. The blood circulation of the placenta.

241

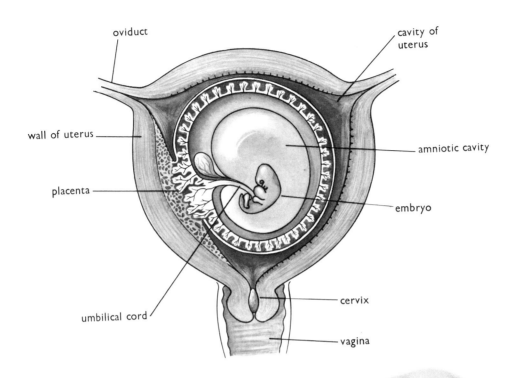

FIG. 21.3. The embryo attached to the uterus by the umbilical cord.

develops it remains attached to the *placenta*, and hence to the mother also, by the *umbilical cord*. This cord has running through it an *umbilical vein* and two *umbilical arteries* connecting the embryonic circulation with that of the placenta. Plate 62 shows an 8-week *foetus*, as the embryo is now called. Plate 63 shows a 14-week foetus with the skeleton stained.

About nine months from the date of fertilisation the foetus is ready to be *born* (Fig. 21.4). The uterine muscles start to contract in order to force the embryo from the uterus: this process is known as *labour*.

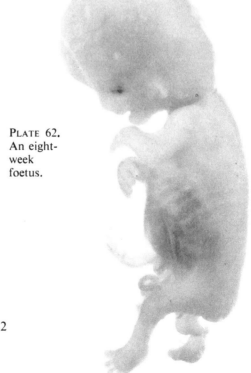

PLATE 62. An eight-week foetus.

242

PLATE 63. An X-ray of a fourteen-week foetus.

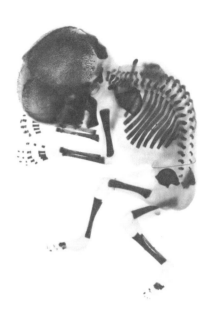

FIG. 21.4. FULL-TERM FOETUS.

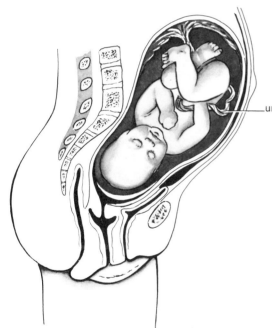

umbilical cord

Rhythmic contractions of the muscles gradually increase in frequency and in strength until the amnion is ruptured and the fluid within it escapes. This is sometimes referred to as 'the breaking of the waters'. More vigorous contractions now force the baby from the uterus and it passes through the greatly distended neck of the uterus, or *cervix*, and down the vagina to the exterior of the body. Lastly, some time after the actual birth, of the child the embryonic membranes and placenta are passed out and form the 'after-birth'.

243

The Special Needs of the Pregnant Woman

Diet. During pregnancy it is especially important to make certain that the diet is carefully balanced. As we have seen in an earlier chapter, growing protoplasm requires a supply of proteins and it is therefore important that these should be stressed in the diet rather than carbohydrates. If carbohydrates form too high a proportion of the diet the mother will put on weight to such an extent that it may make the birth of the child unnecessarily difficult. The total calorific value of the food should be about 10 500 kilojoules a day. Meat, eggs, fish, milk and cheese should appear regularly in the pregnant woman's weekly diet. Milk is especially important at this time because the foetus needs large quantities of calcium for the formation of its bones. If the parent is not getting sufficient milk the foetus may develop at the expense of the calcium reserve in the mother's bones.

The 'old wives' tale' that a pregnant woman should eat sufficient food for two people is not true—if she were to do this she would put on far too much weight. What is true is that she must eat a carefully balanced diet containing a high proportion of proteins and other substances, such as vitamins, which are necessary for growth and development of new tissues.

As well as foods containing protein an expectant mother must eat those which contain plenty of mineral salts and vitamins, such as raw vegetables and fruit, and wholemeal bread. A supply of orange juice, multivitamin tablets, iron tablets and yeast extract is desirable. It is also necessary for a mother to drink plenty of water.

Hygiene. As a mother has to excrete the waste products of the foetus as well as those of her own body it is most important that her skin is kept clean so that it functions efficiently as it will be remembered that some urea is lost through the skin. The bowels should be evacuated regularly and the teeth must be kept free from decay. Free dental treatment is available in this country for a pregnant mother. The importance of this lies in the fact that the poisons from a decaying tooth are continuously poured into the blood stream. The reason why it is advisable for a pregnant woman to drink plenty of water is in order that the toxins and other waste products formed by her own and by the embryo's metabolism may be removed easily.

Clothing. Clothes worn by the pregnant mother must be comfortable and adequate and in no way must circulation of her blood be impaired or her breathing restricted. Maternity clothes should be worn only when they become necessary and low-heeled shoes are essential. High-heeled shoes throw the body out of balance and this is accentuated as pregnancy advances. A doctor will give advice as to the necessity of wearing a maternity girdle at any particular stage but towards the end of pregnancy adequate support of the abdomen can relieve backache which sometimes occurs.

Rest and Exercise. The importance of getting adequate sleep before the birth of the child will be realised when it is remembered that, once born, the child may require to be fed during the night for some time, and owing to this the mother may lose sleep.

During pregnancy the bedroom windows should be open night and day within reason and the mother should take a daily walk to get adequate fresh air into her lungs.

Normal housework should be pursued but reasonable care should be taken not to lift heavy weights. Stretching up should be avoided. Where possible a rest should be taken in the afternoon with the feet raised up.

This reduces the possibility of varicose veins developing.

Antenatal care. In Great Britain Child Welfare Clinics have been set up in most towns. At these centres a mother can pay a monthly visit where her health and the progress of the developing child are checked. This includes a check on her weight, blood pressure and urine. A blood test is also taken to establish her blood group and to see whether or not she is anaemic.

Attitude of mind. Many women still go through pregnancy without any useful knowledge of what is happening and will happen when the baby is born. Very often a childbirth is regarded with dread quite unnecessarily owing to ignorance and fears enlarged by 'old wives' tales'. It should be realised that birth is a natural process and not an illness. Today adequate training for birth is given at relaxation classes in clinics and mothers are taught in simple terms how the baby develops and what will happen at the birth itself.

Some hospitals now encourage the father to be present at the birth so that the experience, which should be a joyful one, can be shared with the mother.

Many hospitals and other centres now teach expectant mothers how to prepare and train for childbirth with the minimum of pain and discomfort. The National Childbirth Trust has begun this work and it is rapidly spreading to most areas of this country. The method is known as *psychoprophylaxis* or *natural childbirth training*.

Family Planning

Methods of *birth control* or *contraception* enable people to plan the number of children they wish to have. This control of family size is important, not only to individual families, but also world-wide—see page 368 concerning the world 'population explosion'.

The commonest forms of contraception involve preventing the sperm reaching the ovum, by means of thin plastic or rubber barriers, thus ensuring that fertilisation does not occur. Another common method of birth control is by means of *contraceptive pills*. These pills contain female sex hormones which prevent ovulation and interfere with the preparation of the uterine wall to receive the blastocyst. (See pages 240 and 247.)

22. Adolescence

Although the growth and development of a person is a continuous process, unmarked by any sudden or clear-cut stages, it is convenient for purposes of description to consider his life to be divided into a number of periods. Thus we have infancy, childhood, boyhood and girlhood, adolescence, youth, manhood and womanhood, middle age and old age. It is with the fourth of these, that is with *adolescence*, that this chapter is concerned.

Adolescence is a term for the process of growing from boyhood or girlhood to the adult state. It is also a word used to describe the period of development from the beginning of puberty to maturity, puberty being the age at which the secondary sexual characteristics begin to develop. These characteristics comprise breaking of the voice, growth of the beard and growth of pubic hair, that is, hair around the external reproductive organs, in the boy. In the girl the changes which occur at puberty include the development of the mammary glands, widening of the hips and redistribution of fat over the body, and growth of pubic hair. At puberty or shortly after its commencement the ovaries begin to produce ova.

The term adolescence is a wider one than the term puberty for it includes not only the physical changes which occur at this period but also certain mental and social aspects as well.

There is an increase in intellectual capacity and the adolescent must begin to give serious consideration to such matters as family relationships and to his or her position in the adult world. Boys start to think carefully about their careers and how best they may earn their living when they become men. Girls develop an interest in home-making and marriage. Both boys and girls start to take more interest in the opposite sex, and make a re-assessment of the roles of men and women in everyday life and in marriage in particular. Whereas in childhood boys may even be antagonistic to girls and vice versa, each comes now to respect the place which the other holds in society.

Adolescents tend to be afraid of acting in a manner different from the group with whom they associate and tend to follow the leadership of those a year or two older than themselves. Thus boys and girls are at this period anxious to follow the most recent fashions and customs set by the 'teenage' idol of the time.

The period of adolescence lasts for six to ten years depending upon the individual. In boys it tends to start a year or two later than in girls. Puberty commences at about 13-14 years of age in boys and 11–12 in girls. This onset of puberty is usually preceded by a sudden growth spurt in both sexes, but as this occurs somewhat earlier in girls they may, at the age of about thirteen years, weigh more and be taller than boys of the same age. Most of the growth in the 'growth spurt' is due to the lengthening of the long bones of the arms and legs and as a result the body may for a time appear awkward in shape and may be unco-ordinated in action. This may sometimes make adolescence a difficult period especially if the adults of the community are lacking in sympathy and in understanding. This feeling of awkwardness may be increased for some time because during adolescence there is often an outbreak of pimples and spots on the skin. This phase usually passes, however, and should not cause undue worry.

It is during the period of adolescence that both boys and girls become capable of reproducing. Spermatozoa are formed in the testes of boys while ova develop in the girls' ovaries. While the sperm are produced continuously in the testes the eggs or ova are only extruded one at a time by each ovary in alternate months. The production of ova follows a regular pattern and it is this which we have now to consider in more details.

We saw in Chapter 20 how the eggs are extruded from Graafian follicles in the ovaries while in Chapter 21 we learned about the subsequent fate of an egg which had been fertilised. Now the uterus wall is prepared under the influence of hormones to receive the fertilised egg. This preparation, however, takes place *even if an egg has not been fertilised* in order that the uterine lining may be ready to receive the egg in good time should fertilisation occur. If the egg remains unfertilised it is shed, together with the thickened tissues of the uterus and a quantity of blood and mucus, as the *menstrual flow*, and the process is called *menstruation*. This flow occurs every 26–30 days, 28 days being an average figure.

The menstrual flow is usually referred to as the monthly 'period' and lasts from 3–5 days. The total quantity of the flow is about 5–8 tablespoons. This is passed to the exterior via the cervix and the vagina. The first few days of the menstrual period may be accompanied by varying degrees of pain. As menstruation occurs regularly and follows the same pattern each month it is often referred to as the *menstrual cycle*.

It should be noted at once that ovulation occurs not at the beginning of the menstrual cycle but in the middle—about halfway between two periods. The cycle begins on the first day of the menstrual flow; thus ovulation occurs about the 14th day of a 28-day cycle.

Reference to Fig. 22.1 will help to clarify the following description. The rhythmic nature of the menstrual cycle is under the control of the anterior lobe of the pituitary gland which secretes three hormones which stimulate the ovary to activity. The first of these hormones is known as the *follicle stimulating hormone* (F.S.H.), the action of which causes ripening of the Graafian follicle which in turn produces the hormone oestrogen or female sex hormone. This hormone is secreted into the blood and is responsible for the development, in the adolescent, of the secondary sex characters, and for their maintenance in later life. Oestrogen has another important function: it inhibits the production of F.S.H. by the pituitary thus ensuring that only one egg is matured during each cycle. As will be seen from the figure, oestrogen from the Graafian follicle operates during the first half of the cycle.

The second pituitary hormone is a companion to the first and causes the Graafian follicle to extrude the ovum. It is known as the *luteinising hormone* or L.H. and causes the extrusion of the ovum to occur about the 13th or 14th day of the cycle, as may be seen in the figure.

Lastly, the third hormone, from the

pituitary, known as the *luteotropic hormone,* or L.T.H., stimulates the corpus luteum to secrete *progesterone.* This hormone has two functions, firstly to inhibit further production of the pituitary hormones and secondly to stimulate the uterus lining to thicken in readiness to receive the egg should it be fertilised. If the egg is not fertilised the corpus luteum degenerates and this, of course, means that the pituitary hormones can again be produced. The egg in this case is not implanted on the uterine wall and is shed with the tissues of the uterus thus completing the cycle. If the egg is fertilised the corpus luteum continues the production of progesterone and this hormone together with oestrogen is necessary for the maintenance of pregnancy.

PRACTICAL WORK ON 20 TO 22

1. Ask your teacher to show a dissected rabbit with the reproductive system displayed. A male and female rabbit are necessary. Draw each dissection. If actual rabbits are not available museum specimens may be used.

2. Examine transverse sections of ovary and testis under the microscope. The high power lens will be necessary to see the sperm. Draw.

3. Examine and draw museum specimens of the placenta. These are usually available from the rabbit or pig. Notice the umbilical cord.

THINKING POINTS ON 20 TO 22

1. Consider why childbirth is often faced

FIG. 22.1. THE MENSTRUAL CYCLE.

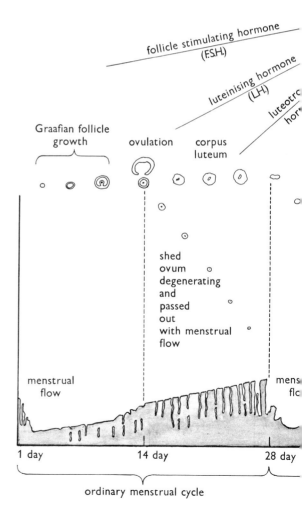

with fear. Why are such fears unfounded nowadays and how did they come about?

2. Adolescence is sometimes a difficult time. Why is this so and why are the fears really not necessary? Discuss this with your teacher and amongst each other.

QUESTIONS ON CHAPTERS 20, 21 AND 22

1. Draw a diagram to show a human foetus at full term *in utero*. Explain how the foetus is enabled to grow before birth. What structural changes occur after birth? (O)

2. Draw diagrams to show (a) the female reproductive organs, (b) the male reproductive organs. Explain how and where a human foetus is formed. (O)

3. Illustrate the way the placenta is situated in the pregnant uterus. Briefly describe its structure and the part it plays in the life of the foetus. (L)

4. Give an account of the position, shape and structure of the uterus. What are the main changes which occur in this organ during the menstrual cycle and how are they brought about? (L)

5. Describe the female reproductive organs and show how the uterus is fitted for its functions. (L)

6. Explain concisely the importance in reproduction of the following: (a) ovulation, (b) fertilisation, (c) corpus luteum and (d) placenta. (L)

7. What hormones are secreted within the female reproductive system, and what is their action on other organs? (L)

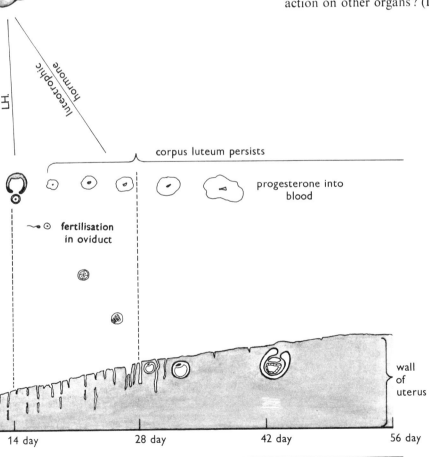

LH.

luteotrophic hormone

corpus luteum persists

fertilisation in oviduct

progesterone into blood

wall of uterus

14 day   28 day   42 day   56 day

cycle ending in pregnancy

Summary of 20 to 22

1. *Charles Darwin* showed that there is a *struggle for existence* in nature and that only the *fittest animals will survive.*

2. *Reproduction* is one of the most distinctive characteristics of living things and is achieved by a variety of methods in both plant and animal kingdoms. Broadly speaking there are two types of reproduction—*asexual* and *sexual.*

3. Reproduction in Man is always sexual, a female gamete (the egg) being fertilised by a male gamete (the sperm); the resulting cell is a *zygote.* Sperm are produced in *testes* and *eggs* in *ovaries.*

4. In human beings fertilisation is *internal*, the sperm being introduced into the body of the female by the male.

5. The fertilised egg develops in the *uterus* of the female where it receives food, oxygen and protection until it is ready to be *born.* The young embryo is attached to the uterus by a *placenta.* The *umbilical cord* joins the embryo to the placenta.

6. The *pregnant woman* must pay particular care to her diet, to hygiene and to clothing.

7. *Adolescence* is the change from boyhood or girlhood to adulthood. *Puberty* is the time during life when sexual developments take place.

8. Various methods of birth control enable the sizes of families to be planned.

23. Genetics

Introduction

Genetics is one of the more modern branches of biology: it is the scientific study of heredity. Heredity is concerned with the way in which characteristics are passed from parents to their offspring and with the variations in characters which occur. It provides an explanation of both the similarities and the differences between individuals and their offspring and its scope includes both plants and animals.

For many centuries Man has been interested in the striking resemblances shown between father and son, mother and daughter, grandparents and grandchildren and so on. For many years, too, Man has tried to improve the quality of his crops and his live-stock. This he has done by carefully selecting 'strong' stock and breeding from it. Little explanation of the excellent results obtained by breeding was available, however, until the work of an obscure Czechoslovakian monk became known and developed. This monk was Gregor Mendel, 1822–1884, whose portrait may be seen in Plate 64. Mendel was abbot at the Augustinian monastery in Altbrunn and it was in the monastery garden that his famous experiments on pea plants were carried out. These experiments and Mendel's interpretation of them resulted in the founding of the modern science of genetics.

It is interesting to note that although Mendel's results were published in the local Natural History Society journal his work remained ignored for more than thirty years and he never achieved fame during his lifetime. When he died in 1884 his funeral was attended by men who honoured him as a good priest and as an inspiring teacher but there could have been none there who realised that they were honouring a great scientist.

PLATE 64. Gregor Mendel.

251

Mendel's Experiments

Mendel realised that in considering any one characteristic of a plant two contrasting conditions often existed. For example, the pea plants which he grew in his monastery garden were either tall or short; the skin of their seeds was either green or yellow and either smooth or wrinkled. When Mendel cross-pollinated the flowers of tall plants over several generations he was able to produce a *pure strain* of tall plants. This process of cross-pollinating over several generations in order to obtain a pure strain is called *selfing*. Similarly a pure strain of dwarf pea plants could be obtained by selfing over several generations. Seed taken from plants which had been selfed in this way always bred true, i.e. tall plants always gave rise to tall plants while dwarf plants gave rise only to dwarf ones. The problem which Mendel set himself to discover was what happened if tall plants were crossed with dwarf plants.

Mendel crossed tall with dwarf plants. These he called the *parental generation*. When the pea pods were ripe on these plants Mendel took the seeds from them and grew them. The resulting generation was called the *first filial* or F_1 generation. Probably Mendel expected this generation to be intermediate in height between the tall plants and the dwarf ones and we can imagine his surprise when he found that all the plants were tall! It looked as if the dwarfness of one parent had been wiped out by the tallness of the other.

However, Mendel did not stop his experiments here: he next took seed from the F_1 generation and grew it, thus obtaining a second filial or F_2 generation. This generation grew into plants which when adult were some tall and some dwarf, and we can again imagine Mendel's surprise when he saw this result. The dwarfness factor had not been wiped out in the F_1 generation but it had been hidden, only to reappear in the next generation! Further by using thousands of seeds Mendel was able to show that the tall and dwarf pea plants were present in the ratio of three to one in the F_2 generation.

Mendel concluded that the characteristics for both tallness and dwarfness were present in the F_1 generation although only one of these characteristics was exhibited. The characteristic which showed in the F_1 generation Mendel called the *dominant characteristic* while that characteristic which was masked in the F_1 generation he called the *recessive characteristic*. Thus, in the case of the pea plants, tallness is dominant to dwarfness, dwarfness being the recessive characteristic. Mendel who knew that the characteristics of the plants must be carried from one generation to the next in the pollen and in the ovules—that is the gametes—concluded that the gametes contained something which caused a particular character to develop. This 'something' he called a 'factor'. Mendel also concluded that *only one of a pair of contrasting characteristics could be present in a particular gamete*. This fact is now known as *Mendel's First Law*. Fig. 23.1 will help you to understand Mendel's results.

Mendel carried his experiments a stage further by breeding pea plants from the F_2 generation. It will be remembered that in this generation three tall plants were found to every one dwarf plant. If the dwarf plants were bred Mendel found that they bred true. On the other hand if the tall plants were bred the F_3 generation obtained from them showed that one third of them gave rise to only tall plants while the remaining two-thirds gave rise to both tall plants and dwarf plants in the ratio of three to one. This result is shown diagrammatically in Fig. 23.1.

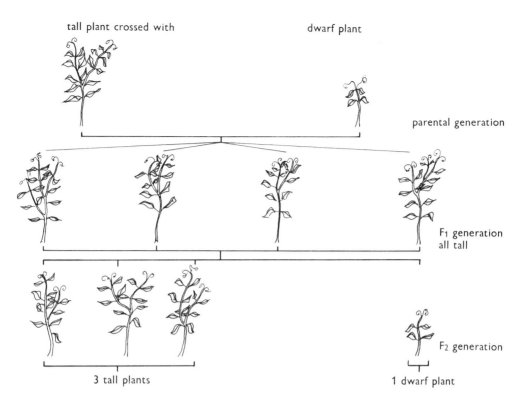

tall plant crossed with   dwarf plant

parental generation

F₁ generation
all tall

F₂ generation

3 tall plants   1 dwarf plant

Diagrammatic representation of Mendel's experiments with pea plants.

a. Cross Pure Tall with Pure Dwarf Plants

T—tallness
t—dwarfness

TT × tt

Tt   Tt   Tt   Tt

Parental Generation—that is the tall and
dwarf plants
Gametes—each gamete contains either the factor
for tallness or the factor for dwarfness. No
gamete contains both
F₁ Generation—all these plants contain the
dominant factor T and are, therefore, tall.
All the plants also contain the recessive factor t
and are therefore heterozygous

b. Cross Plants of the
F₁ generation

All these are tall plants.

Tt × Tt

TT   Tt   Tt   tt

Plants taken from the F₁ generation
Gametes—two out of every four gametes will
contain the factor for tallness and two the
factor for dwarfness
F₂ Generation—tall to dwarf plants in the
ratio of 3:1

c. Cross Plants of the F₂ generation

TT × TT

gametes

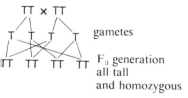

TT   TT   TT   TT   F₃ generation
all tall
and homozygous

Tt × Tt   i.e., heterozygous
plants

gametes

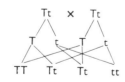

TT   Tt   Tt   tt   F₃ generation
tall to dwarf in
ratio of 3:1

homozygous,
recessive, dwarfs

tt × tt   gametes

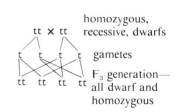

tt   tt   tt   tt   F₃ generation—
all dwarf and
homozygous

FIG. 23.1. MONOHYBRID INHERITANCE.

In Fig. 23.1 TT represents tall plants and tt the dwarf plants. T and t represent the 'factors' present in the gametes. It will be noticed that the TT plants and the tt plants can only give rise to gametes containing the factor for tallness *or* dwarfness. Such plants are said to be *homozygous* for the characteristic of tallness or dwarfness. These are plants of the parental generation. Half the plants of the first filial generation, however, contain 'factors' for both tallness and dwarfness and can thus give rise to gametes for *both* of these characteristics. These plants are therefore known as *heterozygous* for the characteristic of tallness and dwarfness.

Many human characteristics follow this simple Mendelian pattern of inheritance, some of the characteristics being dominant and others being recessive. Dominants include hair lip and negroid hair while recessives include red hair, colour blindness and left-handedness. It is not always that we have clear-cut cases, however, for sometimes dominance is incomplete. For example, if each parent is homozygous for brown eye colour all their children will have brown eyes but if the parents are heterozygous for this particular characteristic their children may have eyes of various shades such as hazel and light brown. The characteristic 'blue eyes' is recessive so that if both parents have blue eyes their children will also have blue eyes. The study of human genetics is difficult because even the largest human family is small compared with the thousands of pea plants, for example, which can be used in plant-breeding experiments. Only when large numbers are used can the results be statistically sound.

Another difficulty in studying human genetics lies in the fact that it is impossible to tell from looking at a person whether he is homozygous or heterozygous for a particular characteristic. Thus considering again the case of eye colour it is impossible to tell if a brown-eyed man is pure strain or a hybrid for that characteristic. If a brown-eyed man marries a blue-eyed woman, provided both are 'pure strains' for eye colour, all the children will be brown-eyed but if the parents are hybrids for eye-colour one in four of the children is likely to be blue-eyed (Fig. 23.2).

Both parents brown-eyed but heterozygous:

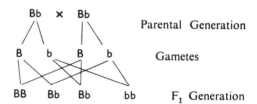

Since B is dominant three children will have brown eyes and one will have blue eyes.

FIG. 23.2. INHERITANCE OF EYE-COLOUR.

The type of Mendelian inheritance we have been considering concerns only one pair of contrasting characteristics and is known as *monohybrid inheritance*. Mendel carried his investigations further, however, by considering how two pairs of contrasting characteristics are inherited. This we refer to as *dihybrid inheritance*. Mendel considered the two characteristics of height and seed colour. He crossed yellow-seeded tall pea plants with green-seeded dwarf pea plants. The characteristic 'yellow' is dominant to 'green' and 'tall' is dominant to 'dwarf'. As we would expect, in the light of what has already been said, Mendel found that all the F_1 plants were tall and had yellow seeds. Then Mendel crossed the plants of the F_1 generation. Considering any two individual parents,

Mendel found that when they were crossed their offspring were present in the proportion of 9 'tall-yellows', 3 'tall-greens', 3 'dwarf-yellows' and 1 'dwarf-green'.

How may this result be explained? The explanation can be seen best in Fig. 23.3.

MALE GAMETES	FEMALE GAMETES			
	TY	Ty	tY	ty
TY	TTYY	TTYy	TtYY	TtYy
Ty	TTYy	TTyy	TtYy	Ttyy
tY	TtYY	TtYy	ttYY	ttYy
ty	TtYy	Ttyy	ttYy	ttyy

The table shows the results of crossing pure tall yellow plants with pure dwarf green plants, the colour referring to the seed coat. Each parent in the F_1 generation produces four different kinds of gametes—TY, Ty, tY and ty.

FIG. 23.3. The inheritance of two pairs of contrasted characters—height and seed colour, in pea plants.

The point to bear in mind is that in the F_1 generation each parent can produce four different kinds of gametes and Fig. 23.3 shows the result of combining them two by two—one male and one female gamete. Mendel concluded that the *characteristics associated in the parents can be inherited independently of each other* or, to express it another way, *each one of a pair of contrasting characteristics can be combined with either characteristic in another contrasting pair*. This is now known as *Mendel's Second Law* or the *Law of Independent Assortment*.

The Mechanism of Inheritance

It will be recalled that in Chapter 1 we saw that the animal cell contains a nucleus surrounded by a nuclear membrane within which nucleoproteins or 'chromatin' are found. In a resting cell, i.e., in one which is not dividing, the chromatin is not present in a clearly recognisable form. However, if a cell which is in the process of dividing is suitably stained it is found that the chromatin appears in definite units. These units are called *chromosomes*. Their importance lies in the fact that they carry Mendel's 'factors', which, as we have seen, is the name he gave to the 'something' which was responsible for passing characteristics from one generation to another. Today these 'factors' are called *genes*. Gamets are formed, as we have seen, from cells of the germinal epithelium in the gonads and it is in them only that characteristics can be passed from one generation to the next.

Although chromosomes are present in all the body cells as well, the gametes are formed by cell division but it is a type of cell division which differs from that of all other cells. The normal body cells (i.e. all except the gametes) divide by a process known as *mitosis* but the gametes are formed by *reduction division* or *meiosis*. A clear understanding of meiosis is made easier by an understanding of mitosis, so we shall study each in turn.

Mitosis (Plate 65). This is the process by which all the body cells divide and it is a process which follows a definite pattern. Fig. 23.4 will help you to understand the following description. At the onset of mitosis the nucleus enlarges, the nuclear membrane and the nucleolus disappear, and the chromatin becomes stainable. When it is stained the chromatin is found to be present as a number of small structures each of which has a recognisable shape. These structures are the

255

FIG. 23.4. MITOSIS, a–i, successive stages.

cell membrane
cytoplasm
nuclear membrane
nuclear sap contains chromatin— not yet stainable
nucleolus
centriole

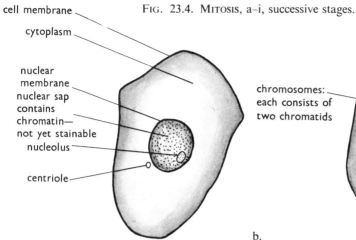

a.
The resting cell

chromosomes: each consists of two chromatids

b.
Chromosomes now visible, nuclear membrane and nucleolus disappearing, centriole has divided

c.
For the sake of clarity this figure and the remaining ones show one pair of chromosomes only. Here the centrioles have moved to opposite poles of the cell

d.
The spindle has formed between the centrioles. The chromosomes are attached to the spindle by the centromeres

e.
The chromatids now repel one another, the centromeres moving apart first

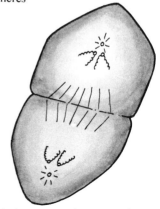

f.
The chromatids have moved to opposite poles; the cytoplasm is beginning to divide

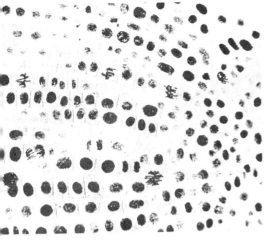

PLATE 65. Mitosis in plant cells.

chromosomes to which reference has already been made. The chromosomes are found to be present in like pairs, one having been derived from the mother and the other from the father, because every cell of the body is derived from the zygote (page 233). The number of chromosomes present is constant for any one species of plant or animal. For example, there are 23 pairs of chromosomes in the body cells of the human being.

A small structure known as the centriole which lies near the nucleus divides into two and each part moves to opposite ends or *poles* of the cell. As they do so a spindle of fibres forms between them. At this stage the chromosomes are seen to be double structures. Each half is called a *chromatid* and is attached to the spindle fibres by a region known as the *centromere* at the 'equator'. The two chromatids formed from each chromosome now repel each other and separate—at first in the region of the centromere—but finally along their whole length and each passes to a pole. The chromatids once they have reached opposite poles take up chemicals from the surrounding cytoplasm to form a new chromatid, which lies alongside the existing one thus forming again a complete new chromosome. The chromosomes now grouped together form a new nucleus at each pole. The cytoplasm of the original cell divides by constriction, as shown in the drawing, and thus two cells have been formed by the division of the original one.

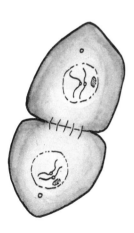

g.
The spindle has almost disappeared, the cyto-plasm is nearly divided, the nuclear membranes and nucleoli are forming

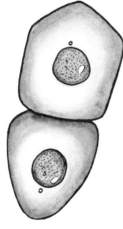

h.
Two new cells have been formed from the original one, each with its own nucleus. The cells now grow to full size

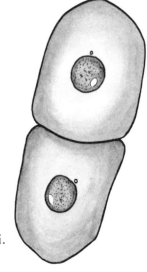

i.
The two cells have now grown to full size. Their subsequent fate would be either to divide again or to become differenti-ated to form specialised cells such as muscle cells, nerve cells or bone cells

Meiosis (Fig. 23.5). This is the name given to the division of the cells which form gametes. Its other name—reduction division —is a good one for it is during meiosis that the number of chromosomes is halved, that is, the gametes have half the number of chromosomes that are found in the body cells. This is readily seen to be essential for if the number of chromosomes were not reduced in the gametes the number present in the zygote, that is in the cell formed by the fusion of two gametes, would be doubled. And again at each generation the number would be doubled so that after a few generations the nucleus would be unable to hold all the chromosomes! Thus we have this position: when gametes are formed they have half the number of chromosomes found in the body cells, and when a zygote is formed by the fusion of two gametes the normal number of chromosomes is restored.

When meiosis takes place there are two divisions to consider. In the first of these divisions the chromosomes become arranged in pairs—one member of the pairs having originally been derived from the mother and the other member from the father. Each member of the pair is split longitudinally so that there appear to be four half-chromosomes lying together. The halves lying next to each other then exchange material by *'crossing-over'*. The significance of this will be considered below. The newly constituted *chromosomes* then separate from one another in much the same way as the *chromatids* separated in mitosis. Thus the two cells formed as a result of this first division contain only half the number of chromosomes of the original cell. The second division takes place at once by a process similar to mitosis. Thus as the result of the double division occurring during meiosis there are four gametes formed, each having half the number of chromosomes

of the body cells. Each gamete has a complete set of characteristics to pass on to the next generation.

Reference to Fig. 23.6 will help you to understand the significance of the 'crossing-over' mentioned in the previous paragraph. It is simply that, since the genes are carried on the chromosomes, when crossing-over occurs there is a change of genes between chromosomes from the two parents. This exchange of genes during gamete formation means that the gametes produced will have different genetic constitutions and hence when two gametes unite at fertilisation greater chances of variation are possible in the inherited characteristics. If the variation is advantageous to the animal or plant which develops from the newly formed zygote, it

FIG. 23.6. CROSSING OVER.

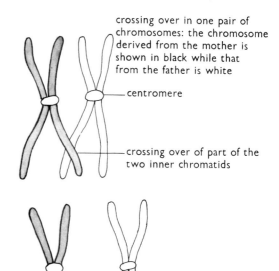

crossing over in one pair of chromosomes: the chromosome derived from the mother is shown in black while that from the father is white

— centromere

— crossing over of part of the two inner chromatids

part of each of the inner chromatids have changed places thus ensuring a change in genetic constitution: this crossing over occurs at stage '*b*' in Fig 23·5

258

FIG. 23.5. MEIOSIS.

a. Body cell just beginning meiosis. The chromosomes have become stainable. Only one pair of chromosomes are shown for the sake of clarity.

b. The centriole has divided and the spindle is forming.

c. The chromosomes are separating. Their separation marks the end of the first division of meiosis.

d. The second meitotic division starts at once—before the cytoplasm has completely divided. Notice that each of new cells forming has only half the number of chromosomes which the original cell had. The centrioles now divide—this heralds the commencement of the second division.

e. Spindles are forming at right angles to that formed in the first division. The chromosomes take up their position at the equator of the spindle.

f. The chromatids are separating as in mitosis. By now the cytoplasm has divided into two and each of these cells is now itself beginning to divide.

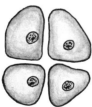

g. The final position: four cells have formed from the original one, each containing half the number of chromosomes as was present in the parent cell: owing to 'crossing over' each of these four cells has a different genetic constitution.

will survive, but if it is of no advantage it will probably be eliminated during the struggle for existence which exists in nature. Variations are made use of by plant and animal breeders in their attempts to improve their live-stock. Many of these changes are effective only under domestic conditions where the animals or plants are grown or cultivated under rather artificial conditions. In the wild state they might well be eliminated. This is particularly true with certain breeds of dogs where, to satisfy current fashions, certain features are developed which would be of no survival value to the dogs in their wild state.

Sex determination and sex-linked characters. The sex of a human being is determined by a pair of chromosomes known as the *sex-chromosomes*. In the female the two chromosomes of the pair are identical but in the male one is smaller than the other. The small chromosome is called the Y-chromosome and the other the X-chromosome. This X-chromosome of the male is identical in appearance with the two chromosomes of the female and hence these are also called X-chromosomes. Fig. 23.7 shows the formation of gametes from the male and female and how fertilisation results in males and females in approximately equal numbers.

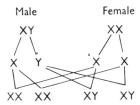

FIG. 23.7. Inheritance of sex. The sex chromosomes in the human being. If XX chromosomes are present the child will be a girl and if XY are present the baby will be a boy. The diagram shows how it comes about that approximately equal numbers of boys and girls are born.

It is interesting to note that certain other characteristics are due to genes on the chromosomes responsible for sex determination. Haemophilia and red-green colour blindness are two such characteristics. These two conditions appear in men but rarely in women as the genes responsible for them are situated on the sex chromosomes. Such characteristics are said to be *sex-linked*.

Gene-complex. So far we have spoken as if each characteristic produced in an individual depends on a single gene or on a pair of genes. But a gene does not always act by itself but in association with other genes. The action of a gene, in other words, may be modified by the presence of other genes. The total gene complement of an organism is its *gene-complex*.

Continuous Variation

The type of variation we have just considered is known as *discontinuous variation*: that is, it is a variation of some marked difference between an individual and its parents, and is due to some genetic change or *mutation*. In contrast to this type of variation there is *continuous variation* in which there is no sharply marked difference but the differences appear to shade into one another. For example there may be slight differences in weight in a litter of kittens—continuous variation—whereas all the kittens may be black except one which is, say, ginger—discontinuous variation. The term 'continuous variation' originated because it is possible to take a large number of individuals and to measure them for some particular characteristic—height or intelligence for example—and to plot a graph of the measurements. Fig. 23.8 will show the results of making one such graph.

1. Who was Gregor Mendel? Explain Mendel's First Law. How may you use this to account for auburn hair occurring in the children of (a) two dark-haired parents, (b) a dark- and an auburn-haired parent, (c) two auburn-haired parents? (O)

2. Describe and explain the results that Mendel obtained by crossing tall and short peas. How is sex determined in Man? (L)

3. Explain how (a) hereditary characteristics are transmitted, (b) the sex of the offspring is determined in Man. (S)

4. In what way does Mendel's First Law help us to understand how characteristics are inherited? Explain why two brown-eyed parents may have both brown-eyed and blue-eyed offspring. (W)

1. Investigate under the microscope sections of plant tissue to show mitosis and meiosis. Draw.

2. Buy a packet of tall pea plant seed and of dwarf seeds. Grow these and try to perform some crosses following Mendel's experiments. This will take several years to complete.

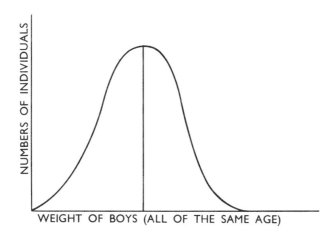

WEIGHT OF BOYS (ALL OF THE SAME AGE)

FIG. 23.8. Continuous variation. The graph is made by plotting the weight of individual boys of the same age against the numbers of boys showing the same weight. Thus the majority of boys will weigh approximately the same and hence the crowding near the 'average' line at the top of the curve. A few boys will weigh much less than the average and a few much more—hence the wide spread of weight at the bottom of the graph.

Summary of 23

1. *Genetics* is the scientific study of *heredity*, that is, the way in which characteristics are passed from parents to children and is concerned with the variations in characteristics which occur.

2. Scientific work on genetics was very limited until *Gregor Mendel* performed his experiments, although Man had long been interested in breeding experiments to improve his live-stock.

3. A *pure strain* may be obtained by crossing similar plants over several generations—tall plants for example—a process known as *selfing*.

4. *Dominant characteristics* mask *recessive characteristics* in the first filial or F_1 generation. The recessive characteristic may reappear in the second filial generation.

5. *Mendel's First Law* states that only one of a pair of contrasting characteristics could be present in a particular gamete.

6. *Genes* are carried on *chromosomes*. Genes are responsible for passing a characteristic from one generation to the next. If an organism has received like genes from each parent at fertilisation it will be *homozygous*; if unlike genes it will be *heterozygous*.

7. Inheritance of one pair of characteristics is known as *monohybrid inheritance*; of two pairs of characteristics, *dihybrid inheritance*.

8. *Mendel's Second Law—the Law of Independent Assortment*—states that the characteristics associated in the parents can be inherited independently of each other.

9. There are two types of cell division—*Meiosis* or *Reduction Division* and *Mitosis*. Meiosis occurs only in the formation of gametes when the number of chromosomes present in the body cells is halved. Mitosis occurs in the formation of new body cells and results in two cells each having the same number of chromosomes.

10. The *crossing-over* which occurs during meiosis ensures that there is an exchange of genetic material and this may result in favourable or unfavourable variations.

11. The sex of a person is determined by *sex-chromosomes*. These chromosomes have genes upon them for other characteristics as well as sex: hence some characteristics are said to be *sex-linked*.

12. Genes do not always act alone to produce a characteristic—sometimes several genes are involved.

13. A sudden genetic change or *mutation* may result in a marked difference between an individual and his parents. The variation may be sudden and marked and is known as *discontinuous variation*. In *continuous variation* there are no sharply marked differences but the differences shade into one another, as, for example, in human height and weight.

24. Habits: Good and Bad

Introduction

Reference was made in Chapter 18 to the part played by conditioned reflexes in the formation of habits. We saw how Pavlov's dogs learned to respond by producing saliva at the sound of a bell. It is important to note that this response continued only as long as it was rewarded. Failure to give the dogs some meat just after the bell had sounded soon resulted in failure to produce saliva. The conditioned reflex and its responses were maintained only as long as they were of value to the dog and as long as they were reinforced by a reward of food. An example of a conditioned reflex in Man is the watering of the mouth when the word 'lemon' is mentioned and this is a possible explanation of the use of lemons in the garnishing of foods!

The biological value of this is obvious and the application of our knowledge of conditioned reflexes to the formation of good habits in childhood will now be considered together with the part played by memory and reason.

Habits of Childhood

We saw also in Chapter 18 that the new-born child commences life equipped with a number of simple reflex actions which enable him to carry out the basic functions of life: his hunger pains result in a sucking reflex action, the stimulus of a full bladder results in its being emptied at once and a sensation of cold makes him cry for his mother's attention.

Early training aims to convert some of these simple reflexes into conditioned reflexes so that the responses are made at suitable times and in appropriate places. Thus this type of training is one which disciplines the natural functions.

A second type of training aims at tidiness, cleanliness, etc.—that is, habits which do not come 'naturally' but have to be taught. To assist in this learning, incentives are necessary; for example, parent's approval in a child of about two years of age is frequently rewarded by rapid learning of the desired habit. Unfortunately this phase in which the child delights to please does not usually last long but is followed by a 'contrary' phase during which he does not seem to know what he wants. Hence it is important that he is trained as far as possible in good habits before this contrary phase is reached! As a child becomes older, memory and reasoning begin to play their part in habit training and a child can see why certain actions are harmful and others beneficial. For example, after a certain degree of mental development a child can *understand*, because of his increasing knowledge, that continual sweet-eating will lead to tooth decay.

Finally, habits of mind need to be cultivated from the earliest years. The child must learn to see himself against a background of other children and of adults and he must learn to fit into their company and to get on with them. Attitudes of unselfishness, tolerance and thoughtfulness must be encouraged.

As a child grows older he must link consciously each habit with the reason behind it. This will reinforce the habit. This point should be kept in mind as we now consider a number of childhood habits.

One thing worth noting is that a young child enjoys *regular* activities and looks forward to such times as meals and the daily bath. Regularity helps establish the physical pattern of a good habit. For example, the stomach becomes used to being active at regular times and similarly needs regular periods of rest. The child can be taught while still quite young that it is desirable to have a varied diet and that certain foods are better for him than others. For example, a child is likely to drink a suitable quantity of milk if he (or she) knows that by doing so the teeth will remain attractive.

A good natural appetite may be spoilt by too great an insistence on correct table manners: meal times are to be enjoyed and a gradual development of good social habits will result.

Regularity is also important in connection with rest and sleep. As at mealtimes, the body becomes used to a regular rhythm of activity and rest, and interruptions of this rhythm are likely to lead to unhappiness. A child should sleep contentedly and awaken refreshed. The amount of sleep required depends upon the age and upon the individual. It is important to realise the need for fresh air in the bedroom which should always be well ventilated.

The need for sleep, exercise and for good posture have all been considered in Chapter 6 and it is important that good attitudes towards these are developed during early childhood. Exercises and postures are especially important in early childhood because it is at this time that the bones are being formed.

It is also important that children should learn to wash their hands before meals and after visiting the toilet—the reasons for this will become clearer when the chapters on bacteria and disease have been studied. One may not expect a child to keep clean while at play but he can be taught the importance of washing before meals. Children should also be taught, as early as possible, the importance of nose breathing and the use of a handkerchief. The reasons for these practices should be explained as soon as the child is old enough to understand them. Gradually as understanding develops a child will learn to prefer cleanliness to dirt and this becomes reinforced strongly at adolescence when the importance of attracting the opposite sex becomes apparent.

In all this training it is most important to maintain a happy relationship between parent and child, and a reasoned caution in connection with dangerous things such as fire, gas, electricity and traffic.

In the second year of a child's life imitation of adult behaviour and that of other children becomes an important factor in learning. A child loves to copy its mother and this may help in the formation of good habits. The attitude of parents towards toilet training varies a great deal, some parents 'potting' a child almost from birth while others wait until the end of the first year before beginning to do so. It is important to avoid excessive strictness in toilet training because doctors have noticed that many adults and children with nervous complaints have had very early and severe training. They tend to be fussy about cleanliness and take neatness to extremes while their personality may become nervous and irritable. Punishing a child for 'wetting' is the worst possible treatment to give him, for, although this may force a child to be clean and dry early, it frequently results in serious trouble later on: it may result in his becoming so tense that his bladder cannot fill to its full extent and hence he needs to empty it very often. Thus when he goes to school he may need to be 'excused' frequently while at night he may become a persistent 'bed-wetter'. The best method of toilet training is possibly to watch the child until he appears ready to learn, and then to give him all the encouragement he needs so that the happy relationship between him and his mother may be maintained. It seems futile to 'pot' a child until his bladder is large enough to retain the urine for about two hours. Naturally the age at which this is possible varies with each child. The first stage in the child's becoming trained will be when he tells his mother that he *is* wet, the second stage occurs when he begins to tell his mother *just after* he has passed urine, and the third stage is when he tells his mother when his bladder is full, so that she is able to put him on the toilet *before* he passes the urine. Before this last stage is reached there will have been many 'accidents' and much patience will have to be shown by the mother but this will be well rewarded. With regard to defaecation, insisting that the child sits on the 'pot' for a long time only frustrates the mother and may have the effect of making the child determined to 'hold on' to his faeces as if it were a part of his body or a cherished possession and may result in a life-time habit of constipation. If a child defaecates at the same time each day it is, of course, reasonable to 'pot' him at this time thereby associating in the child's mind the 'pot' and the faeces so that he soon establishes the habit of defaecating at the same time each day in the same place. A child is not fully toilet-trained until he can go to the toilet on his own and cope unaided with his clothes,

cleaning himself, washing his hands and dressing himself. All these actions require a high degree of co-ordinated muscular effort and this cannot be expected of him until he is between two-and-a-half and three years old. Some children may take even longer than this period to become fully trained.

While severe toilet training may be the cause of bed-wetting it must not be imagined that it is the only one. A child who is upset by being left with strangers while the parents go out, for example, may become tense, and this may also lead to bed-wetting. Any great emotional upset or unusual excitement is likely to have a similar effect. Sometimes the emotional stress of the arrival of a new baby brother or sister may cause a child who has for some time been dry, day and night, to start bed-wetting. Here again the cure for the bed-wetting is not to blame or punish the child but to try to gain an insight into the underlying cause of it. If bed-wetting is continued beyond the age when the child should normally be dry it is called *enuresis* and this may persist even into adolescence in exceptional cases.

Nervousness, tension and worry may cause a child to develop other habits in childhood which may return during adolescence. For example the natural interest which a child shows in its genitalia, or external sex organs, is perfectly healthy. He likes to explore them in just the same way as he likes to explore his toes—to him this is part of learning about himself and the whole exciting new world into which he has been born. It is most important that a child should be told that all parts of his body are wholesome and good, and any attempt by his mother to prevent his exploring his body fully will only increase his interest, and may result in his having an unhealthy attitude to the sexual parts. An unhealthy interest in the sex organs may also develop if a child is deprived of the comfort of his mother's love; lacking her love may lead to his seeking comfort from his own body.

If the child is allowed to explore himself fully his natural curiosity will soon be satisfied and his attention will pass to other things. At about two-and-a-half years of age a child becomes curious as to why boys and girls are different and this should be explained to him (or her).

We have already seen that there is a basic instinct to suck in young children. This is obviously of biological advantage for it ensures that the baby will obtain its milk. If a child has had insufficient suckling when he is young he may suck his thumb or finger or a piece of blanket in order to satisfy this need. It is interesting to note that puppies fed by dropping milk into their mouths, instead of being fed by their mothers or from a bottle, miss the satisfaction of sucking to such a degree that they will suck one another's paws until the hair is completely removed. Generally a baby stops thumb-sucking by the time he is a year and a half old but may return to it for comfort when he is in pain or when he is tired or worried. To attempt to restrain a child from sucking his thumb only makes him do it more. The habit of thumb-sucking may affect the shape of the milk dentition and this is why some mothers prefer to give their baby a dummy as this does not affect the teeth and keeps a child quiet into the bargain: however, it is not usually considered very hygienic to use a dummy, for it so easily becomes dirty as it is frequently dropped on the floor.

Nail-biting is a habit of childhood which is a sign of nervousness and tension. A child who bites his nails does not realise that he is doing so and therefore nagging him about it has no effect on the habit. Again the parent should aim at finding the cause of the habit and when he has done so the anxiety may be removed so that the child again feels secure.

Another habit which may develop when a child is between two and three years of age is *stuttering*. This is again a sign of tenseness and it may arise when a new baby is born into the family or when a parent has to leave the child for a long time. Stuttering tends to run in families and is commoner in boys than in girls. A child of two years of age tends to speak in phrases and in an attempt to form sentences may find himself at a loss for words and stuttering may result. This habit provides yet another example of the need for a parent to get to the bottom of the child's problem, and to understand rather than to scold.

The new-born child makes his needs known to his mother by crying and when these needs are not immediately satisfied he becomes frustrated and eventually very angry. As a child begins to realise that he is an individual and has a will of his own he gets angry when his mother or father suggests anything which is contrary to his wishes. A young child has not yet acquired a flow of language and abuse to deal with the situation and so feels frustrated and loses his temper. A *temper-tantrum* occurs when a child is seriously thwarted and will show itself quite clearly—the child yells and screams and throws himself on the floor and bangs it with his fists. These tantrums usually occur between the ages of one and three years. A mother can do a great deal to side-step these outbursts by being tactful in her handling of the situation. If the child sees how much power he can wield over his mother by these temper-tantrums they tend to become more frequent. For the sake of both mother and child it is advisable that these tantrums are avoided wherever possible. As the child becomes older his anger takes the form of words to express his feelings and real tantrums become less frequent as he learns self-control.

266

As a child becomes older and mixes with other children he almost inevitably picks up from them '*bad language*'. This may take the form of 'swear' and 'dirty' words. He may not even understand what these words mean but will continue to use them if he finds that they shock his parents. Using this language gives him a sense of importance, makes him feel grown up and gives him a feeling of power over his parents. This habit must be countered by the parents' appearing not to be shocked, or the child will only swear the more, as it gives him some pleasure sometimes to annoy them. Obviously parents cannot expect a higher standard of behaviour, including the use of language, than they themselves set.

A young child usually has a very vivid imagination which will be greatly enriched by listening to stories. The child later will begin to make up stories of his own and will bring into these other people and events known to him. At this stage a child is uncertain where real events begin and imagination ends, and there is no need to make him feel guilty if he appears to be telling lies at this stage of his development. After all, he does not accuse his mother of lying when she tells him fairy stories. The child should, however, soon be taught the differences between truth and falsehood. If 'fibbing' persists after the child is about four years of age it usually means that he finds his world of make-believe more satisfying than the real world in which he lives, and he uses these made-up stories to escape from real life. When an older child finds himself in an awkward situation he may lie to get out of it and if he finds that this succeeds he will begin to make it a habit. This is undesirable because as he becomes older people begin to realise that they cannot trust his word.

When a child is under about three years of age he has no sense of what belongs to him and what belongs to other people. Taking what does not belong to him fills him with no sense of guilt. After a child is six or seven years old *stealing* has more serious consequences as he now knows what this involves. Children sometimes steal when they have plenty and this is frequently a sign of unhappiness at home or at school.

It is important that the parents do not over-burden the child with a sense of undeserved guilt, as the humiliation of this may build up a resentment against them and this may even result in the child's stealing again. Parents must not on the other hand make too light of the incident but must clearly show the child that he has indeed done something which is wrong.

Finally it must be stressed that good habits of childhood are best engendered by a happy relationship between parents and their children. During the early years the role of the mother in the development of the little personality cannot be over-emphasised. It is her love that will give the child his sense of security, not only when he is young but in later life as well. He depends upon her to such an extent that his future life, and the stability of his personality even after he is grown up, may be affected by her treatment of him as a child. The good habits which a child's mother teaches him while he is yet young will be the foundation of his behaviour as an adult in society. The importance of the relationship between the mother and the father is also great. If the child is brought up in an atmosphere of happy relationships his own life will be happy too, and his development more stable than if he is constantly in an atmosphere of nagging and unkindness. The respect which a child sees his parents hold for one another will largely determine his attitude to the opposite sex and this will consequently affect his choice of a marriage partner and the success or failure of his marriage. A person who has himself enjoyed a happy childhood will find that providing the same for his own children comes almost naturally.

Some Habits of Later Life

Some of the habits of childhood are carried into adult life but in this section we shall consider a few habits which frequently begin during adolescence.

Alcoholism and alcohol. An alcoholic is a person who is unable to refrain from drinking excessive amounts of alcohol in the form of spirits, beers or wines. Alcoholism is not the same as heavy drinking: a person may be a heavy drinker but he may not necessarily be an alcoholic. In the case of the alcoholic it is not a question of will-power—the power to stop when he has drunk a certain amount— he just cannot control the craving for alcohol. Alcoholism is best regarded as a disease from which a proportion of the population suffers and it requires special treatment. Unfortunately a person does not know whether he will become an alcoholic until after he has started the habit of drinking, by which time it is too late to stop it easily. About 6% of drinkers are destined to become alcoholics. Of these some will soon realise that they are alcoholic but others do not develop the symptoms of alcoholism until perhaps 10–15 years later.

The symptoms of the alcoholic are that he consumes his drinks very quickly, begins drinking early in the day, drinks long before and after a social drinking occasion and, in addition, he may try all manner of tricks to conceal his drinking habits from his friends and family. The alcoholic frequently finds it difficult to face life and seeks escape from it by drinking. Often he may have had an insecure childhood.

Alcoholics are found in all social classes and in all ranges of intellectual ability. Some of the physical effects of alcohol taken in excess are a marked loss of appetite, disease of the liver and loss of muscular control due to the effect of alcohol on the nervous system. *Delirium tremens* is a violent form of mental disturbance and can be caused by the excessive use of alcohol. It is characterised by delusions, trembling and mental distress, and is frequent amongst alcoholics. One sad result of a person becoming alcoholic is that he is frequently shunned by his friends, and even by his family, with the result that he is lonely and therefore has more time to drink, which he does to a greater and greater extent in an effort to escape his responsibilities.

The social stigma attached to alcoholism prevents many sufferers from seeking help and thus it is not generally realised how large is the problem. For example it is not often known that in the U.S.A. there are an estimated $4\frac{1}{2}$ million alcoholics. The country with the highest proportion is France followed by the U.S.A., Switzerland and Sweden. In Britain there are about 100,000. There are about five times as many men alcoholics as women.

Alcoholics Anonymous is an organisation, now world-wide in its influence, which was started in 1935 by two recovered alcoholics— a New York broker and an Ohio physician. Their aim was to found an organisation which would help others break the habit. Its success largely depends on former alcoholics helping those who are still sufferers from the disease. The alcoholic lists his past errors and admits them to another human being and undertakes to make amends. He strives to follow a simple code of living which avoids all alcohol. In this he is helped by reformed alcoholics.

Current medical research aims to find means of diagnosing a potential alcoholic

PLATE 66.
Cirrhosis of
the liver of an
alcoholic.

before the habit is formed.

Alcohol, of course, has its effects on everyone who drinks it quite apart from the serious effects seen in alcoholics. It has a very rapid effect on the tissues of the body, as it is a simple chemical in structure and needs no digestion, and is absorbed directly through the stomach wall into the blood stream. This ensures rapid distribution to all parts of the body. Contrary to popular belief alcohol has an anaesthetic effect, depressing and reducing the sensitivity of the central nervous system in proportion to the amount present in the blood. Alcohol is slowly oxidised in the tissues and, as this oxidation is accompanied by the evolution of heat, gives a sensation of warmth. Small amounts of alcohol are said to relieve tension or fatigue and to increase appetite. In larger quantities alcohol causes an increase in self-confidence, an inhibition of mental processes and a reduction of guilt and anxiety. Speech becomes loud and the behaviour irresponsible. Further drinking results in disturbed co-ordination and ends in stupor. The speed of a person's reactions to stimuli is decreased by drink and this leads to inefficiency at work and to danger on the roads.

It is important to remember that alcohol taken in conjunction with certain drugs has a dangerous effect.

It is worth noting that drunkenness costs a country a considerable amount, for drunken people must be kept in hospital, the police station or rehabilitation centres. The problem of drunkenness, although serious in Britain, is even more so in some other countries. In the vine-growing areas of France, for example, some children of under seven years of age suffer from *delirium tremens*.

Smoking. Pipe-smoking was the most popular form of smoking when it was first introduced into this country in the sixteenth century. Since those times there has always been argument as to whether smoking has a harmful effect on the body or not. Until recently no scientific research had been carried out on this question. Cigarettes are now the most popular means of smoking tobacco and three-quarters of the male population and half the female population of Britain smoke. The habit is increasing amongst school children.

According to the report of the Royal College of Physicians of London, published in 1962, smoking has been shown to have definite ill effects on the body. Cancer and other serious diseases affect smokers more frequently than non-smokers, and this danger increases with the number of cigarettes smoked. The report caused many doctors to give up smoking altogether and only half the doctors in this country now smoke and less than a third of them smoke cigarettes (Fig. 24.1). Advertising on the television and in the Press has been very often directed at young people. Eleven million pounds were spent in 1960 in Britain on advertising tobacco, It is interesting to see from Fig. 24.2 that while the number of deaths from cancer other than cancer of the lungs, and from tuberculosis, is decreasing, deaths from lung cancer are rapidly increasing. (The steady rate of deaths from bronchitis is probably due to the increasing use of antibiotics.)

The smoke inhaled when tobacco is smoked contains very many different components some of which are present in quantities too small to be harmful. Nicotine is present in sufficient quantity to affect, in time, the nervous system, kidneys, digestive tracts, blood vessels and the heart. Minute quantities of substances which are known to be cancer-causing agents are present in cigarette smoke. Other components of tobacco smoke have serious effects on the lungs themselves by irritating the bronchioles.

It has been shown that the death rate from lung cancer increases steeply with the increase of cigarette consumption. Heavy smokers have a death rate thirty times that of non-smokers owing to cancer of the lung.

Cigarette-smoking seems to have by far the most serious effect on the lungs when compared with that due to cigar- or pipe-smoking. This is because cigarette-smokers inhale the smoke more deeply. Air pollution may also be a cause of lung cancer but smoking is of more general application (Fig. 24.3).

Lung cancer (Plate 67) occurs in only a small minority of smokers but the incidence increases with the number of cigarettes smoked. Tobacco tar produces skin cancer in animals when painted on their skin, and microscopic changes which may precede the development of cancer have been found in the lungs of smokers. At present there are 12,000 people a year in Britain under sixty-five years of age who die of lung cancer.

Chronic bronchitis especially in middle-aged and elderly men also seems to be linked with smoking—heavy smokers being the most affected. The lungs damaged by constant irritation of tobacco smoke may be very badly affected when smog, for example, settles in the atmosphere. Smoking may also affect the lungs in such a way as to lessen their resistance to other diseases such as tuberculosis, especially in middle-aged and elderly people.

Heavy smoking impairs athletic performance and makes factory workers especially liable to accident. It also depresses the appetite and for this reason too much weight may

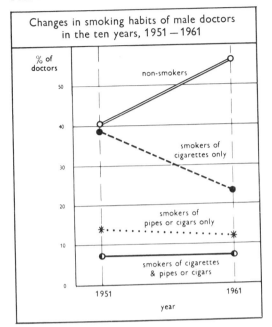

FIG. 24.1.

Changes in smoking habits of male doctors in the ten years, 1951 — 1961

% of doctors — year

non-smokers
smokers of cigarettes only
smokers of pipes or cigars only
smokers of cigarettes & pipes or cigars

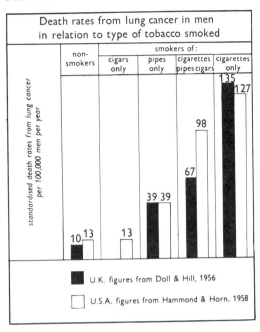

FIG. 24.3.

Death rates from lung cancer in men in relation to type of tobacco smoked

standardised death rates from lung cancer per 100,000 men per year

■ U.K. figures from Doll & Hill, 1956

□ U.S.A. figures from Hammond & Horn, 1958

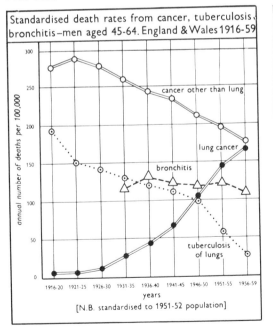

FIG. 24.2.

Standardised death rates from cancer, tuberculosis, bronchitis—men aged 45-64. England & Wales 1916-59

annual number of deaths per 100,000

cancer other than lung
lung cancer
bronchitis
tuberculosis of lungs

years

[N.B. standardised to 1951-52 population]

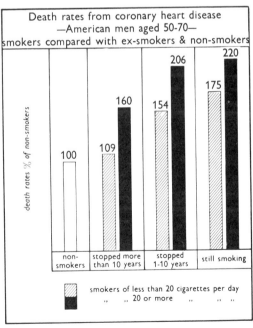

FIG. 24.4.

Death rates from coronary heart disease —American men aged 50-70— smokers compared with ex-smokers & non-smokers

death rates % of non-smokers

non-smokers — stopped more than 10 years — stopped 1-10 years — still smoking

▨ smokers of less than 20 cigarettes per day
■ „ „ 20 or more „ „ „

271

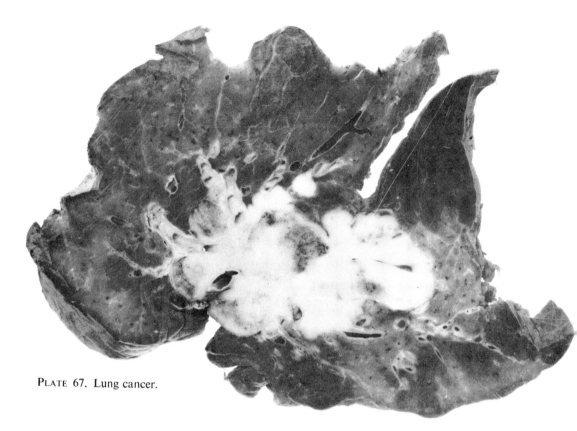

PLATE 67. Lung cancer.

PLATE 68. Emphysema of the lung.

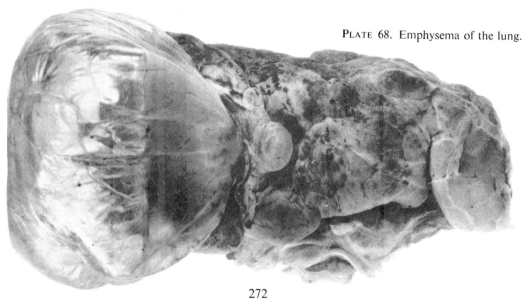

be lost. Smoking also tends to prevent ulcers of the gut from healing quickly.

Cancer of the mouth, throat and oesophagus occurs more often in smokers than in non-smokers.

The report of the Royal College of Physicians associates coronary heart disease and other diseases of the vascular system with excessive cigarette-smoking. Coronary heart disease, which is failure of the blood supply to the heart muscles, is becoming increasingly common, especially amongst sedentary workers (Fig. 24.4).

The reasons why people smoke are many and varied. Intelligent children tend to smoke less than the less able but all children tend to copy the habits of their parents. Some people may smoke for subconscious reasons while others smoke to relieve tension or to help concentration.

People who smoke heavily are frequently neurotic and restless by nature. The narcotic drug nicotine in cigarette smoke can cause an addiction and for this reason, once the habit is firmly entrenched, many people find it hard to break. When a heavy smoker attempts to break the habit he often becomes irritable and nervous. Social pressure, largely due to advertisements in the Press and on television, has encouraged smoking by making it appear to be the 'correct' and 'adult' thing to do.

A heavy smoker of thirty-five years of age has a chance of one in twenty-three of dying within the next ten years of his life, while the risk for a non-smoker of similar age is only one in ninety. Amongst non-smokers one man in six of this age will die before he is sixty-five while amongst heavy smokers the figure is one man in three.

A change to cigars or a pipe will lessen the risk of the harmful effects as will the use of more efficient filters. As no one can predict which individuals in the population will be harmed by smoking it is wise to think carefully before commencing the habit and to balance carefully the risks to health against the benefits. It is interesting to note that there was a sharp drop in cigarette-smoking after the Royal College of Physicians Report was published, but that this was maintained only for a short while, and now cigarette-smoking is as heavy as it has ever been. People will not accept as true that which they do not wish to believe and they also take a short-term view of this habit because the serious effects of smoking may not become evident for many years.

It has now become accepted in medical circles that smoking is dangerous to health, and weight is given to this view from the fact that several anti-smoking clinics are now in operation.

Drug Addiction. A drug is any substance—other than food—which is used to prevent or to treat a disease. For many centuries Man has used various preparations from plants to cure diseases without having any knowledge of the actual substances within the plant which caused the cure. *Digitalis*, for example, is a drug which is extracted from foxglove plants and is used in treating heart troubles. The foxglove plant was used for many years before the actual substance, digitalis, was isolated by chemists. Nowadays many drugs can be made synthetically in laboratories. Fortunately for mankind many of the newer drugs, as well as some of the older kinds, are very effective as pain-killers. A tremendous amount of research is now carried out on the production and use of drugs (Plate 2) and not only for their use in physical medicine but also for treatment of certain mental disturbances.

The effect of even small doses of drugs is so powerful that great care must be taken in their administration for even slight variations in the amounts taken may be dangerous. For this reason most drugs are obtainable only on receipt by a chemist of a doctor's prescription.

For example, sleeping-tablets may be prescribed for insomnia, but only by a qualified doctor, for taken in too great quantity they may be extremely dangerous.

Great as is the benefit which Man has derived from drugs there is one aspect of their use which, unfortunately, has brought misery to many people. This is because many drugs are habit-forming and some people, who obtain and take the drugs without medical advice, find that the habit cannot be broken. Such a physical dependence on a drug is called drug *addiction*. Addiction does not usually start as a result of taking drugs on prescription but from experimenting at parties and dances in the hope of heightening the pleasures experienced at such gatherings. This is a modern problem for until recently drug addicts were more or less confined to people who had serious emotional disturbances or who were unable to cope with stresses of everyday life—people of the type mentioned under the section on alcoholism. It is now unfortunately fashionable for young people to dabble in drug-taking without realising the serious dangers involved. A more or less casual acceptance of a drug in the hope of being 'high' or getting 'kicks' has resulted in the formation of a habit whose grip it is almost impossible to break. Those who consider such a course should think very carefully before taking the *first drug* for it is not generally realised how rapidly habits may be formed and how difficult they are to break. As with alcohol, a person who becomes a chronic addict may develop such a craving that he becomes amoral or criminal, even killing in order to obtain his supplies. Drug addiction has no sex or class barriers.

Drugs fall into two main classes—the *stimulants* and the *depressants*. The former increase cellular activity causing the heartbeat, respiration rate and most other metabolic activities to increase. Depressants have the reverse effects and cause dulling of the senses and a slowing of the metabolic rate.

Some of the dangerous drugs, which at all costs one should have the courage to refuse, however forcefully they are offered, are given in Table 14 together with some of their effects.

Once a person has become an addict he will require help to break the habit. Some drugs, such as the opiates and barbituates, cause a tolerance to develop in the addict, that is, greater and greater doses are required to achieve the same result: these sufferers need hospital treatment to break the habit. The principles in breaking the addiction are to cut off the supply of the drug and to find the basic reason why the addict cannot face life without drugs.

People frequently become involved, quite unwittingly, in drug rings—that is the illegal buying and selling of drugs, one addict causing others to begin the habit. A 'reefer', for example, may be offered in place of a cigarette and a single smoke may be sufficient to start the habit. The problem of drug addiction, especially amongst teenagers in the U.S.A., has become so serious that an organisation known as Addicts Anonymous has been set up on a similar basis to Alcoholics Anonymous. In Britain the problem is still relatively small but is rapidly becoming greater. One result of this is that the number of people brought before the Juvenile Courts contains an ever-increasing proportion of addicts. Especially is this true of those who have mixed alcohol with other drugs. The drug amphe-

Depressants	Opium Morphia Heroin	Is smoked—common in Oriental countries—causes tolerance in user. Administered by hypodermic needle) Causes moral, economic and spiritual breakdown. Administered by hypodermic needle)
	Alcohol	Is taken in the form of a drink. Person may become alcoholic, may develop cirrhosis of liver, coma, D.T.'s and death.
	Salicylic Compounds	Particularly aspirin. May cause delirium, vomiting, heart irregularity and mental dullness if taken in excess.
	Barbiturates	Form base of common sleeping-tablets. Cause accidental death by overdose, or suicide. May cause paralysis and memory defects.
	'Tranquillisers'	Inhibit worry and stress. In excess can be dangerous. Sometimes used for 'Exam Nerves'.
Stimulants	Cocaine	In small doses exhilarating. In greater doses causes hallucinations, delusions. Causes development of criminal tendencies.
	Marijuana	N. American homologue of Indian hemp. Injected or smoked as a 'reefer'. Causes eyes to become very light sensitive. Causes confusion, depression, delirium, delusions, depravity and causes addict to commit violent acts when taken in large doses.
	Amphetamine e.g. Benzedrine	Once known as 'Purple Heart' drug. Habit forms quickly. Medically used for fatigue and depression. When mixed with alcohol is known as a 'Benny'. Under its influence violent crimes are committed.
	Caffeine	Found in small doses in tea, coffee and cocoa. Has a mildly stimulating effect and when used initially it causes a loss of appetite and for this reason excessive drinking of these stimulants is sometimes employed to reduce weight.
Hallucinogens	Lysergic Acid	A very dangerous drug. Its effects are variable. Causes hallucinations, e.g. that one can fly.

TABLE 14. SOME DRUGS AND THEIR EFFECTS

tamine, for example, if taken as a stimulant before a party or dance and followed by alcohol has a disastrous effect, the person becoming quite irresponsible in his behaviour. Under those conditions it has been known for dreadful acts of violence to be committed even leading to death. The long-term physical effects of such abuse of the body are difficult to calculate but the degree of suffering both of the addict and of his family are easily seen.

QUESTIONS ON CHAPTER 24

What do you understand by the term 'habits' and what is the value of training young children in good habits? List the habits you would try to establish in connection with personal cleanliness, sleep and exercise, explaining why you consider each important.

THINKING POINTS

Ask your teacher to hold a discussion group on the formation of habits. Consider the effects of various habits, in the discussion, and what your own attitude should be towards them. What effect does advertising have on the formation of habits? How far does the restricting of advertising interfere with the rights of the individual?

1. Light was thrown on habit-formation by Pavlov's work on dogs.

2. A child starts life equipped with a number of reflex actions which enable him to carry out the basic functions of life: early training aims to convert these simple reflexes into conditioned reflexes. Incentives are useful in early habit formation. Regularity helps to establish a habit.

3. Imitation of adult behaviour is an important factor in learning, particularly during the second year of a child's life.

4. Young children show interest in all parts of their body and the use of each part should be explained as far as possible.

5. Nervous tension in a child's life may show itself in the form of undesirable habits such as nail-biting and stuttering.

6. Good habits are best formed in childhood by a happy relationship between parents and children.

7. Alcohol taken in excess may be dangerous. An alcoholic is a person who is unable to refrain from drinking excessive amounts of alcohol. Alcoholism is a disease which may lead to cirrhosis of the liver, *delirium tremens* and other physical and mental disturbances. Alcoholics Anonymous is an organisation which aims at helping alcoholics.

8. There is a direct link between smoking and health. Cigarette-smoking is more harmful than pipe-smoking. Deaths from lung cancer are much higher amongst heavy smokers than amongst non-smokers.

9. Drugs have brought great benefit to mankind but their mis-use leads to great misery. A physical dependence upon drugs is called addiction.

10. Drugs are either stimulants or depressants.

11. Illegal drug rings are common in the U.S.A. and the illegal use of drugs is increasing in this country.

12. Drugs if taken in conjunction with alcohol can be particularly dangerous.

25. Bacteria and Viruses

Although Man has been conscious of disease from the earliest times, a scientific study of these unhealthy conditions of the body has only occurred during the last few centuries. Early Man looked on disease as a punishment sent by a vengeful god for sins committed. In medieval times diseases were thought to be caused by 'night' or 'bad' air. The 'cure' for these diseases was magical, and quackery was widely practised. Herbal remedies were, however, sometimes effective and even today some of the old prescriptions are useful. Later, owing to the careful observation and recording of diseases and their effects, a more scientific approach was made.

In 1660 *Robert Boyle* stated that the person who could discover the cause of fermentation could explain the cause of illness and as we shall see later this 'prophecy' was well founded.

Galileo, 1564–1643, discovered how to grind lenses for magnifying small objects and *Robert Hooke* in 1660 arranged lenses to form the first compound microscope. Hooke was also the first person to observe and name the 'cells' in cork tissue. *Anton van Leeuwenhoek*, 1632–1723, a Dutch draper, was also interested in lenses and magnified scrapings from the teeth and drops of dirty water up to 270 times their normal size. He thus became the first man to observe bacteria and he left accurate records of their appearance at this magnification. It was the discovery of these minute organisms that led to the breakdown of the theory of *spontaneous generation*' which held that organisms could arise directly from non-living matter without having any living ancestors. The sudden appearance of moulds on sealed jars of jams and preserves would seem logically explained by the theory of spontaneous generation to anyone who knew nothing of the existence of bacterial and fungal spores.

Louis Pasteur, 1822–1895, put forward the *germ theory* after some observations on fermentation and so fulfilled Boyle's prophetic statement. This germ theory stated that diseases were caused by microbes present in the air and that these same microbes were the cause of fermentation and putrefaction. Pasteur said that all living things could arise only from living ancestors and could not be created spontaneously from non-living substances.

Robert Koch, 1843–1910, discovered the bacterium which caused anthrax in cattle and Man, and he also isolated the bacterium which causes tuberculosis. Koch also discovered how to grow ('culture') bacteria outside the living body under laboratory conditions. He thus paved the way for greater knowledge of diseases and the bacteria which cause them and, most important, how some of them could be cured.

Another very important application of the increasing knowledge of bacteria was made

PLATE 69. Alexander Fleming.

by *Joseph Lister* (1827–1912)—namely that of antiseptic surgery. He realised that deaths resulted not only from the wounds a patient had received, but also from the infection of their wounds by bacteria particularly from the instruments used by the surgeon. Lister used carbolic acid to kill the microbes on the instruments and in the air of the operating theatre.

Sir Alexander Fleming (Plate 69), 1881–1955, discovered that the mould *penicillium* secreted a substance which killed the bacterium *staphylococcus* which causes boils and which also causes wounds to go septic. The substance secreted from the mould was later isolated and named penicillin: this substance was the first *antibiotic* discovered. Since that time, 1928, many other antibiotics have been discovered and like penicillin have proved of inestimable value to mankind.

Thus the story of the study of bacteria provides many examples of really great discoveries which have been made to the benefit of mankind as a whole. Frequently at the time the significance of the discovery has not been realised, and indeed several of the great men whose names are associated with important advances in the study of

disease have had difficulty in getting their ideas accepted by their colleagues and by the general public. Pasteur and Lister in particular met with considerable opposition and scorn: fortunately for mankind their personalities were such that they did not easily give in when faced with difficulties.

More about Bacteria

The microbes first observed under the lens by Leeuwenhoek are today studied with the help of a compound microscope or an electron microscope. Small microbes which can only be seen in this way are termed microorganisms and include some fungi, some algae, protozoa, bacteria and viruses. In the remainder of this chapter we shall deal with the structure and functioning of the bacteria.

Bacteria are unicellular micro-organisms with a cell wall of protein and fat and are up to 0·01 mm. in length: many are far smaller. Despite the fact that cellulose is absent from their walls and that chlorophyll is rarely found within them they are, as a group, more akin to the plant kingdom than to animals. It is thought that they possibly may represent a group of organisms from which the plant and animal kingdom have evolved.

The cytoplasm of each bacterial cell contains granules of food reserve and the nucleus is not centralised but diffuse in structure, the nuclear material being scattered about the cytoplasm (Plate 70 and Fig. 25.1). Coloured stains are used in the study of bacteria and the nucleus stains differently in different types of bacteria and this fact aids in their identification. The individuals of a given species of bacterium may vary greatly in size depending on the conditions under which they are cultured. Their form may also be affected by differing conditions.

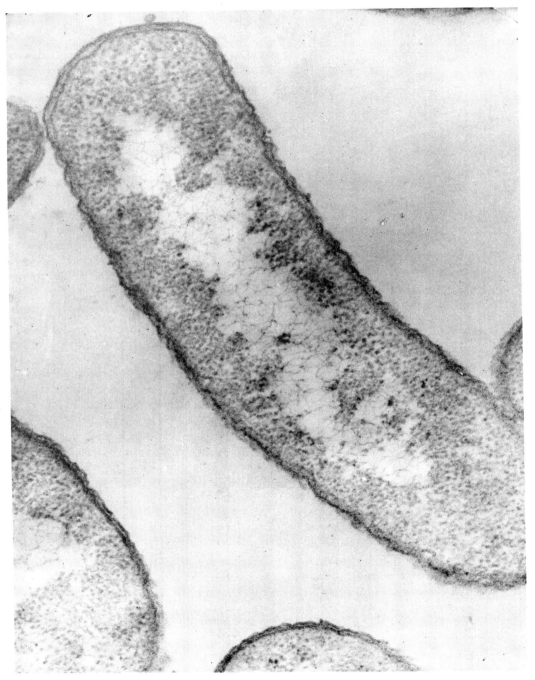

PLATE 70. A single bacterium under electron microscope (approximately × 107,000).

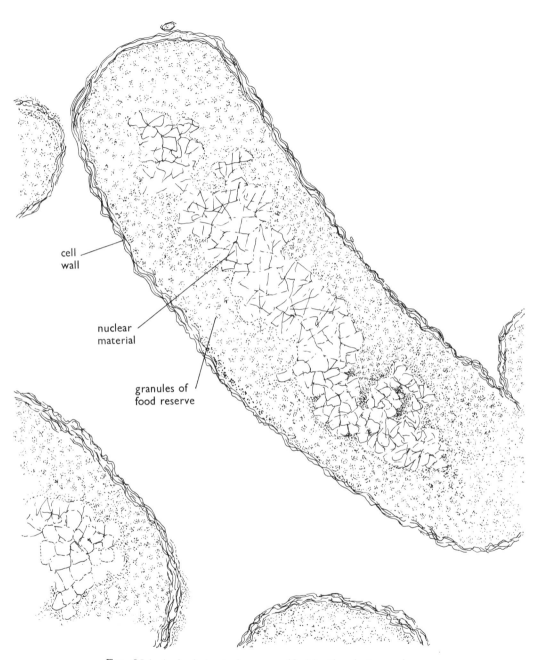

cell
wall

nuclear
material

granules of
food reserve

FIG. 25.1. A single bacterium magnified by the electron microscope.
Drawn from PLATE 70.

281

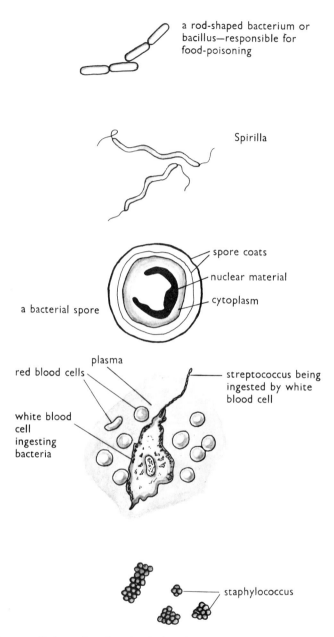

a rod-shaped bacterium or bacillus—responsible for food-poisoning

Spirilla

spore coats

nuclear material

cytoplasm

a bacterial spore

plasma

red blood cells

streptococcus being ingested by white blood cell

white blood cell ingesting bacteria

staphylococcus

Spherical bacteria are called cocci—when in chains they are known as streptococci; when in groups staphylococci

FIG. 25.2. TYPES OF BACTERIA.

282

The bacteria are divided broadly into three groups by their shape (Fig. 25.2). A bacterial cell may be spherical, rod-like or spiral. Spherical types are called *cocci*, rod-like varieties are termed *bacilli* (Plate 71) and spiral kinds are known as *spirilla* A spiral type may have one twist only along its length or many twists depending on its conditions of growth, that is, upon the factors of its environment. The appearance of the cells, then, is not a sure guide to the identification of bacteria. Some bacterial cells have smooth walls and may be enclosed in as many as three membranes or capsules. Some bacteria have a long thread-like extension of the cytoplasm, protruding beyond the cell membrane, and this structure is called a *flagellum*. Some bacteria have no flagellae but others have one or more by means of which they may move. Others move by undulations of the body. The cocci themselves may occur in groups, in pairs, or in chains depending upon the species. When in groups the cocci are known as *staphlococci*, when in chains they are called *streptococci* and in pairs *diplococci* (Fig. 25.2).

One of the amazing things about bacteria is the rate at which they reproduce. At normal air temperature a bacterium takes about an hour to divide but at 21°C this rate is increased to one division in 15–40 minutes. At this speed of division, at the end of an hour one bacterium will have given rise to 16 individuals. Try to calculate the number of bacteria produced at the end of 24 hours from one 'parent'—the figure soon becomes astronomical. The usual method of division of the cells is by binary fission in which the parent cell nucleus gathers together and divides and this is followed by a separation of the cytoplasm into two daughter cells which in turn divide soon in the same way.

Under certain adverse environmental con-

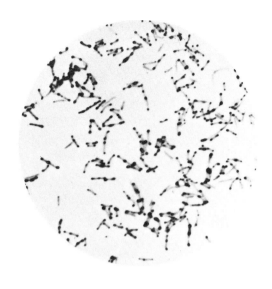

PLATE 71. Diphtheria bacilli.

ditions some bacteria are able to survive in the form of spores (Fig. 25.2). One bacterial cell produces one spore only. The cytoplasm of the bacterium becomes concentrated and forms round itself a protective coat: this spore is far more resistant to environmental change than was the 'parent' cell. This, as we shall see later, makes the control of certain disease-causing bacteria, such as *anthrax*, *tetanus*, *gas gangrene* and *botulism*, very difficult.

In order to identify and study bacteria extensively they are cultured under controlled conditions in a laboratory. The usual method of culture is to grow the bacteria on jelly in a Petri dish or test-tube which has previously been sterilised. The jelly, which is known as agar-agar, is produced from seaweeds and is very well suited to this purpose. Meat extract or fruit juice is added as a food supply for the bacteria (Fig. 25.3). The dish or tube is then sealed from the air by a lid or a plug of cotton wool to prevent the entry of unwanted bacteria and fungi. The jelly is then ready for *inoculation* which is the name given to the introduction of the bacterium under study. A bacterial cell placed on this jelly and kept at a suitable temperature will divide rapidly to produce a colony which will have the definite characteristics of that particular bacterial species. The colonies vary in shape, colour, smoothness, etc., and it is by these characteristics that the bacteria are usually identified. If the lid of a Petri dish is accidentally left off, thus exposing the jelly to the air, contamination of the colony being cultured will occur, for unwanted bacterial and fungal spores of various kinds will fall upon it.

As bacteria have such an unusual rate of cell division they are widely used in studying genetics and biochemistry. The effect of one micro-organism upon another is the basis of the development of the antibiotics already referred to on page 279.

Bacteria are found in soil, air and water and especially in decaying material. In fact it is by their useful decaying activity that the surface of the earth is scavenged of its dead animals and plants (see page 39).

The vast majority of bacteria are saprophytes, that is, they live on the dead and decaying remains of plants and animals. A minority are parasitic, that is, they live on or in another living organism. It is in this connection that they cause disease of the body. Bacteria are transmitted from place to place in many ways but mostly through the air on water droplets, or in food or in waste matter from animals.

The growth of bacteria is encouraged by warmth, moisture and a suitable food supply. Dirty, insanitary and overcrowded conditions supply a very suitable environment for their growth and harmful activity.

a. The lid of the sterile Petri dish has been raised and the nutrient jelly is being poured in

b. The lid has been replaced. The bacteria are growing on the jelly

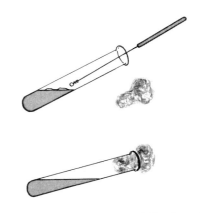

c. Bacteria are placed on the jelly slope from a wire loop and the cotton wool immediately replaced

FIG. 25.3. Two methods of culturing bacteria.

284

Bacteria enter the body through the nose, mouth, skin and wounds.

Extremes of temperature discourage the growth of bacteria. Above about 55° C most bacteria are killed by the heat except those which form spores—these are more resistant. The optimum temperature for bacterial growth is between 37–40° C. At the other end of the temperature scale bacteria cannot survive temperatures below −20° C and most are unable to multiply at temperatures below freezing point. Typhoid bacteria are, however, able to live in ice. Dehydration will also kill bacterial cells. Extremes of acidity and alkalinity will discourage their growth but many bacteria can tolerate quite a high concentration of acid. Ultra-violet light kills some bacteria and, as this wavelength occurs in sunlight, exposure to the sun will kill them.

Such facts as we have just given are important, for it is upon a knowledge of the conditions which bacteria can and cannot tolerate that the practice of sterilisation depends. Certain chemicals and boiling water kill all but the most resistant bacteria and all can be killed by steam at high pressure.

It must not be imagined, however, that all bacteria are harmful. Only about 10% are *pathogenic* or disease causing. In most bacterial diseases it is not the presence of the bacteria themselves which causes the disease but the toxins or poisonous enzymes which they produce. These may seriously upset the metabolism of the normally healthy tissues. In fact it is possible to filter out all the bacterial cells from a solution and by injecting the filtrate still cause the disease to develop as the toxins are chemicals in solution and are filter-passing.

Bacteria cause milk to sour and other foods to spoil by causing putrefaction to occur but generally bacterial action when controlled is of great benefit to Man.

The scavenging action of bacteria has already been mentioned in connection with decay of the bodies of plants and animals. By this activity nitrogen is returned to the soil in a form in which it can be re-used by living plants to build up proteins.

The Vitamins K and B_2 are also manufactured in the large intestine of Man by the activity of some harmless bacteria. Similar bacteria occur in the intestines of plant-eating animals. The bacteria digest the cellulose walls of the plants, which the animals eat, thus releasing the valuable food substances within the cells.

The process of fermentation in wine-production is also brought about by bacteria and they are essential in the manufacture of vinegar, cheese and butter.

The sewage from large towns and cities is treated by certain bacteria to render it harmless (see Chapter 32).

Thus it can be seen that the activity of bacteria is by no means a complete disadvantage; in fact without bacteria Man would not be able long to survive.

Viruses (see frontispiece)

In 1892 *Dimitri Iwanowski*, a Russian bacteriologist, found that sap taken from a plant infected with mosaic disease could induce the disease in a healthy plant even when the sap had been filtered. Mosaic disease affects plants by causing a mosaic pattern to appear on the leaves. Bacterial cells cannot pass through a fine filter—it appeared that something other than bacteria was causing the disease. It was not until 1935, however, that *virus particles* were isolated in the pure state by *Wendell Stanley*.

The term 'virus particle' is used rather than 'organism' or 'cell' because viruses can be crystallised in what appears to be a non-living form, and then returned to the living cells of a host plant or animal, when they again show living characteristics. The virus is therefore said to be on the border between the living and the non-living. Virus particles can reproduce but only within the living cells of the host. The type of reproduction shown by viruses is called *replication* and the results of this process are that the 'offspring' have the same characteristics as the 'parent'. That is, virus particles can pass on inheritable characteristics and this is, as we have seen, a feature of living things.' Thus tobacco mosaic virus taken from one plant and injected into another plant causes the second plant to have tobacco mosaic disease and no other.

The fact that viruses cannot be trapped by even the finest filters is an indication of their minute size. Only the largest kinds of virus, e.g. that which causes the disease known as *psitacossis*, can be revealed by the light microscope so that the electron microscope (Plate 7) is used to study their structure. The virus particle causing *poliomyelitis* is 27 nanometres long and the tobacco mosaic virus is 300 nanometres long.

Viruses are named by the disease they cause because although they themselves are a recent discovery the disease in many cases has been known for a long time: thus we have the following viruses—tobacco mosaic virus, common cold virus, influenza virus, smallpox virus and yellow-fever virus—giving rise to the diseases of those names.

Virus particles show regular symmetrical shapes, e.g. some are cubic, and others are helical (double spiral). All have an outer protective protein coat and an inner core of a substance called nucleic acid which is the genetic material, that is, the material which passes on the inheritable characteristics.

Some idea of the minute size of virus

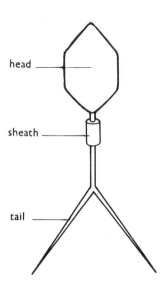

FIG. 25.4. A BACTERIOPHAGE.

particles can be gained from the fact that some viruses infect bacteria. These viruses are called *bacteriophages* or 'bacteria eaters' (Fig. 25.4). A bacteriophage is tadpole-shaped and has roughly a hexagonal head and narrow tail by means of which it attaches itself to the 'victim' bacterial cell. It then injects its own nuclear material into the cytoplasm of the bacterium leaving its own protein coat outside. The whole metabolism of the bacterium is drastically altered by the invasion of the virus nuclear material and the cytoplasm becomes governed by it. In fact the virus really takes over the control of the bacterial cytoplasm and uses it for its own ends, namely, to replicate, thus producing more virus particles each complete with protein coat and tail. Up to 200 new virus particles may be formed within one bacterial cell before its cell wall splits releasing the new particles. These new viruses are then able to infect other bacteria cells. The splitting of the bacterial cell wall is called *lysis,* and the whole cycle from infection to lysis takes only twenty minutes.

While much virus research is carried out using bacteria as hosts, a great deal is also done on tissue taken from freshly killed rats, mice and monkeys.

Viruses are transmitted in a similar way to bacteria. Some people can act as carriers of the disease without showing any symptoms themselves. For example, infectious jaundice can be transmitted to a healthy person from a carrier who was a blood donor.

Virus diseases are of importance not only to the health of Man himself, but also to that of many of his domestic animals and cultivated plants. Some of these diseases are: rinderpest or cattle plague, rabies, foot-and-mouth disease, distemper in dogs, enteritis of cats and fowl plague; and in plants, stunting of growth, leaf curl, tumour formation and mosaic diseases. Most of these plant diseases are transmitted by sucking insects.

For many years there have been suggestions that there may be some connection between viruses and the disease cancer. Although no virus is as yet known to be the cause of cancer in Man, several are known to cause cancer in animals. In 1910 *Peyton Rous* discovered a virus which would cause tumours in chickens. In 1960 *polyoma virus* was found to cause cancer in mice and other rodents. This virus is called the *SE polyoma virus* in honour of its discoverers, *Drs. Stewart* and *Eddy.* In 1962 Dr. Eddy discovered the *simian virus* or *SV*40 which causes cancer in monkeys. This is the first known virus to cause cancer in a primate.

26. Disease

Introduction

Both the terms 'health' and 'disease' are difficult to define. Health implies a well-being of mind, body and spirit which enables life to be fully enjoyed. A healthy person enjoys refreshing sleep and is able to relax easily. The body is in good condition, free from over-weight, alert and adaptable.

Most people, however, from time to time experience an ill-defined feeling of not being one hundred per cent fit—many people suffer from eye-defects, headaches, poor digestion, decaying teeth and constipation. These and other ailments take from life its natural exuberance and considerably lessen its enjoyment. With only a little knowledge of the structure and functioning of our bodies many of these minor ailments can easily be avoided.

Disease could be defined very broadly as any condition of the body which makes a person lose his sense of well-being. In a narrower sense disease is more specific and is not just a 'dis-ease' but refers to some definite ailment which shows clear symptoms; for example, toothache is a clear symptom of a decayed tooth or abscess beneath it.

Some diseases, such as haemophilia, are inherited while in others—hay-fever, for example—the likelihood of a person's becoming a sufferer from it appears to be an inherited factor. We have already met with deficiency and other nutritional diseases in Chapter 10. A nutritional disease will in addition to its own effects lower the resistance of the body to attack by disease-causing organisms such as bacteria and viruses.

Some occupations bring their own particular hazards to people employed in certain industries. Coal-miners, for example, frequently develop diseased lungs owing to exposure to dust and grit in the air of the mines. People who work in industries where lead and mercury are used are also exposed to the dangers of poisoning.

Sometimes when a person has a healthy body it can quickly become a diseased one by over-indulgence in food, drugs or alcohol. Irregular meals and insufficient sleep and exercise predispose the body to disease from other sources and lessen body vitality.

When we speak of a healthy person we are usually referring to his or her body, and to the way in which it functions, but we must also realise that the mind of each person is related to health. The inter-action of mind and body is not generally realised and the effect that the one has upon the other is remarkable. Stammering in young children may sometimes be caused by unexpressed worry and in adults worry can lead to gastric upsets such as indigestion and even ulcers in the alimentary canal. We have already seen in the chapter on the endocrine system how even slight variations in the volume of their secretions can affect the temperament of people as in the case of over-activity or under-activity of the thyroid gland: this shows the close link between the body and the mind.

By far the most obvious cause of disease and the one which immediately springs to mind is that brought about by the invasion of a healthy body by disease-causing organisms. These may be bacteria, viruses, fungi or protozoa. Other parasites—that is— organisms which live on or in the body of an animal and gain food and shelter from so doing—also cause disorders which may be very serious. Examples of parasites are worms, fleas, bugs, lice and mites some of which may even serve as disease carriers by introducing harmful organisms into the body. For example, a mosquito, while it may by sucking a small quantity of human blood do little harm itself, may introduce, in the process, the very harmful malarial parasite.

Thus we see that diseases are of several types and may be due to a variety of factors— inherited, nutritional, occupational, mental and parasitic. In this chapter we shall be concerned with those diseases caused by the parasites known as bacteria and viruses.

The Connection between Hygiene and Disease

Throughout Man's history he has been plagued by disease, famine and wars. Very often unexplained diseases caused the death of large numbers of the population while crop failures led to widespread malnutrition and consequent suffering. So far as we can tell from the records existing, infant mortality has always been very high, and the expectation of life relatively short compared with today. Even in this country a century ago a labourer could expect to live for about twenty-five years only but today the age of seventy or more is the expected extent of a

man's lifetime in Britain. It is, however, difficult to know the exact extent of Man's life in past centuries and in other countries because careful records were not kept. In India today of every thousand children born alive about 150 die before they reach their first birthday owing largely to malnutrition. In that country the expectation of life is about the same as it was in this country one hundred years ago. The high infant mortality rate and low expectation of life in many of the under-developed countries today are due to a combination of factors such as malnutrition and disease encouraged by unhygienic living conditions.

A hundred years ago in this country the sewage from towns drained directly into the rivers from which water supplies were taken. This untreated sewage frequently contained disease-causing organisms which could thus easily reinfect the whole population. Garbage from the kitchens was left to putrefy in large heaps in the streets where dogs and birds scavenged amongst the filth. It is, incidentally, interesting to read in old books and diaries that a large bird of prey, the kite, was a common scavenger in Tudor England. With improved sanitary conditions these birds disappeared from the London scene and are now confined to a small area of Wales where they live, not in towns, but in remote country districts feeding not on garbage but on rabbits and other small mammals.

In past centuries, under such insanitary conditions as then existed, it is not surprising to find that the death rate was very high and that epidemics (i.e. infectious diseases affecting a high proportion of the population of a country) would kill large numbers of people. Little understanding of the causes of epidemics was gained until Pasteur's work on disease and putrefaction became generally accepted. After this an attempt was made to render sewage harmless and to obtain purer water supplies for homes.

The high death rate amongst infants and the low expectation of life were not due entirely to contaminated food and water but also to unhygienic conditions in hospitals. This state of affairs was in turn due to a lack of understanding of the relationship between bacteria and putrefaction, particularly in surgery.

The Work of Louis Pasteur and Joseph Lister
(Plates 73 and 72)

Pasteur was very interested in the phenomenon of fermentation because the wine industry in France was threatened by ruin owing to souring of the wine. Fermentation is brought about by the action of a fungus, known as yeast, which occurs naturally on the skin of the grapes from which the wine is made. When Pasteur examined samples of wine he found yeast cells in the 'good' and in the 'sour' wine. But in addition to the yeast cells Pasteur found in the sour wine some rod-shaped structures: it was these, he concluded, which were making the wine turn sour. He found similar structures in sour milk. He found that after heating good wine to 55° C souring did not occur. Pasteur recommended that this heat treatment be applied on a large scale and by so doing he

PLATE 72. Joseph Lister.

PLATE 73. Louis Pasteur.

saved the French wine industry. The rod-like structures which Pasteur observed were, of course, bacteria and these were killed by being heated to 55° C.

Today milk is heat-treated in the process known as Pasteurisation, a name used in honour of Pasteur. In this process the dangerous bacteria are killed without impairing the flavour of the milk or destroying its vitamin content.

The best-known work of Pasteur is, perhaps, that which he carried out in connection with fermentation and putrefaction. He was convinced that the air was the source of infection in these two processes and set out to prove his theory.

Pasteur knew that when he placed dust which he had trapped from the air on a sterile, fermentable liquid it caused the liquid to ferment. His most famous experiment in this connection was one in which he sterilised broth in glass flasks whose necks were then drawn out into the thin curved shape shown in Fig. 26.1. The sterilisation was, of course, brought about by heating the broth in the flasks. The ends of the necks of the flasks were then sealed in the laboratory. The sealed flasks were then carried to several different places such as a city, a field and the top of Mt. Blanc. The seals were then broken to admit the air. After exposure for some time the flasks were taken back to the laboratory and carefully observed. It was found that in none of the flasks did fermentation take place because any microbes occurring in the air, which was now present in the necks of the flasks, were trapped in the bend of the tube. When Pasteur tilted the flasks so that the broth came in contact with the thin necks of the flasks, and then allowed the broth to return to the flask, fermentation began. The broth in the flasks exposed in Paris fermented more quickly than in those which had been opened on Mt. Blanc. Pasteur concluded that microbes were carried about in the air, and that the air of the city contained more microbes than the air of the mountains and fields, and that fermentation and putrefaction were brought about by their activity.

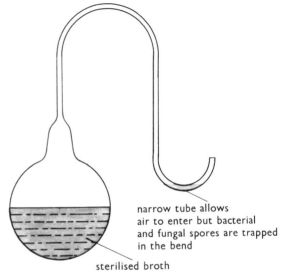

narrow tube allows air to enter but bacterial and fungal spores are trapped in the bend

sterilised broth

FIG. 26.1. The Type of Flask used by Pasteur.

Although Pasteur started his work on fermentation as early as 1858 it was not until seven years later that Joseph Lister, when reading about Pasteur's work, realised the connection between pus formation in wounds and bacteria. The bacteria from the air and from surgical instruments caused the wounds to putrefy. Lister realised that wounds should be kept free from anything which might take bacteria into them and he thus revolutionised hospital practice by spraying carbolic acid into the air of the operating theatre and by washing hands and instruments in carbolic acid. The results of Lister's work were remarkable and the death rate due to bacterial poisoning dropped dramatically.

Infectious Diseases (Table 15)

These diseases are sometimes termed communicable diseases as they are spread from an infected person to a healthy one in several ways. When a person becomes infected it means that the disease-causing organism has entered his body and has begun to grow and develop there.

The course taken by an infectious disease usually follows a pattern. The disease-causing organism, or *pathogen* as it is called, enters the body, which immediately resists this invasion. If the body fails to check the invasion quickly the disease begins to establish itself.

Between the time the pathogen first enters the body and the appearance of the disease symptoms the organism is growing rapidly in numbers. This period is called the incubation period and no symptoms have begun to manifest themselves.

While the organism is being incubated in the body, the toxins produced by its metabolism begin to accumulate and are dispersed throughout the body in the blood. Frequently it is the presence of these toxins only which cause the symptoms to develop. Occasionally the foreign proteins of the pathogen itself may cause the disease. In one or two diseases, e.g. diphtheria and tetanus, the pathogens stay at the site of infection and only the toxins are released into the blood stream.

When the phagocytes of the blood have failed to check the increase in numbers of the pathogen, another mechanism is used to halt the progress of the illness. The temperature of the body rises rapidly and this discourages bacterial growth. The period when the temperature is at its maximum is known as the 'crisis' after which the temperature returns to normal and recovery begins. If the disease is a serious one and the body cannot resist the invasion then the person will die. If recovery occurs, then the bodily defences set up will confer a certain degree of *immunity* to this particular disease for a certain length of time. Immunity, as we shall shortly see, is the power a person has to resist a particular infection.

Some other signs of a developing infectious disease are shivering, sickness, diarrhoea, sore-throat, headache or rash. Some or all of these symptoms may be present depending on the disease.

If a disease occurs with just an occasional apparently unconnected case here and there in a community the disease is said to be *sporadic*.

A rapidly spreading disease which affects a large proportion in a certain area is called an *epidemic* disease. An example of this type of outbreak occurred in 1964 in Aberdeen when typhoid became epidemic.

If a disease sweeps across whole countries or even continents it is called a *pandemic* disease. An example of this was the Black Death disease which killed about one-third of England's population in the fourteenth century.

Some diseases are always present, with varying degrees of seriousness, in particular areas. These are *endemic* diseases—e.g. yellow fever is endemic in certain tropical countries.

Some diseases—dysentry, for example—may occur in more than one form. They may begin as sporadic diseases, become epidemic or may remain as endemic diseases in a certain area.

Diseases may be very serious and bring death to many people, or they may be quite mild. Some of the more serious ones are *notifiable* to the Ministry of Health and a note of some of these will be found later in this chapter.

292

TABLE 15. SOME INFECTIOUS DISEASES

Disease	Some Main Symptoms	Agent	Usual Age for Attack	Incubation	Quarantine for Contacts	Isolation	Precaution to Prevent Spread of Disease
Scarlet Fever	Bright scarlet rash—white around mouth. Skin peels.	Bacterium	1–14 years	2–5 days	10 days	For 4 weeks or until no discharge	Burn materials infected with discharge from ear, nose and throat. Milk supply should be investigated.
Diphtheria	Highly infectious. Pain in limbs. Bacteria located in throat. Was once a 'killer' disease. Now under control in Britain.	Bacterium	All ages	2–10 days	Contacts vaccinated if Schick Test positive	Until three negative swabs obtained. Usually 4 weeks.	Babies vaccinated. Infected material burnt. Notifiable disease.
Measles	Highly infectious. Sharp cough, head cold and rash.	Virus	Usually children	10–14 days	16 days	2 weeks	Isolation of patient. Antibiotics now prevent death occurring from complications following attack of measles, e.g. pneumonia.
German Measles	Mild disease. Rose red rash begins on face. Glands in neck swollen.	Virus	All ages	14–18 days	3 weeks	1 week	Nose and throat secretions are infectious. Can be dangerous for a mother to take this disease in the first few months of pregnancy.
Mumps	Swollen and painful glands at angle of jaws. Virus spread on crockery, etc.	Virus	All ages. More serious in older person	17–21 days	3 weeks	3 weeks or 7 days after swellings have subsided	Secretions from nose and throat infectious. Handkerchiefs, etc., should be boiled.

TABLE 15. SOME INFECTIOUS DISEASES (continued)

Disease	Some Main Symptoms	Agent	Usual Age for Attack	Incubation	Quarantine for Contacts	Isolation	Precautions to Prevent Spread of Disease
Whooping-cough	Spasmodic attacks of coughing with characteristic 'whoop' sound. Can be a serious disease.	Bacterium	Usually children up to 5 years	8–10 days	3 weeks	6 weeks	Inoculation in infancy as precaution. Secretions, sputum and vomit all infectious. Danger of bronchitis as complication.
Chicken-pox	Highly infectious crops of red pimples with pearly heads. May leave scars if scratched.	Virus	Any age. More serious in older person.	17–20 days	3 weeks	Until all the scars have been shed.	Droplets from vesicles and secretions both highly infectious. Notifiable only when smallpox in the area.
Smallpox	Occurs in epidemics. Serious disease. Infection spreads rapidly. Now under control in Britain.	Virus	Any age	12–14 days	3 weeks. All contacts traced and isolated.	Until every scab has gone. Leaves scars on skin.	Notifiable disease. Strict isolation. Scales, scabs and secretions infectious. Home disinfected. Hospitalisation or re-vaccination of all possible contacts.
Typhoid Fever	Serious disease. Transmitted in food or water. Hospitalisation. High temperature, with diarrhoea or constipation.	Bacterium	Any age	7–21 days	Usually none but supervision is required.	Until there have been 3 consecutive negative cultures in faeces and urine.	Strict barrier nursing. Use of vaccines. Investigation of sewage, water and milk supply. Kill flies, cover food, search for carriers.

TABLE 15. SOME INFECTIOUS DISEASES (continued)

Disease	Some Main Symptoms	Agent	Usual Age for Attack	Incubation	Quarantine for Contacts	Isolation	Precautions to Prevent Spread of Disease
Poliomyelitis	Sporadic or epidemic. Attacks brain and spinal nerves. May paralyse. If respiratory muscles affected may cause death.	Virus	Children, young people and middle-aged.	5–10 days	3 weeks	6 weeks	Notifiable disease. Barrier nursing. Spread by flies on food or drink. Salk vaccine now available. Babies vaccinated as precaution. Nose and throat secretions infectious.
Dysentry (a) Amoebic (b) Bacillary	Severe vomiting and diarrhoea. High temperature. More common in tropics. Carried by flies. Very weakening.	(a) Protozoan (b) Bacterium	All ages	2–8 days	14 days	Until one week after temperature is normal.	Stools and urine infectious. Notifiable disease. Barrier nursing. Search for carriers. Investigation of milk and water supply. Bacillary dysentry—vaccination as preventive measure.
Summer Diarrhoea (Gastro-Enteritis)	Epidemic disease. Spread by flies, and unsanitary conditions. Usually occurs in hot weather when flies are abundant.	Bacterium	All ages. Dangerous in young babies. Death rate reduced to one-quarter in last half century.	1–2 days	None	None	Stools and any materials in contact with patient infectious. Diarrhoea and vomiting. Starvation while disease still active —boiled drinks only.
Common Cold	Fever, followed by sub-normal temperature, headache and secretions from nose. More prevalent in colder weather.	Virus	All ages	2 days	None	None	Avoid crowded places. Cover nose and mouth when coughing and sneezing. Vitamin preparations give greater resistance to disease. Much research to find cure.

TABLE 15. SOME INFECTIOUS DISEASES (continued)

Disease	Some Main Symptoms	Agent	Usual Age for Attack	Incubation	Quarantine for Contacts	Isolation	Precautions to Prevent Spread of Disease
Influenza	Acute highly infectious epidemic or pandemic disease. Complications may cause death.	Virus	All ages	1–4 days	7 days	Until temperature is normal and no further discharges.	Avoid crowds, changes in temperature and fatigue. Secretions from nose and throat infectious.
Pneumonia	Acute infection of lungs. May arise as complication of other illness. High fever.	Bacterium	All ages. Dangerous to very young and old.	Short but not known with certainty.	None	None	Notifiable disease. Lobar or bronchopneumonia. Chilling of body lowers resistance.
Malaria	Disease common in tropical countries. Under control in Britain. Occurs cyclically and may return for years after initial attack. High fever and shivering.	Protozoan. Spread by mosquito while feeding on human blood.	Usually adults	8–10 days	None	None	Spraying of stagnant water. Use of mosquito nets at night. Kill adult mosquitoes. Use of drugs.
Tuberculosis	A disease of overcrowded conditions. Persistent cough, night sweats, etc. Spread by coughing, sneezing, kissing. May be spread by milk (Bovine T.B.). Affects lungs, joints, glands, bones. Under control in Britain.	Bacterium	All ages	Not known	None	Until all evidence of active disease has disappeared. Treatment in open-air schools and hospitals.	Notifiable disease. B.C.G. vaccination of school children if tuberculin tests are negative. Sputum highly infectious. Mass X-ray units detect disease at early stage. Most people have a resistance to this disease.

TABLE 15. SOME INFECTIOUS DISEASES (continued)

Disease	Some Main Symptoms	Agent	Usual Age for Attack	Incubation	Quarantine for Contacts	Isolation	Precautions to Prevent Spread of Disease
Syphilis	Causes insanity, blindness, heart disease, deafness, death. Still-births in children. One of venereal diseases. Becoming very common in Britain.	Spirochaete (Protozoan)	Young people and adults. Child may be born with syphilis of a syphilytic mother.	2–6 weeks	None	None	Treatment free in confidential clinics. Care in use of public lavatories. All discharges are infectious. Education of the public. High percentage of cases curable if reported early enough.
Gonorrhoea	Causes sterility, blindness, arthritis, heart disease and death. Another venereal disease. Becoming common in Britain.	Bacterium	Young people and adults.	3–6 days	None	None	
Ophthalmia neonatorum	Discharge from the eyes of new-born infants infected by gonococcus bacteria from the mother during birth.	Bacterium	New-born infants.	3 days	None	None	Notifiable disease. Baby isolated. Mother may be treated before its birth. Eyes treated at birth. Spread by towels, sponges, etc. Infected by the discharge

The Spread of Infectious Diseases

Infectious diseases can be spread in several ways.

Droplet infection is the term given to the way in which some air-borne diseases are transmitted. 'Germs' collect around small particles of moisture in the air which is breathed, coughed or sneezed out of the nose or mouth of an infected person. A healthy person who breathes in these particles may contract the disease. The germs may settle on the ground, or on food, or may contaminate open wounds. Some diseases spread in this way are German measles, diphtheria, whooping-cough, influenza, etc. The particles may dry out and become part of the dust and, when later disturbed, infect healthy people. Tuberculosis bacteria can remain latent in this way for a considerable period.

Some insects and domestic animals may act as *vectors* or carriers of disease to Man. The mosquito spreads malaria, and the rat flea spreads plague to Man. Fleas and lice may also be disease-transmitters. Flies are a notorious source of disease owing to their unpleasant habits.

Close personal contact is a method of transmitting some diseases especially of the lungs and skin. Venereal diseases are also spread in this way.

Food and water which have been contaminated by pathogens pass on dysentry, cholera and typhoid. These water-borne diseases are especially prevalent in areas where sanitation is poor. Milk is a very common source of infection as it is as nutritious for the bacteria as it is for the human beings. Tuberculosis of bones (Plate

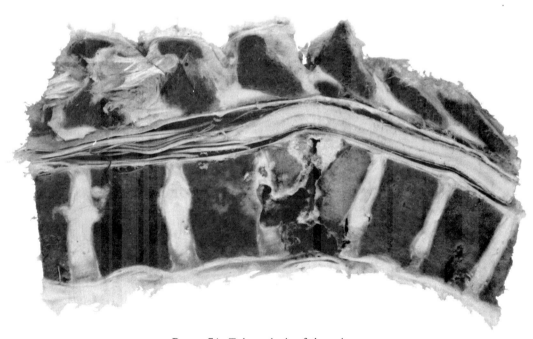

PLATE 74. Tuberculosis of the spine.

74) and glands can be carried in untreated milk from an infected cow. Food can be contaminated at its source, or during its preparation. Unwashed hands may act as a vehicle for food-poisoning because the skin and nails may trap germs. A break in the skin by a scratch or cut will allow germs to enter the body but washing of the wound and treatment with an antiseptic can prevent infection.

Some germs can enter a hair follicle as when a stye forms at the edge of an eye-lid.

Objects which are used and handled by an infectious patient are sometimes the source of fresh outbreaks of disease. Smallpox can be spread in this way. Few other diseases are spread in this manner but children sharing pencils, towels, mugs, etc., may pass disease from one to another rapidly. Some infectious diseases of the intestines are spread easily by contact with lavatory seats and their surroundings so that it is important to wash the hands after each visit to the toilet. Mattresses and blankets used by tubercular patients can retain spores of the tubercle bacillus and crockery and cutlery can also spread this disease. Where people use baths, toilets and bathrooms communally, great care must be taken to keep toothbrushes, flannels, etc. clean and not in contact with each other when stored.

It is possible to avoid, or at any rate to lessen, the chances of catching infectious diseases by taking certain simple precautions, which, if they were taken by the whole population, would help to prevent the spread of disease generally and so gradually to improve the health of the nation. For example, the use of a handkerchief to prevent the spread of 'germs' from the nose and mouth when sneezing and coughing would help to lessen the chance of passing the diseases known as 'common cold' and 'flu'.

If it is possible we should avoid crowds when we have colds. Breathing through the nose is very important, for as we saw in an earlier chapter, the nose filters the dust which we breathe and it thus to some extent prevents germs from reaching the lungs.

Spitting is not only unpleasant but dangerous, for the phlegm ejected may contain bacteria or viruses. For example, tuberculosis may be spread by this dirty habit.

Sudden changes of air temperature such as may occur when leaving a centrally heated room and entering a cold atmosphere may chill the body and this seems to lessen its resistance to infection. Hence we see the importance of wearing warm, dry clothing when passing from a warm building to the outside air.

Vitamin A is important in our diet for it helps to increase the body's resistance to disease by keeping the mucous membranes of the nose and mouth in good condition.

The progress of an infectious disease in an area can be curtailed by isolating any infected persons, by keeping the 'contacts' under observation, by immunisation and sometimes by excluding the suspected cases from schools and other crowded places. The precautions taken will depend largely on the seriousness of the disease. Preventive measures taken in childhood greatly lessen the risk of infection in later life, e.g. vaccination and inoculation (see page 301).

Some Common Terms used in Connection with Infectious Diseases

A *carrier* is a person who has 'taken' a disease and is incubating it. During this time he may pass it on to others. A carrier may also transmit the disease when the symptoms are in evidence. A convalescent patient may pass on virulent germs in his faeces and urine.

A *contact* is a person who has been with another diseased person, even one who has developed the disease after their meeting.

Quarantine is the term applied to the longest length of time to elapse between contact with the disease and the onset of the disease itself. Contacts may or may not need to be isolated during quarantine but this depends on the seriousness of the disease.

An *infectious person* is one who has 'taken' the disease and is capable of transmitting it to another healthy person. This infectious stage occurs only after the pathogen has had time to increase greatly in numbers.

Immunity is the power a person has to resist a particular infection. Some people have greater immunity than others but none of us is immune to all diseases. It is important to note that a person who has had certain diseases, such as typhoid for example, may then act as a carrier without showing symptoms of the disease, because he gained immunity when he first had it.

Disinfection kills all living organisms. It can be made effective by chemicals in liquid form or as gases. An *antiseptic* is a weaker solution which prevents the growth and multiplication of bacteria.

Disinfestation is a term used when D.D.T. or other chemicals are used to kill vermin which may be transmitting disease, e.g. killing rats and mice in infested property.

Disinsectisation is a method of killing insect disease vectors—i.e. those insects which may carry disease such as lice, fleas and bugs.

To *sterilise* means to kill any living micro-organism, e.g. by steam or by boiling water or by chemicals.

In *aseptic* surgery germs are prevented from getting near a wound by the sterilisation of everything which comes into contact with the patient's flesh. Instruments, gowns, hands and gloves and even the air of the operating theatre are made sterile.

Chemotherapy is the treatment of disease by chemicals which are introduced into the body, e.g. the well-known sulphonamide drugs. M. & B. are examples of these, and by their action within the body the rate at which bacteria can multiply is slowed down. This enables the phagocytes to engulf the invading germs before their effects have become too serious.

Antibiotics are chemicals extracted from micro-organisms, usually fungi, which will destroy germs. The bacteria which cause boils and styes can be killed by using strepto-mycin, which is an antibiotic extracted from a fungus. Other antibiotics are penicillin, aureomycin and terramycin.

Immunity to Disease

We saw in Chapter 8 that bacteria are harmful in two ways. Certain proteins occurring in bacteria are dangerous to human beings and in addition their waste products, or toxins, are harmful. There is in the body a strong reaction to the foreign proteins of the bacteria. These proteins act as *antigens* and cause the production of *antibodies*, that is, substances which coat the surface of the bacteria thus making them readily engulfed and digested by the phagocytes which were described in Chapter 8. The antibodies are produced in the liver, spleen and lymphatic nodes.

The harmful effect of the bacterial toxins is overcome by the production of *antitoxins*.

Now, once a disease has been contracted, the antibodies formed during the course of the disease remain in the blood and give an *immunity* to that particular disease. The immunity gained by the production of antibodies in a person's body due to the presence of disease-causing organisms

PLATE 75. Edward Jenner.

is called *acquired immunity*. In addition to this acquired type of immunity there is a *natural immunity* to certain diseases, especially those which are prevalent in a given geographical area, for the continual presence in the locality of certain diseases means that it is very likely that a person may have received small doses of the micro-organism causing the disease—'doses' which have been large enough to stimulate the production of antibodies without being large enough to cause the disease symptoms to appear. Naturally a healthy person is more resistant to disease than is one who is 'run-down' owing to under-nourishment or fatigue. It is interesting to note that, although influenza is not usually regarded as a disease to which there is natural

immunity, Tristan de Cunhans brought to this country after the volcanic eruptions on their island in 1961, suffered severely and even fatally from it—a disease not normally known in their country.

There is also an immunity known as *inherited immunity* in which a baby receives antibodies from its mother either through the placenta before birth or in the mother's milk after birth. The immunity thus gained by the infant is only effective for the first few months of its life, and later it must produce its own antibodies.

The acquired type of immunity may be of two kinds: either it is *active immunity* or it is *passive immunity*. In the active kind the body produces its own antibodies to fight the infection, this production being stimulated by the antigens of the invading bacteria or artificially by injections of small doses of bacteria which have been prepared and weakened in a laboratory. The injected preparation is called a *vaccine*. Vaccines were used by Pasteur who discovered, almost by accident, that a stale culture of the micro-organism causing chicken cholera gave immunity to a chicken injected with it.

Long before *Pasteur*, however, *Edward Jenner* (Plate 75) had conferred active immunity on people against their developing the dreaded disease called *smallpox*. He carried out the first *vaccinations* without a real knowledge of the processes involved. His was a courageous step forward and has brought great benefit to mankind throughout the world. Jenner was an English country doctor. He had heard a milkmaid say that she could not contract smallpox because she had had cowpox. This might have sounded like an 'old wives' tale' to Jenner but he thought carefully and commenced to observe and to record all that he could about his smallpox and cowpox patients. Cowpox is a relatively mild disease usually affecting cattle but frequently infecting human beings who come into contact with cows. Smallpox is a deadly disease which was very common in Jenner's time. As a result of his observations Jenner became aware of the interesting fact that only rarely did a person contract smallpox if he had previously suffered from cowpox. Jenner was persuaded by these observations that in some way cowpox could confer a form of protection against the more serious disease. In 1796 he took a step which must have demanded great courage: he extracted some of the discharge from the cowpox sore on the arm of a young woman and transferred it into the arm of a boy. At the point of introduction of the discharge a sore developed on the boy's arm. Six weeks later Jenner deliberately injected the boy with the discharge from a *smallpox* sore: the boy did not develop the disease! Thus Jenner had successfully performed the first vaccination. The word vaccination is derived from the Latin 'vacca' which means 'a cow'. As a result of Edward Jenner's work, smallpox was almost wiped out in this country before 1880, whereas before his time it had been a terrifying scourge. In 1898 vaccination was made compulsory but today it is voluntary: it is still widely practised as a wise precaution, for occasionally smallpox is reintroduced into this country by people from abroad. What had happened in Jenner's vaccination was that the antigens for cowpox had stimulated the boy's body to produce antibodies. These were effective not only against cowpox but also against the closely related disease, smallpox.

As is so often the case when great discoveries are made, Jenner at first met with opposition but later he became very famous and was received by King George III, by the Duke of York, who made vaccination compulsory in the army and by the Duke of Clarence who made it compulsory in the navy. Parliament granted Jenner £10,000 in 1801 and a further sum of £20,000 in 1807. Jenner, like many medical men, had a great interest in nature and he was the first to point out that it was the robin and not the lark which first heralds the coming of the dawn. Also like many great men his work inspired others to search yet further into the mysteries of living processes and, indeed, Pasteur himself was inspired by Jenner's work.

Nowadays vaccines are not taken directly from one person or animal and injected into another but 'pure' cultures are made either from living organisms as in the case of smallpox or else from dead bacteria as in typhoid vaccine.

Passive immunity is an immunity conferred on a patient who is already suffering from a disease: his own body system takes no part in the production of antibodies. Instead, as there is no time for the patient to make antibodies, large doses of *serum* containing the necessary antibodies and antitoxins are injected into him. The serum is taken from an animal, usually a horse, that has previously been immunised by injections of the appropriate vaccine. The passive immunity is conferred in an emergency as, for example, when a person is already suffering from diphtheria or when he may have become infected by the tetanus bacillus from the soil.

It should be noted that, while passive immunity may be conferred by injections of the vaccine when the disease is well under way, an active immunity may be given against the same disease as a *preventive* measure. Thus against diphtheria a *passive* immunity may be given as described in the preceding paragraph and also an *active* immunity may be conferred by injection of A.P.T. (alum precipitated toxoid) before the disease is contracted. Thus immunisation against diphtheria is advisable when a child is about ten months old—and again later in life, normally just before school age.

Nowadays a preventive measure can be taken against a considerable number of dangerous diseases. For example it is usual to give to infants, of about 5–6 months old, what is known as a three-in-one injection against whooping-cough, diphtheria and tetanus. Vaccination against poliomyelitis is now common as a result of research work in America. Poliomyelitis is an acute infectious disease of the central nervous system. It sometimes causes paralysis but this is an occasional occurrence in what is otherwise a mild disease frequently widespread. Here we have a good example of a disease which may be carried by people who themselves are not affected by it. The various journeys made by these unrecognised carriers explains the haphazard scattering of cases which may become an epidemic of the disease. The first safe polio vaccine was produced by an American, Dr. Jonas Salk, Professor of Medicine at Pittsburgh University. This was a killed-virus vaccine given by injection. A live-virus vaccine was devised by Dr. Albert Sabin and this has the advantage that it can be given by mouth. It is likely that the polio virus is transmitted in contaminated water, food and milk and the importance of keeping flies from these is obvious.

Tuberculosis: a Disease Frequently Associated with Poor Living Standards

Tuberculosis (Plate 74) has been known to mankind since ancient times and it is a chronic epidemic disease in every country of the world. The name tuberculosis derives from the fact that one symptom of the

PLATE 76. Wilhelm Röntgen.

disease is the formation of small 'tubercles' or lumps in various parts of the body. Tuberculosis is a very serious and even deadly disease and this fact, together with its widespread occurrence, make it an important topic for study.

For centuries the disease took its toll unchecked, especially of young people, for its cause was unknown and effective treatment therefore impossible. In 1882 Robert Koch observed the tubercle bacillus for the first time and thus the scientific study of the disease became possible. This study was also greatly assisted by the discovery in 1895 of X-rays by the German physicist Wilhelm Röntgen (Plate 76). X-rays which have passed through a diseased tissue leave a shadow of the diseased part on the photographic plate. This enables detection of the diseased part of the body to be ascertained.

303

From an historical point of view it is interesting to note that in 1650 in England and Wales one in five deaths was due to tuberculosis of the lungs. This high death rate continued until the middle of the nineteenth century when there was a decline in the death rate probably as a result of better living conditions. After World War II the rate again increased and was checked, fortunately, by the discovery and use of more effective antibiotics. Work in America has shown that whereas the majority of the adult population had come into contact with the disease at the beginning of the century, today's figures indicate that a minority only of the adult population have been in contact with the scourge. This gives some indication of the great advances made in ridding the country of tuberculosis.

Tuberculosis is caused by a bacterium called the *Mycobacterium tuberculosis*. It is a killing disease and its progress does not follow the usual pattern of infectious diseases. Death will result unless the disease is checked. There are two types of tuberculosis. *Bovine* tuberculosis affects both Man and cattle, while the second type affects Man only. This is known as *human* tuberculosis or *consumption*.

Bovine tuberculosis infects bones, glands, joints and the alimentary canal and is transmitted in untreated milk from infected cows. It is this type of tuberculosis which causes death in young children fed on contaminated cow's milk. In this country most herds are now *attested*, that is, the cows have been passed as free from tuberculosis. Pasteurisation of milk also kills the tuberculosis bacteria. Boiling the milk will, of course, also kill the microbes.

Human tuberculosis is transmitted from one person to another by droplet infection or by the inhalation of dust containing dried bacterial spores. The most usual type of human tuberculosis is therefore that of the lungs and once established here the microbes may travel to and infect almost any other part of the body. Tuberculosis is not an inherited disease although the tendency to lack resistance to its attack may be. Most people have gradually built up a resistance to this disease but a few have not. The bacteria may remain within the body in a dormant condition and cause disease only when the body resistance becomes lowered because of fatigue or worry. Where living conditions are poor and the environment faulty the disease can thrive. This was evident from the numerous deaths due to tuberculosis in Victorian slums. Malnutrition, as is always the case, lowers the resistance of the body to the ravages of disease.

In this country tuberculosis in all its forms is a notifiable disease but it is now under control. However, in many countries, especially those which are under-developed, tuberculosis is still a major problem.

The symptoms of tuberculosis in the early stages are loss of weight and continuous tiredness. Later a persistent cough develops, night-sweating occurs, there may be difficulty in breathing and there may even be blood coughed up in the sputum.

If tuberculosis is detected in its early stages, then cure can be easily effected. Later, the parasite is far more difficult to control. In 1943 mass radiography was introduced as a measure to detect cases of tuberculosis. X-rays of the chest are taken and where infected tissues are present further treatment is essential. (Many healthy people show old tuberculosis scars on the X-ray plate indicating that the disease was active at one time in their past life but has since been overcome by the body's own resources.)

Only when the atmosphere is highly

charged with tuberculosis microbes is it likely that the disease will be contracted by a healthy person. This is why children of tubercular parents tend to get the disease. If a person has had some contact with an infected person he may not have developed the disease but will have inhaled sufficient germs to give him immunity. Various 'susceptibility' tests have now been developed which indicate whether or not a person has had contact with an infected person. One of these tests is the *Mantoux* test where the toxin of tubercular bacilli is injected into the skin of the forearm. If a positive reaction develops it shows that a person has been in contact with tuberculosis and has had infection or still has it. He will then be X-rayed, treated if necessary, and any contacts will be asked to attend a clinic for investigation. If the test is negative it means that the person has had no contact with the tuberculosis and so he is vaccinated against infection. This vaccination is called the B.C.G. (Bacillus Calmette-Guerin) vaccine in honour of the two Frenchmen who first prepared it. The B.C.G. vaccination has been given to school children since 1953 when they are about thirteen years of age.

Antibiotics such as streptomycin, and more recently, drugs like viomycin, seromycin and pyrazinamide are proving effective. Where the disease has progressed to its later stages surgery may become necessary. More usually the disease is curable if the patient is isolated in a sanatorium where rest, good food and fresh air will help self-healing of the tissues. When treatment is completed great care must be taken to ensure that a relapse does not occur. The environmental factors of food, housing and employment are all-important in the patient's final recovery. One important advance in dealing with tuberculosis was made by Varrier-Jones working in Cambridge. In 1914 he set up a village settlement for tubercular patients in which not only the sufferer but his whole family could live together in the open countryside and where they could work at useful employment under careful medical supervision.

Thus we see that tuberculosis is a disease which may truly be described as a *social disease*, that is, one which is encouraged by certain social factors. Fresh air, good food, exercise and hygienic living conditions all help to prevent its spread while malnutrition, overcrowding, dirty surroundings and fatigue encourage its advance. Certain undesirable habits such as spitting and coughing without covering the mouth will tend to be dangerous for they obviously will help transmit disease.

The Venereal Diseases

These diseases are frequently referred to as 'social diseases', not because they are confined to one social class nor, as in the case of tuberculosis, because they are associated with poor living standards, but because of their widespread nature. They are, indeed, no respecters of class or position but attack rich and poor alike. They form a group of communicable diseases and are, in fact, the earliest known infectious diseases. They are all passed from one person to another during sexual intercourse. There are some five venereal diseases but only the two most common need concern us here. These two are *gonorrhea* and *syphilis*. *Both are very serious diseases but both can be treated if reported in the early stages of the disease*. The most certain way of not contracting one of the venereal diseases is to avoid sexual intercourse outside marriage. Promiscuity and prostitution are two of the social problems which are as yet unsolved and which are responsible for the serious and rapid increase in the number of cases of venereal disease reported to the medical authorities.

Gonorrhea. This is the most prevalent of the venereal diseases and one of the oldest known to Man. Chinese writings five thousand years old mention gonorrhea and it is also referred to in ancient Arabic, Greek and Roman records. The micro-organism causing gonorrhea was discovered by a German, Albert Neisser, after whom it is named— *Neisseria gonorrhoeae.*

Gonorrhea is almost always caught by direct contact but it may be passed from a mother to a baby during birth and this may lead to the child's becoming blind. The incubation period in men is usually from two to three days but it may be as long as ten days. The onset of the disease is accompanied by an itching or burning sensation when urine is passed. Pus may be passed with the urine. This symptom may disappear after the first week of the disease but this does not mean that the disease has been cured: it goes on developing slowly and if left untreated may lead to arthritis—a painful condition of the joints—to heart disease, to blindness and even death. This may also happen in women but in that sex the disease is likely to go undetected for some time during which they may be passing it on to men. The treatment of gonorrhea has now fortunately improved and advanced stages of the disease are rare owing to the discovery in 1937 of the *sulphonamide* drugs.

Syphilis. This is the most serious of the venereal diseases; not only does it affect the genital organs of both sexes but also attacks the heart and the spinal cord and brain. This disease, too, is an ancient one some evidence suggesting that it was known in ancient Greece. It was reported as occurring amongst Columbus' crew in 1493 when they returned from America to Spain.

The organism causing syphilis is a protozoan called *Treponema pallidium* (Fig. 26.2). This organism, like that responsible for gonorrhea, was discovered by a German worker. He was Fritz Schaudinn and he made the discovery in 1905. The disease is transmitted by personal contact, chiefly during copulation, but it may also be passed by kissing and by contact with articles soiled by the pus from the discharge of an infected person.

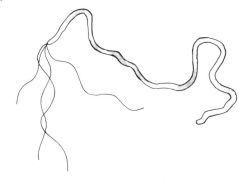

FIG. 26.2. *Treponema pallidum.*

For convenience's sake, three stages in the disease of syphilis are recognised. The primary stage lasts during the incubation of the disease and this may be from 10–90 days. A sore appears usually at the place where infection has taken place, although sometimes the sore may be hidden inside the sex organs. If the sore appears it may do so as a pimple or a blister, or it may be an open sore. At this stage the infected person is very dangerous to other people as the sore is full of the germs. The second stage of the disease occurs usually in 3–6 weeks and the symptoms are a body rash, sore throat or fever. Hair may fall out in patches; the rash may also be patchy, occurring, perhaps, on the hands and feet only instead of on the body. Not infrequently, shallow ulcers develop on the lips or in the mouth and, in women, in the vulva. At this stage the disease may be passed on by kissing as well as by sexual intercourse. Like the primary signs of the disease the symptoms of the secondary stage may pass away without treatment but this is not because the disease has been cured. Quite the opposite is, in fact, true. The disease is by this time firmly established in the body and it may begin to attack the heart, blood vessels and brain. This is the third or tertiary stage and this may not develop for a very long time—somewhere between one and twenty years. The final effect on the brain is that a form of insanity develops. The disease of syphilis can be treated: the first effective drug was discovered in 1909 by Paul Ehrlich who used an arsenic compound called '606' as it was his 606th experiment which was successful. Later, better methods were developed and penicillin is effective. Unfortunately the germs may become resistant to penicillin—the stronger germs survive and breed offspring which are penicillin-resistant.

It is important to remember that although both the diseases just described are dangerous, contagious and easily spread, if detected in time they can be treated and cured. The important point is that they must be reported at once: treatment must be sought; a doctor must be consulted as soon as a person suspects that he or she has contracted venereal disease. The feelings of shame which may be felt by a young person who has caught the disease may prevent him from seeking advice: this is a pity when the disease can be so terrible in its effects not only upon the infected person but upon the unborn generation. Remember that gonorrhea can cause injury to the sexual organs, sterility, arthritis, blindness and death and that syphilis can cause insanity, deafness, heart disease, paralysis, blindness and death. It is also worth noting that unlike many other infectious diseases the venereal diseases do not give any form of immunity. A person once cured is in no way immune to further infection.

The venereal diseases are not contracted from food, water or from the air and are rarely, if ever, caught from utensils or lavatory seats: they are caught by close bodily contact usually through sex relations outside marriage. The seriousness with which the increase in the number of people who contract one or other of the venereal diseases is emphasised by the fact that in many American States health laws require people who are getting married to have blood tests to show whether or not they have the disease and one state prohibits the marriage of persons who are found to have the disease.

27. Some Other Harmful Organisms

Introduction

In the last two chapters we have studied bacteria and viruses and their harmful effects in some detail. It must not be imagined, however, that these organisms are the only ones which attack human beings. Others will form the subject of this chapter.

Many groups of animals contain species which are harmful to Man; some of these are *external parasites*, while others live within the body and are known as *internal parasites*. Examples of the former type are fleas, bugs, lice and mites, and of the latter, protozoa and worms. One group of plants, the fungi, provides three examples of parasites in Man: those which cause athlete's foot, ringworm and stomatitis. (There are many other parasitic fungi but these others affect only plants.)

We shall also be considering in this chapter other animals which, while not actually causing diseases in Man act as *carriers* by transmitting diseases to him. Some of these, such as the house-fly, for example, merely act as carriers, the germs being carried passively on parts of their bodies or in their excreta, while in others the parasite grows and develops, part of its life-cycle actually occurring in the tissues of the carrier and another part in Man. In this latter case the animal carrying the disease-causing organism is known as a *vector*.

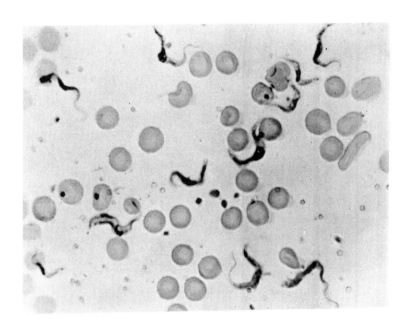

PLATE 77.
Trypanosoma gambiense.

Fungi Causing Disease in Man

Ringworm. This is an infection of the skin of the scalp or beard area. The fungal spores enter the hair follicles, and begin to live there parasitically. Patches of yellow crusted scales develop, and these are dotted with the stumps of destroyed hairs. The hairs which fall out are highly infectious, being covered with fungal spores. Brushes and combs are similarly affected and in this way the disease is spread.

Athlete's foot. This is another skin disease affecting especially the area between the toes. It is transmitted from person to person on the floors of changing rooms, and by footwear borrowed from an infected person. Many swimming-baths have arrangements such as foot-baths containing solutions which curb the spread of this infection.

Stomatitis or **Thrush.** This disease occurs especially in the mouths of young babies, appearing as tiny flakes. Thrush is caused by a yeast-like fungus and can be transmitted on dirty feeding utensils.

Protozoa

Protozoa are unicellular, amoeboid animals, most of which are quite harmless to Man. *Entamoeba coli* exists in the colon of Man, feeding on the bacteria which live there and it is quite harmless. *Entamoeba histolytica* causes amoebic dysentry. It contaminates water supplies in areas with poor sanitation. The *Entamoeba histolytica* causes severe ulcers in the colon and they later encyst in a hard case which passes out with the faeces of the infected person. This may lead to the contamination of food or water, as the encysted *Entamoeba* are carried by flies, and thus the disease may rapidly spread. Care should be taken, therefore, to wash carefully fresh, uncooked fruit and vegetables. The disease leads to frequent attacks of diarrhoea. The incubation period is from three to four weeks.

Sleeping sickness is a very common tropical disease and is spread by the *tsetse fly*. The disease is caused by a protozoan known as *Trypanosoma gambiense* shown in Plate 77. It is found in the blood of infected people and its minute size may be gauged by comparison with the red blood cells shown in the photograph. It causes fever, lethargy and eventually death if not treated. The tsetse fly spreads the parasite by sucking it up in blood of infected people. When it bites a healthy person it injects a fluid, the purpose of which is to prevent the blood from clotting. With this fluid many of the parasitic trypanosomes are injected into the body of the victim. If another fly sucks the blood of an infected man it takes in the parasite which undergoes rapid multiplication in the stomach of the fly and from there travels to the salivary glands and thence to the next human to be bitten. The tsetse fly is, of course, the vector in this disease.

Another disease caused by a protozoan is *malaria*. This is a disease which has been a great scourge to mankind throughout the ages. It was known in Greek and Roman times and during the Middle Ages it was called 'the Ague'. It was thought to be caused by the 'bad' air arising from swamps and marshes and thus derived its present name. The symptoms of the disease are fever, which recurs at regular intervals, anaemia and weakness and frequently death. It is probably the greatest single cause of disease and death in the world although it has been wiped out in many areas including Europe and North America. The story of the scientific investigation of malaria and its subsequent control is one well worth telling because once an understanding of the cause of the disease

PLATE 78. Manson.

life-cycle of the parasite begins in Man when slender *sporozoites* are injected from the salivary glands of the female mosquito. These sporozoites are taken in the blood of the human being to the liver where they rapidly multiply for about twelve days. During this time the parasites are absent from the human blood and thus during this time the victim is not a danger to other people. After the twelve days have passed the parasites leave the liver cells and enter the red blood cells. Here they undergo further multiplication to form merozoites which in turn form gametocytes. At this stage if the gametocytes are taken into a mosquito the gametocytes develop both male and female forms which undergo a type of sexual reproduction in the

was known an attack could be made upon it.

The men responsible for the discovery of the cause of the disease are shown in Plates 78 and 79. Sir Patrick Manson, 1844–1922, was a British physician who was born in Aberdeen and who took a medical degree at the University of Aberdeen. He later went to China as the head of a missionary hospital. In 1889 he returned to Scotland and in 1899 he went to London where he assisted in founding the London School of Tropical Medicine. Manson was the first to announce the theory that malaria was spread by a mosquito. In 1892 he persuaded Sir Ronald Ross, 1857–1932, to investigate the possibility and during that decade he discovered that the mosquito *Anopheles* was, indeed, the vector. For his work on malaria Ross received the Nobel Prize in 1902. The actual life-cycle of the malarial parasite, *Plasmodium*, was described by two Italians, Grassi and Bignami. The

PLATE 79. Ross.

310

PLATE 80. Mosquitoes feeding on human blood.

mosquito. The zygotes resulting from the fusion of male and female gametocytes bore into the stomach wall of the mosquito where they encyst. In the cyst the zygote undergoes repeated division to form many sporozoites once more. The cysts break and release the sporozoites into the insect's blood and thus they quickly find their way into the salivary glands.

A knowledge of the life-history of the malarial parasite enables an attack to be made on the disease by killing the vector (Plate 80). This has been made in many parts of the world on a very large scale by draining ponds, swamps and marshes where the mosquitoes breed. The larvae (Plate 81) of the mosquitoes develop in water and removing the water deprives them of their habitat. Pouring oil on the water also helps control the disease because the oil blocks the breathing tubes of the mosquito larvae and pupae (Plate 82) and thus brings about their

destruction. Insecticides such as D.D.T. are used to kill the adults and infection is avoided by sleeping under mosquito nets. The life-cycle of the plasmodium is shown in Fig. 27.1.

PLATE 81. Mosquito larvae.

PLATE 82. Mosquito pupae.

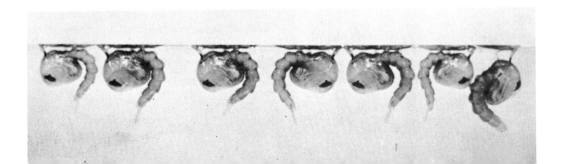

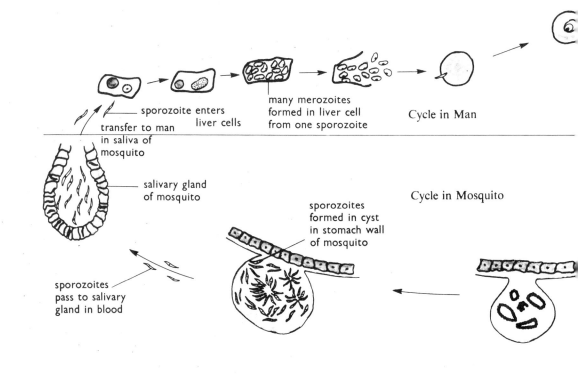

sporozoite enters liver cells

transfer to man in saliva of mosquito

many merozoites formed in liver cell from one sporozoite

Cycle in Man

salivary gland of mosquito

Cycle in Mosquito

sporozoites formed in cyst in stomach wall of mosquito

sporozoites pass to salivary gland in blood

FIG. 27.1. THE LIFE CYCLE OF *Plasmodium*.

Syphilis is a disease caused by a protozoan. This disease was described in Chapter 26.

FIG. 27.2. *Ascaris*.

mouth

Male

anus

Female

Worms

Several animals belonging to various classes of invertebrates and generally grouped together loosely as 'worms' are parasitic in human beings. They tend to be more common and more serious in tropical countries because the climate and conditions there favour them. However, a number are found also in temperate regions.

Common Round Worm. *Ascaris lumbricoides* (Fig. 27.2). This worm is not unlike the earthworm in appearance and is from 15–40 cm in length and pale grey, white or pink in colour. It is an inhabitant of the small intestine where it feeds on the food of the host. Both male and female worms occur and

312

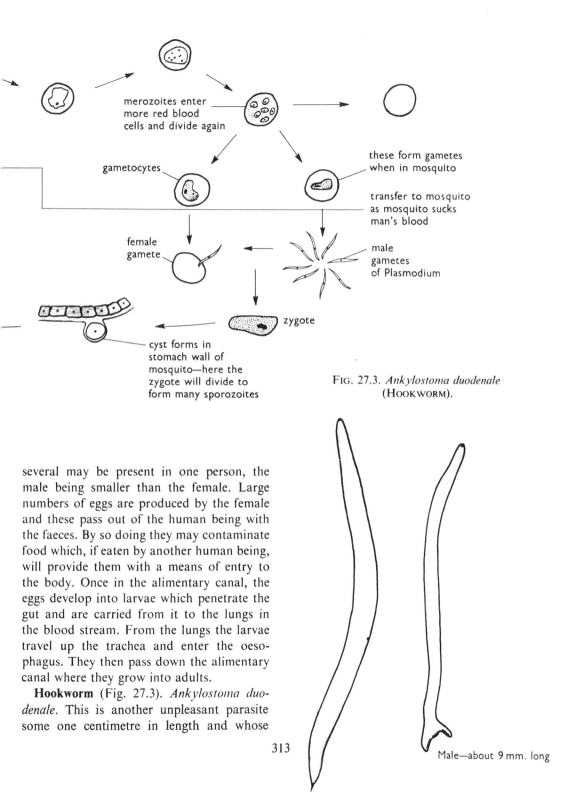

merozoites enter more red blood cells and divide again

gametocytes

these form gametes when in mosquito

transfer to mosquito as mosquito sucks man's blood

female gamete

male gametes of Plasmodium

zygote

cyst forms in stomach wall of mosquito—here the zygote will divide to form many sporozoites

Fig. 27.3. *Ankylostoma duodenale* (Hookworm).

several may be present in one person, the male being smaller than the female. Large numbers of eggs are produced by the female and these pass out of the human being with the faeces. By so doing they may contaminate food which, if eaten by another human being, will provide them with a means of entry to the body. Once in the alimentary canal, the eggs develop into larvae which penetrate the gut and are carried from it to the lungs in the blood stream. From the lungs the larvae travel up the trachea and enter the oesophagus. They then pass down the alimentary canal where they grow into adults.

Hookworm (Fig. 27.3). *Ankylostoma duodenale*. This is another unpleasant parasite some one centimetre in length and whose

313

Male—about 9 mm. long

Female—about 12 mm. long

mouth is equipped with hooked spines which are used to hold it on to the duodenum. The eggs are laid in the intestine and they pass out with the faeces. Hookworm is common in tropical countries where people walk bare-foot through wet grass, for the eggs hatch into larvae which can bore through the bare skin. They pass into the blood stream to the duodenum where they attach themselves by their hooks.

Threadworm. *Oxyuris vermicularia*. This is another parasite of the alimentary canal. It is quite common amongst young children. The worms appear in the faeces as tiny white threads. The eggs are taken in by mouth from fingers which have become dirty with a child's faeces or from books and toys contaminated with eggs. In the stomach the egg capsules dissolve and the embryos pass to the intestine where they develop into adults. The fertilised females are present in large numbers in the colon and are passed out as well as the eggs with the faeces. The females move to the anus at night and cause intense irritation. The child scratches itself and thus gets more eggs on the fingers. During thumb-sucking and nail-biting the eggs are transferred to the mouth. The symptoms of the disease are intense irritations of the anus, sleeplessness and even convulsions. Prevention of infection is by means of keeping the nails short and clean, by frequent changes of night clothes and bed linen.

Tapeworms (Fig. 27.4). These worms are intestinal parasites characterised by having two hosts, part of the life-cycle occurring in one host and the rest of the life-cycle in another. Frequently the two hosts are referred to as the primary host—that in which the adult parasite occurs—and the secondary host. They are all flat, tape-like creatures whose bodies are divided into segments. At the front of the adult worm is a head equipped with hooks and suckers by means of which it clings tightly to the intestine of the primary host. No mouth is present on the head and the worm has no gut, for its food has already been digested by its host and in liquid form it is absorbed by the skin of the worm all over its body. To prevent the body of the adult worm becoming digested by the enzymes of the host a thick cuticle is present. Anti-enzymes secreted by the worm neutralise the enzymes of the host. As the worm has little need to move and as it is living in a dark, stable environment, locomotor and sensory organs are much reduced or absent altogether. Eggs are produced in vast numbers. The worm possesses both male and female reproductive organs, that is it is *hermaphrodite* (Plate 83), and fertilisation of the eggs is followed by their rapid development until each of the segments at the end of the worm is little more than an egg-sac. Two or three segments actually break away from the worm each day and pass out of the host in the faeces.

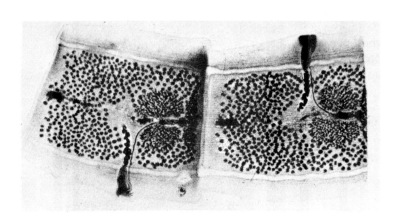

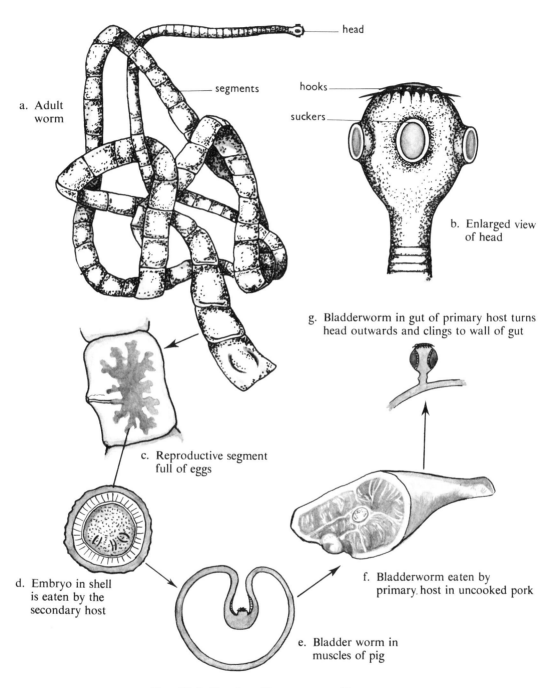

a. Adult worm

head

segments

hooks

suckers

b. Enlarged view of head

g. Bladderworm in gut of primary host turns head outwards and clings to wall of gut

c. Reproductive segment full of eggs

d. Embryo in shell is eaten by the secondary host

e. Bladder worm in muscles of pig

f. Bladderworm eaten by primary host in uncooked pork

FIG. 27.4. THE LIFE-CYCLE OF THE TAPEWORM.

Should these be eaten by the secondary host they undergo further development. When the secondary host is eaten—for it always forms the food of the primary host—the worm again enters the primary host where it develops into an adult worm.

Tapeworms are rare in Britain now but common in many under-developed countries where living conditions are still primitive. The worms are prevented from spreading by good sanitation, by cooking meat well so that the high temperature kills the larvae and by regular meat inspection. The Pork tapeworm, *Taenia solium*, is some $1\frac{1}{2}$–4 m long and one victim may have several worms at the same time. The secondary host is the pig which is infected by human faeces. In the muscles of the pig a bladder-worm develops which, if eaten by a human, will develop into an adult worm, thus completing the life-cycle.

The Beef tapeworm, *Taenia saginata*, has the adult stage also in the human being. This worm may reach a length of 6–7 m. The tiny head, which is about the size of a small pin, has four suckers to grip the gut wall. As in the case of the pork worm the secondary host is the one which forms part of Man's diet and thus easily gets back into Man. The symptoms of infection are indigestion and a tremendous appetite. *Taenia echinococcus* is a third tapeworm but it differs from the two just described in that Man is the secondary host and dogs are the primary host. It is a small worm about one centimetre long and it holds the dog's intestine by hooks and suckers. The end segments are passed out with the faeces and may contaminate drinking water or food. The cysts containing the embryos occur in Man's liver, lungs or brain. The worm is common in Australia and other sheep-farming countries.

Insects and Disease

Many insects are important to Man in relation to disease. We have already noticed the important part played by the anophelene mosquito in transmitting the protozoan parasite responsible for malaria.

Insects are a very varied and widespread group of animals and are therefore capable of spreading disease in every country of the world. As is well known the bodies of insects are protected by a hard exoskeleton (page 62) and are divisible into the three regions, head, thorax and abdomen. Each of these regions is segmented. The sense organs of insects are well developed and many, such as mosquitoes and flies, are able to fly rapidly from place to place. Reproduction is rapid especially in hot weather and in hot countries so that a sudden spell of summer weather may quickly bring the appearance of swarms of disease-carrying flies.

The House Fly—*Musca domestica* (Plate 84). This animal's life-cycle takes from 10–12 days only from egg to adult. The eggs are laid in moist, warm places such as refuse dumps and manure heaps. About 100 eggs are laid at a time and 4 or 5 batches may be laid in one season. The larvae (Plate 85) hatch in about 24 hours and feed for 4 or 5 days before turning into the pupal stage (Plate 86). As pupae they rest for a few days and then emerge from the pupal case as flies. The hairy bodies carry germs easily and as they may fly straight from a manure heap to human food the danger of spreading bacteria is obvious. Disease bacteria may also be carried in the saliva of the fly and spread when it feeds on Man's food and in addition germs are dropped in the faeces. House flies are responsible for carrying such germs as those causing enteric fever, dysentry, epidemic diarrhoea and cholera. Flies may be killed with various insecticides and their spread prevented by covering food and refuse bins.

Blue Bottles. Various species of blue bottles spread disease-causing organisms in much the same way as the house fly. They, however, lay their eggs in meat and in decaying animal matter, and it is therefore important to keep meat covered especially in hot weather when blue bottles abound.

PLATE 84. The adult house fly.

PLATE 86. Pupae of house fly.

PLATE 85. Larvae of house fly.

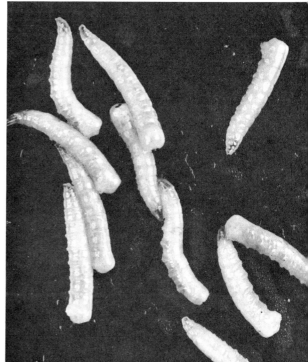

In addition to the flying insects just considered, which are not parasitic upon Man's person, there is a group of insects which form ectoparasites on human beings. These are the lice, fleas, bugs and mites shown in Fig. 27.5.

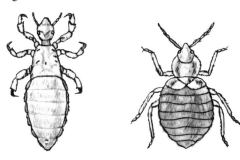

FIG. 27.5.
THE LOUSE (*Pediculus*).   THE BED BUG (*Cimex*).

The lice are flat, wingless insects which live amongst the hair in various parts of the body. The head louse, *Pediculus capitis*, as the name implies, is found in the hair of the head where it may lead to impetigo as the result of scratching. The insect hangs on to the hair with claws which occur on each of the six feet. The head is equipped with a sucker with which it sucks the blood of the host. The female louse lays eggs and sticks them on the hair with a cement-like substance: they are referred to as nits.

The body louse, *Pediculus corporis*, is very similar to the head louse and is responsible for carrying such important diseases as typhus and relapsing fevers. The eggs are laid on clothing especially in folds and seams.

The pubic louse, *Pediculus pubis*, as the name implies, is found in the hair of the pubic region.

All the lice may be dealt with by the use of D.D.T. and frequent baths and washing of the hair should prevent spread and infection by these unpleasant and dangerous creatures.

The human beings in most of the world are also a prey to fleas. These creatures are, like the lice, a nuisance and irritant to the skin but may also be dangerous, for they carry disease. The human flea, *Pulex irritans*, is shown in Fig. 1.1. It is like all fleas, flattened from side to side, a shape which enables it to move easily amongst the hair of the body and head. The legs are long and enable the flea to jump, and the feet are hooked at the end. Fleas may live for several months but they die quickly if deprived of food. The food is, of course, blood sucked from the host.

The rat flea, *Xenopsylla cheopsis*, is responsible for carrying bubonic plague from rats to Man.

Fleas lay their eggs in bedding, dust or rubbish and the larvae hatch in 2 weeks and reach the adult stage in 5–6 weeks. D.D.T. is effective against fleas and frequent clean bedding is essential. Old infected bedding must be burned.

Cimex lectularius, the bed bug (Fig. 27.5), is another external parasite which sucks human blood and may be responsible for spreading disease. It causes intense irritation of the skin. It does not normally live on the body but in cracks in walls and floors and it comes out at night to feed. The adult female lays up to 200 eggs. Bugs are interesting in that they can live for as much as nine months without food—a point of contrast with fleas. Bugs are best destroyed by fumigation of rooms infested with them and by D.D.T. sprays.

Finally one animal, *Acarus scabiei*, may be considered here although it is not an insect, for it causes the common disease of scabies. The adult is a *mite*, not an insect, and it burrows in the skin and lays its eggs there, causing an intense irritation. It occurs mostly between the fingers and toes.

318

1. Prepare some nutrient agar solution and pour some into each of four Petri dishes and four test-tubes held on a slope (Fig. 25.3). All dishes and tubes must first have been kept in boiling water for ten minutes to sterilise them. Expose one dish in the fresh air of a field or park, a second dish in a town, a third dish in a dusty room, by removing the lids for five minutes in each place. The fourth dish is kept as a control—no bacteria or fungi should develop on it. Keep the dishes with their lids on for a week and observe the gradual growth of bacteria and fungi. Explain the differences in the amount of growth in the three dishes which were exposed to the air for five minutes.

Inoculate the agar solution on the slopes with matter from different objects, e.g. a dirty handkerchief, a rotten apple, dust from the road and horse dung. Replace the cotton-wool plugs and observe the growth of bacteria and fungi which soon occurs. The warmer the room in which the cultures are kept the quicker will be the rate of growth.

2. Prepare a hay infusion by dropping a small quantity of hay in a beaker of water and bringing it to the boil. Remove the flame and allow the solution to stand for three days. Then look at a drop of the solution under the high power of the microscope. Observe the bacteria.

3. Examine microscope slides of as many of the animals and fungi mentioned in the last three chapters as you can. Draw them.

4. Draw specimens of the larger animals mentioned, e.g. *Ascaris* and the house fly.

5. Take water from a pond and look for the larvae and pupae of mosquitoes.

QUESTIONS ON CHAPTERS 25, 26 AND 27

1. What observations or experiments have you made that have convinced you that micro-organisms can be carried by air or hands? How is such information related to questions of personal hygiene? (C)

2. What is meant by 'immunity'? Embodying your own experiences, show how immunisation is being employed in the health services of this country. (C)

3. Describe and explain the arrangements and precautions that you would suggest for an ordinary home in order to minimise the danger to health from the house fly. (C)

4. What are the *three* main routes by which infection may enter our bodies? Name *two* diseases for each route. Describe the various ways of preventing these diseases. (O)

5. How may the spread of disease-causing organisms be prevented? Explain the steps which are being taken to prevent outbreaks of (a) cholera, (b) smallpox, (c) polio-myelitis. (O)

6. Explain the terms (a) immunity, (b) vaccination, (c) immunisation. How could you obtain immunity from (i) smallpox, (ii) whooping-cough, (iii) measles? (O)

7. Smallpox occurs rarely in Great Britain and diphtheria has been practically eliminated. How has this been achieved? If a case of smallpox is found what steps can be taken to prevent an epidemic? (L)

8. Tuberculosis is a disease caused by bacteria and spread by the method of droplet infection. Explain carefully what is meant by 'a bacterium' and by 'droplet infection', showing why bacteria are so easily spread from one person to another, and why they are so difficult to destroy. What precautions can the individual take to prevent spread of infection by the droplet method? (RSA)

9. Give an account of the life history and habits of the house fly. Explain clearly why the fly is a dangerous pest and list the methods which can be used to control it. (RSA)

10. Describe the appearance, life history

and habits of the head louse *or* the bed bug *or* the flea. State the nature of the surroundings in which the pest you choose breeds and the dangers it causes. How can these dangers be avoided? (RSA)

11. State what is meant by the term 'infection' and give a list of three types of organisms which cause it. Explain the methods by which the body can defend itself against these organisms. (RSA)

12. The conditions under which milk is produced and distributed are controlled by strict regulations. Explain why this is necessary, stating the ways in which the milk may become contaminated (infected) at the farm and dairy and the reasons why milk which has become contaminated can very easily spread disease.

List the precautions that should be taken at the farm and dairy to prevent contamination of the milk. (RSA)

13. List the main substances present in milk and say why it forms an important part of our diet. What is meant by the term 'T.T. milk'? Explain the conditions under which T.T. milk is produced and say why these conditions are necessary. What precautions have been taken to keep the milk fresh from the time it leaves the farm until it reaches your doorstep? Give reasons for the precautions you mention. (RSA)

14. Give a brief account of the life history of the house fly. Why are flies dangerous to Man? Describe briefly any precautions against flies which the housewife should take when storing foods and disposing of kitchen waste. (O)

15. Give an illustrated account of the life history of the house fly. Name *two* diseases which it helps to spread. What precautions can be taken to prevent this spread? (W)

16. Describe experiments you have carried out, or have seen, to demonstrate the presence of micro-organisms in milk. Why do micro-organisms readily thrive and multiply in milk? What are the differences between the processes of pasteurisation and sterilisation of milk, and what does each achieve? (W)

17. Distinguish between (a) natural immunity, (b) active immunity and (c) passive immunity, the last two being produced artificially. Give an example of each type of immunity. (S)

18. Discuss the way in which the danger of illness and death from (a) diphtheria, (b) scarlet fever, (c) smallpox, (d) typhoid fever, has been largely overcome in this country. (S)

19. Disease can be spread by the following:
    (a) drops of moisture
    (b) biting insects
    (c) bath towels.

State the kinds of disease spread by each of these; explain how the disease-causing organisms are spread and how such spread can be prevented. (RSA)

20. Outbreaks of (a) smallpox, (b) typhoid have occurred in this country in recent times. Explain how these may occur and discuss the measures that are taken to keep them from becoming widespread. (J)

21. What are the chief types of micro-organisms that can cause disease? Give an example of each type. Describe any experiments you have performed to show the presence of micro-organisms in the air or on your body, and give *three* good rules of healthy living designed to prevent harmful infection by these organisms. (J)

Summary of 25 to 27

1. The scientific study of bacteria has only been possible since the invention of the *microscope*. *Van Leeuwenhoek* was the first to see *bacteria* under a microscope.

2. The most famous name connected with bacteria and disease is that of *Louis Pasteur* whose work led to the breakdown of the theory of *spontaneous generation*, and to his *germ theory*, which stated that some diseases were caused by *microbes*.

3. *Robert Koch*, who discovered the bacteria which caused anthrax in cattle and tuberculosis in human beings; *Joseph Lister*, who introduced sterile conditions into surgery and *Alexander Fleming*, who discovered penicillin, are other names famous for their work in connection with disease.

4. *Bacteria* are microscopic organisms, some of which are harmful to mankind and some of which are beneficial. They are surrounded by a cell wall within which is the cytoplasm and a diffuse nucleus. Bacteria are classified according to their shape. They can survive adverse conditions by forming a protective coat. Bacteria can be cultured on agar. Disease-causing bacteria are known as *pathogens*.

5. *Viruses* occupy a position intermediate between living and non-living things for they can exist in a crystalline state. Viruses are much smaller than bacteria. Some diseases caused by viruses are common cold, influenza, smallpox and poliomyelitis.

6. Disease is frequently due to the invasion of the body by other organisms, not only bacteria and viruses, but also fungi, worms, protozoa and fleas, bugs or lice.

7. There is a close link between disease and hygiene for many disease-causing organisms are able to live only in dirty conditions.

8. *Infectious diseases* are spread by droplets in the air, by vectors or in food or water. German measles, diphtheria, whooping-cough are examples.

9. *Immunity* may be natural, acquired or inherited. *Edward Jenner* conferred immunity upon people by vaccinations against smallpox.

10. *Tuberculosis* is a disease associated with poor living conditions. Its incidence has been greatly reduced in this country during this century.

11. *Venereal Diseases* are dangerous and the number of cases treated annually is increasing alarmingly.

12. *Fungi* cause the diseases known as *ringworm, athlete's foot* and *thrush*.

13. *Protozoa* cause some diseases such as *sleeping sickness* and *malaria*.

14. Various kinds of worms may infect Man—*Ascaris, Ankylostoma, Oxyuris,* for example.

15. Insects are closely linked with disease for not only do some act as *vectors* but others, such as the house fly, spread bacteria and viruses.

28. Skin Care and Clothing

We have seen in Chapter 15 that the functions of the skin include temperature regulation, excretion of a small amount of waste substances, protection against infection and sensitivity. These functions can only be satisfactorily carried out when the skin is kept clean.

With regard to temperature regulation Man has more difficulty than most mammals because his skin is almost hairless. From the earliest times Man has used clothing of some kind to minimise the effect of a fluctuating external atmospheric temperature. The earliest type of clothing was made from the skins of animals which had been hunted and killed for food. Later Man learned how to weave yarn from natural fibres such as wool and cotton. The thickness of garments made from these materials could be altered to suit the regional and seasonal climatic variations. Clothing was made in the home by the mother of the family and only during the last century or two has clothing been made on a commercial scale. Today not only are different types of clothing made on a vast scale in large factories but the natural fibres have been largely supplemented by artificial fibres such as nylon.

Healthy skin should be supple and elastic, and should be kept clean by thorough daily washing or bathing. Soap and warm water is the best way of cleaning the skin as the soap is able to dissolve away the grease in the skin which traps dirt. During the day dust, bacteria and dead cells accumulate on the surface of the skin and these should be removed daily. The secretion produced by the sebaceous glands is poured into the hair follicle and thus makes its way to the surface of the skin. If it is not frequently removed by washing it clogs the pores of the ducts from the sweat glands and prevents their functioning adequately. This sebum, as the secretion is called, mixes with sweat and dirt and forms a plug in the opening of the pore and so forms a *blackhead*. If further neglected, the blocked pore can become infected by bacteria and a septic spot or *whitehead* is formed. The final stages of such neglect may be *acne*—an unsightly chronic skin infection. When skin has over-active sebaceous glands, it is said to be greasy in nature and needs special care and cleansing.

The health of the skin depends also on a balanced diet and a vigorous blood circulation. The blood brings oxygen to the skin cells and removes waste products from them. Exercise and fresh air help to keep the skin healthy. Sunlight causes a chemical change within the skin and Vitamin D is formed. Exposure to sunlight will also produce in the skin a tan which gives it protection against the burning rays of hot sunshine. Over-exposure should be avoided as sun-burning may otherwise result. Darker-skinned people tend to acclimatise better than fair or auburn-haired people whose skin may often turn red, peel and blister with the slightest amount of exposure to sunshine. It is important to introduce short periods of exposure at first when sunbathing commences after the winter months. This is especially important as far as babies are concerned, for their skin is very sensitive. The action of wind on the skin surface tends to stimulate the blood supply and is therefore of great benefit. A cold shower has a similar effect but is not as cleansing as a warm bath.

Special care should be given to the skin of the hands and feet as these take much of the wear and tear of daily activity. The feet need to be washed every day and dried carefully expecially between the toes, as soft corns can easily develop if drying is not thorough. Breaks in the skin which occur when soft corns develop between the toes may allow bacteria to gain entry.

Modern detergents are sometimes harmful to the skin because they dry it by removing the sebum which would normally keep it soft and smooth. Certain industrial occupations can also cause skin damage because of exposure to harmful chemicals. For this reason barrier creams are applied to prevent such harmful effects or alternatively rubber gloves may be worn.

Changes in the texture of the skin and in the amount of its glandular activity tend to occur in adolescence. It is at this time that young people become most conscious of their personal appearance. All too frequently young people fail to pay attention to a balanced diet, regular emptying of the bowel, regular cleansing of the skin and daily exercise in the fresh air. The cumulative effect of this neglect may be a 'spotty' skin. In order to hide these flaws, girls often apply make-up to conceal the blemishes instead of getting to the root of the trouble. Too little care in choosing the correct make-up for the skin type, an inefficient removal of the make-up at the end of the day, will only make matters worse.

The hair should also be regularly washed and should be brushed and combed daily. Massage of the scalp often improves the condition of the hair and spirit shampoos may be used to correct the type of hair which becomes greasy very quickly. Unwashed hair traps dust and dirt easily and, as we have seen in an earlier chapter, it may form a home for lice.

The purpose of wearing clothing is to assist in the control of heat loss due to climatic changes such as wind and rain. Clothing also protects the body from over-exposure to the rays of the sun. Footwear protects the skin from mechanical injury such as might be caused by thorns and stones. Clothing is also used to adorn the body to give pleasure to both the wearer and to other people.

In very hot climates little clothing is worn so that sweat can evaporate from and cool the body over as large a skin area as possible. People who are native to hot climates have skins which are dark in colour and which are thus protective against the sun's rays. Light-skinned people living in hot climates need to wear light, loose clothes to protect them from very hot sun. The clothes should be loose so that air can circulate between the skin and the material in order that the sweat may easily evaporate. It should also be absorbent. White clothes are usually worn in hot climates as the white colour *reflects* some of the sun's rays. We can now see why tennis players and athletes wear white clothing. Black surfaces *radiate* heat better than do those which are white and thus a black skin will cool a person better than a white skin.

In cold climates and in cold weather clothing should be worn which will enable the body to retain its heat. A layer of still air against the body surface prevents heat loss. Several layers of thinner clothes are better than one layer of thick material as more air is trapped between the layers. Wool and fur conserve body heat well but wool is wind-proof only if it is very densely woven. Leather is a better wind-proof material but does not let excess sweat evaporate. Frequently anoraks are made of wind-proof nylon with an inner, warmer lining for use under conditions of exposure to great cold or strong winds.

In hot weather the body needs to be able to get rid of excess heat quickly, and so a large proportion of the body surface should be bare. In cold weather, however, the body needs to conserve heat and it is very important to ensure that a high proportion of the skin is covered to prevent loss of heat. It is pointless to wear a thick winter overcoat if a large part of the legs, the hands, the face and neck is uncovered. Such exposed areas may amount to as much as 40% of the skin surface and heat loss will then be considerable.

As we saw in an earlier paragraph it is largely the air trapped in or between layers of clothing which insulates the body against heat loss and for this reason wool is a warmer fabric than cotton for it holds nearly twice as much air between its fibres as does cotton. Cellular cotton underclothing may be quite warm, for the meshwork of cotton traps the air in much the same way as natural wool. It has the advantage that it is more easily washed than wool.

In a climate with marked seasonal changes of temperature one type of clothing is not suitable throughout the year. The clothing chosen for any particular season depends on the need to retain body heat or to conduct it away.

The air layer around the skin receives the body's excess heat and moisture. The clothing which is around the body will either let this heat and moisture escape or it will help retain it. Thus materials may be either 'warm' —such as wool, which will conserve this heat —or 'cool'—such as cotton, which will quickly allow the heat to escape. Between these extremes are many intermediate types of fabrics. Plastic materials are the best moisture retainers but are used only for outer rain-proof garments as they do not allow any body moisture to escape.

Clothing should never be so tightly fastened as to restrict the flow of blood anywhere, but clothes which fasten comfortably at the neck, waist, wrist and ankles help to conserve body heat and are thus so frequently worn in cold climates and in cold weather. In hotter conditions the clothing should always be loose to allow air to circulate freely.

Great care should be taken in the fitting and suitability of footwear. Any shoes which cramp the feet or, by the height of their heels, throw the body off balance should be avoided. Footwear may be made from rubber, leather or plastic. Rubber and plastic are cheaper than leather and are quite hard-wearing, but completely prevent moisture loss from the feet. Leather allows the perspiration from the feet to escape and in this respect is preferable to rubber. Wellington boots are useful out-of-doors in wet weather, but they should be changed at school or at work for indoor shoes, and the inside of the boots given time to dry before being worn again.

For the same reason, winter boots should not be worn all day. In hot weather open meshwork sandals are cool and comfortable.

There is a real danger of clothes catching fire in rooms where an open fire—solid fuel, gas or electricity—is used. This danger is greatest where little children are concerned as night-clothes and party dresses catch fire so easily. Nowadays fabrics are available which are flame-proof but the safest measure is to cover the fire with a close-mesh fireguard.

Elderly people and children are especially liable to get chilled by a sudden change of

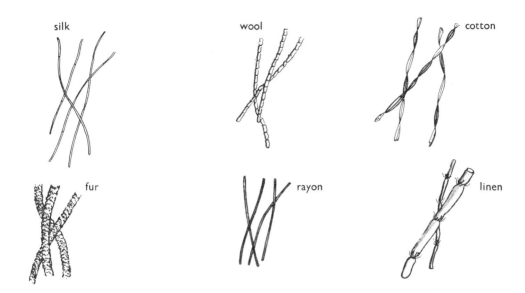

silk wool cotton

fur rayon linen

Fig. 28.1. Some fibres used in clothing.

temperature even within the same day and for this reason they should always have warm clothing available.

Lastly, it should be noted that clothing materials are of both vegetable and animal origin and today many are manufactured from synthetic or 'man-made' fibres. These materials, which are of vegetable origin, are rayon, cotton, linen and rubber. Materials derived from animals are wool, silk, fur, leather and feathers. New synthetic fabrics are constantly being produced and some of these are nylon, terylene, acrylic fibre, dacron, etc. With such a bewildering array of new materials a housewife may be at a loss how to launder them all correctly but a coding system is now in existence which assists her in choosing the correct method. This code is indicated on the article or fabric at the time of purchase. A summary of the characteristics of some of the fabrics available is given in Table 16.

QUESTIONS ON CHAPTER 28

1. Show how a knowledge of the properties of clothing materials and of the functions of the skin is helpful in choosing suitable clothing for different seasons of the year. (L)

2. What is meant by the term *good conductor of heat*? Air, cotton and wool all play a part in controlling the amount of heat lost from the body. Explain why woollen blankets are better than cotton sheets in controlling the heat lost from the body. Describe how hot water radiators heat a room and explain why they are better for this purpose than a coal fire. (RSA)

3. Show how a knowledge of the properties of clothing materials and of the functions of the skin is useful in devising suitable clothing for different seasons of the year. (J)

TABLE 16. SOME FABRICS USED FOR CLOTHING PURPOSES

Fabric		Origin	Nature	Heat Retention	Moisture Retention	Washability	Strength	Uses
Cotton	P	Fibres found surrounding seeds of cotton plant.	Fibres 1–2¼" long. Spun into yarn.	Cool fabric. Loses heat easily.	Very absorbent. May be made into cellular materials.	Non-shrink. Can be boiled.	Quite strong.	Under and outer garments.
Linen	P	Fibres in the stems of flax plants.	Rounded and jointed fibres spun into yarn.	Cool fabric. Loses body heat quickly.	Absorbent.	Shrinks slightly. Can be boiled.	Very strong.	Shirts, jackets, suits, bed linen. Expensive.
Rayon	P	Cellulose from plants, wood pulp.	Filaments of cellulose dissolved in solvents and spun into threads.	A cool fabric. Very inflammable.	Does not absorb moisture well.	Washes quite well.	Fair.	Underclothing, dresses. Inexpensive.
Rubber	P	Milky latex tapped from rubber trees.	In almost any form.	Holds heat well.	Is waterproof.	Needs no laundering.	Dependent on thickness.	Wellington boots, waterproof garments. Need ventilation holes to allow perspiration to escape or lining to absorb moisture.
Synthetic Materials		Chemical origin.	In almost any form.	Variable. Includes nylon, acrylic fibres, terylene, etc.	Variable. Nylon is not absorbent.	Very easy. Dries rapidly. (Drip-dry sometimes.)	Very strong.	Variable price. Can be treated to be non-iron, and to hold pleats almost permanently.

TABLE 16. SOME FABRICS USED FOR CLOTHING PURPOSES (continued)

Fabric	Origin	Nature	Heat Retention	Moisture Retention	Washability	Strength	Uses
Plastic	Coal tar.	Almost any form.	Retains heat with variable efficiency depending on thickness.	Waterproof.	No need to launder.	May tear easily and is destroyed on overheating.	Outer garments—rainwear, etc. Shoes and boots. Inexpensive
Wool A	From the hair of certain animals —usually the sheep.	Overlapping scales along each hair. Contains natural fats.	Retains heat very well due to air trapped between fibres.	Absorbs moisture. Is fairly waterproof when densely woven.	Shrinks badly in too hot water. Washes well in lukewarm water.	It is only a strong fabric when woven closely.	Under and outer garments. Sometimes combined with other fabrics for strength. Light to wear but expensive.
Leather and fur A	Skin and hair of certain animals.	Skins may be cut and treated.	Retains heat very well. Warm and windproof.	Non-absorbent. Leather is waterproof.	Furs are cleaned and leathers may be polished.	Leather is very strong and is variable in thickness. Fur is quite hard-wearing.	Outer garments. Shoes, gloves, etc. Expensive
Silk A	Threads from the cocoon of the silk worm.	Very fine smooth threads.	Warm.	Not very absorbent. When closely woven is wind-resistent.	Washes well in warm water.	Very strong. but fine. Wears quite well.	Underclothing, blouses, shirts, scarves, dresses etc. Very expensive.

A—indicates animal origin.   P—indicates plant origin.

Summary of 28

1. Because Man has an almost hairless skin, temperature control must be assisted by the use of *clothing*. The type of clothing worn varies in different parts of the world owing to climatic variations.

2. *Blackheads* may form if the skin is not kept clean. These may turn to *whiteheads* and even result in a condition known as *acne*.

3. The health of the skin depends on a *balanced diet, fresh air* and *sunshine*, and a *vigorous blood circulation*.

4. Several layers of light clothing are warmer than one layer of thick clothes because they trap air between them.

5. Clothing must never be so tight as to restrict the blood circulation. Special care should be given to footwear.

6. Sudden changes of temperature are liable to cause chilling especially of elderly people and young children.

29. More about Food: its Storage, Preservation and Preparation

Introduction

Many centuries ago in this country food was grown, harvested and consumed within a given area and this is still the case in some countries. However, nowadays, foods which are plentiful in one country may be shipped many thousands of kilometres to other countries which do not produce them. Within any given country food crops can only be grown in certain seasons and it is important in this case to *store* and *preserve* this food for times of scarcity.

Although many foods may be eaten raw a great many can be improved in taste and texture by *cooking*. Whenever food is handled —in its preservation, preparation or transport —there is danger of its becoming contaminated through a general lack of *hygiene*.

Preservation of Food

Foods can be spoiled and made unfit for human consumption by being accidentally damaged or bruised; by undergoing natural decomposition due to the presence of enzymes in the cells; they may go rancid by oxidation of their fatty contents; or they may become contaminated by micro-organisms.

Some older methods of food preservation are still in use in country districts but their place is gradually being taken by newer methods. *Salting* of meat is one of the earliest methods of food preservation. The salt within and around the flesh prevents bacterial growth by extracting water from the bacteria. The *smoking* of fish and meat also prevents decay and the addition of acids such as vinegar in *pickling* foods has a similar effect. Most of you will be familiar with the addition of considerable quantities of sugar to fruit in jam making: the sugar acts as a preservative. All these methods may result in a loss of food value and flavour. *Bottling* is a method of food preservation in which all air is excluded from sterilised containers by filling them to the brim with boiling syrup or water. The heating which then follows kills any micro-organisms present within the jar. Some fruit may lose some of its Vitamin C content when bottled but generally the colour and flavour of the food is retained.

Newer methods of preservation of food aim to retain colour, flavour and food value. They may be considered under the headings of dehydration, canning and refrigeration.

Dehydration. Bacteria and other micro-organisms can only multiply in the presence of moisture and dehydration prevents their growth by removing up to 95% of the water content of the food. The food is first scalded to prevent enzyme action and it is then dehydrated. To ensure efficient dehydration the food must be finely divided.

Dehydration results in a loss of flavour and of some food value. The total weight of the food can be reduced in this process by as much as 80% and its bulk by up to 90% due to drying. For this reason dehydrated food is of great value where weight and bulk have to be kept at a minimum. Where dehydrated food forms the basis of a diet vitamins in concentrated form should also be taken.

Canning is now a major industry and involves the extraction of oxygen to prevent the oxidation of food, and the heating of the food to kill micro-organisms and to destroy enzymes. The inside of the cans is usually lacquered to prevent acids in the foods from dissolving some of the metal which would be a source of danger to the consumer. One of the important factors in canning is that the food should be picked and canned as quickly as possible. Constant research into methods of picking, peeling and coring fruit, and in handling other types of food rapidly, by mechanical devices, has resulted in greatly improved products.

Invention of new canning machines has led to a tremendous increase in the speed of output of cans: in the early days of canning the tins were cut and shaped by hand and the tops and bottoms soldered on. A hole was left in the top of the can through which the food was forced and then the tin was sealed and processed. A single canner could produce about sixty cans in a ten-hour day. Nowadays a single assembly line in a modern factory can produce up to a thousand cans a minute.

Carelessness in the handling of the food to be canned at any stage may lead to infection by micro-organisms or by poisons—contaminated water is one obvious danger and this may have been responsible for the outbreak of typhoid in Aberdeen in 1964.

Canning preserves food values to a maximum degree as each tin acts as a pressure cooker, thereby reducing the cooking time during which vitamins may be destroyed.

Refrigeration depends on the principle that micro-organisms cannot multiply in temperatures just below the freezing point of water and thus the rate of spoilage and decay is slowed up considerably. Refrigeration will not kill micro-organisms and when frozen food is allowed to thaw it should be cooked and eaten immediately. Once frozen food has been allowed to thaw it should not be refrozen, in order to keep it longer, as after a period of cooling bacteria are even more active than usual.

Deep freezing to a temperature of $-10°C$ or less enables food to be kept for far longer periods than does refrigeration to just below the freezing point of water. Meat frozen in this way may keep for up to a year. Fruit and vegetables which are *deep* frozen must also be *quickly* frozen or else ice crystals form in the cell sap, and will completely destroy the food: this becomes evident as soon as it thaws.

Refrigeration does not alter the flavour or colour of the food and its food value is also retained. Refrigerated food should be kept in moisture-proof wrappers and containers as it will otherwise quickly lose moisture and the texture of the food will be destroyed. The time for which frozen food may be kept depends on the temperature in the refrigerator. Some manufacturers indicate on the food packet how long the food may be kept safely at different temperatures.

The main modern forms of food preservation just described enable a supply of varied foodstuffs to be obtained during the whole year and not only when it is in season. Prices are kept at a more even level, and this, of course, helps to make good food available to everybody.

Preparation of Food

Many foods can be eaten without any preparation other than careful washing. Most foods, however, are made more digestible and appetising by being cooked by one method or another. The heat applied in cooking liquefies fats, breaks up meat fibres and starch grains, and often hot food is more palatable than that which is cold. Cooking also delays decomposition of food as micro-organisms are destroyed by prolonged heating. The sight, taste and smell of well-prepared and attractively served dishes stimulates the salivary glands and gives an appetite.

Different methods of cooking are used in different parts of the world depending upon the type of food available and on the climate of the country under consideration. *Roasting* or baking involves cooking by direct heat as on a spit, or in an oven by indirect heat. Roasting is usually begun at a high temperature which causes a juice-retaining layer to be formed on the surface of the food and then the temperature is lowered and maintained for some time to ensure even cooking throughout.

Frying is a very quick method of cooking as hot fat can reach very high temperatures. *Boiling* is a method of cooking food in a liquid. It has the advantage of retaining or even adding to the water content of the food but the disadvantage that some of the food value may be lost by dissolving out into the liquid. This liquid, known as stock, can be used for soups, sauces and gravies and thus some of the food value which leaves the food and enters the liquid can be recovered. *Stewing* is a long, slow method of cooking in a closed vessel and the liquid is usually kept below boiling point. *Steaming* is another long, slow method of cooking unless the steam is under high pressure as in a pressure cooker. In this case the cooking time is far shorter than in other methods. Pressure cooking also conserves the food value very well but according to some people causes a loss in flavour. *Grilling* is a quick way of cooking relatively thin slices of food and it retains flavour and juices very well.

In spite of the advantages of cooking food it should be remembered that some vitamins are easily destroyed by prolonged cooking as they are unstable at even moderate temperatures. This is why green vegetables should be cooked rapidly in a small quantity of water and consumed as soon as possible after cooking. The fact that heat destroys many vitamins means that fresh fruit and vegetables must be included in the diet. Salads containing freshly picked lettuce, raw carrots and uncooked tomatoes are excellent as are fresh fruit salads.

Food Hygiene

In order to maintain a high standard of hygiene care must be taken by all people who handle food whether it is in its production, packing, distribution, sale or preparation. Unfortunately standards of hygiene are not always as high in Britain as they should be due to a failure of individual people to realise the seriousness of the dangers involved. Persons who come into contact with food should be scrupulously clean in their personal habits. A plentiful supply of hot water, soap and clean towels must be available in all places where food is handled. The hands must always be washed thoroughly before food is touched and after the toilet has been visited. In food factories a cap and overalls should be worn. Any sign of infectious disease should immediately be reported. Because nowadays many people eat together often in large canteens and restaurants a careless act on the part of one person may lead to many others becoming ill. For example, a person suffering from a septic finger can easily become the source of infection by staphylococci. Thus we can see the importance of covering cuts, spots and boils. Coughing and sneezing over exposed food can also lead to food poisoning. Smoking should not be allowed near food.

Many shops still exhibit fish, meat and other goods without covering them, thus leaving them exposed to flies which, as we have seen in Chapter 27 and Plate 87, carry bacteria. In addition food so exposed may be handled by shoppers who may unwittingly spread disease by so doing.

PLATE 87. Bacteria growing on plate exposed for one second to fly feet.

Some shop assistants may be seen handling food and money quite regardless of the fact that the money may be harbouring germs. Obviously pets should not be allowed in food shops and restaurants as they may carry

a whole variety of bacteria and other organisms harmful to Man. Any unhygienic practices observed in shops or canteens should be reported to the Medical Officer of Health as a public duty. The shop shown in Plate 88 is an excellent example of good hygiene for the food is well covered and the surfaces and floors are easily washed. The shop is light, clean and well ventilated and the assistant is wearing a clean white coat.

Even before food reaches shops it may be made unfit to eat by being damaged during transport or storage. The food may already have become infected by pathogens; the animal from which the food has been made may itself be infected by the tuberculosis bacillus or tapeworm eggs. Rigid inspection of all carcases has almost eliminated danger from these sources, however. The danger from contaminated milk is discussed in Chapter 26.

The addition of chemicals in the artificial colouring and flavouring of foods is also strictly controlled in this country in order to prevent poisoning.

The most notorious sources of food poisoning are re-heated meat dishes, meat pies, sausages, ice cream, synthetic cream and fish. This danger can be avoided by purchasing food from reliable firms and by avoiding 'dirty' shops and restaurants.

In order to keep food in good condition many firms use insulated and refrigerated vans to transport their products. Food must be stored in a cool dry place, free from rats and flies and out of the reach of other animals. Many foods keep best in a refrigerator but where this is not possible several devices can be arranged to keep cheese, milk and meat cool. For example, milk may be cooled by standing the bottle in cold water and covering it with a wet cloth. Evaporation from the cloth causes cooling and may help to keep the milk below the temperature at

PLATE 88. Hygienic foodshop.

333

PLATE 89. Modern kitchen with hygienic working surfaces.

which bacteria thrive. Fruit and vegetables should be stored in a place which is dry and in which air may freely circulate round them. They should be consumed as quickly as possible and bruising them should be avoided.

With regard to food hygiene in the home the floors and walls of the kitchen should be made of easily washable materials. Surfaces of cupboards and work tops must preferably be smooth in order that food and dust may not be trapped on them. Adequate ventilation, heating and lighting should be provided—it must not be forgotten that sunlight kills bacteria. Plate 89 shows a modern kitchen with easy-clean surfaces, stainless steel sink unit and adequate lighting. Whether the kitchen be old or new, special attention should be paid to drains and sinks so that they may be kept free of grease and dirt. Kitchen waste should be placed in an easily cleaned container

which can be frequently emptied into a rat-proof dustbin which has a tightly fitting lid. The dustbin should be raised slightly above ground level as this helps to prevent it from rusting when it becomes wet. Plate 90 shows a most unhygienic back-yard providing suitable conditions for rats to forage in and as we saw in Chapter 27 these animals are dangerous for they spread disease. The two species of rats found in Britain are shown in Plates 91 and 92.

A plentiful supply of hot water should be available to keep washing up as hygienic as possible. Detergents may be used as necessary. Dishes can be left to dry on a rack as long as the detergent has been thoroughly rinsed away. Tea towels and washing-up cloths should be boiled regularly because to use a dirty tea towel on a washed plate may spread germs. Dish-washing machines wash

PLATE 90. Rat-infested back-yard.

PLATE 91. Brown rats.

335

PLATE 92. A black rat.

and dry at high temperatures thus helping to kill bacteria. Cutlery, glass and china should be kept scrupulously clean as dirty utensils spread disease from one user to another. Cracked glass and china should be disposed of as the cracks harbour micro-organisms. When tables are laid for a meal cutlery should be lifted only by the handles and not by the parts which will go into the mouth. Cups and glasses should be held by their bases when the table is laid.

It will be noticed that the recommendations contained in this chapter are largely matters of courtesy and common sense but that underlying them are scientific reasons which, if fully understood, provide the key for improving the health of the nation.

QUESTIONS ON CHAPTER 29

1. Enumerate the unhygienic practices that you might see in the course of a day that began with buying food for a packed meal and went on to a coach trip and picnic. State why each practice quoted is a menace to health. (C)

2. Every summer brings outbreaks of food poisoning. Explain the reasons for this, and suggest the ways in which such outbreaks can be avoided. (C)

3. In the light of any unhygienic practices you have seen in foodshops and feeding establishments, draw up what you feel is an ideal code of hygienic behaviour for such places. Discuss the value of your recommendations. (C)

4. Outbreaks of food-borne diseases continue to give concern in this country. How do you account for such outbreaks? Suggest a code of hygienic behaviour for preparers, vendors and consumers of food that would lead to improvement. (C)

5. What advice should be given to an inexperienced housewife about the hygienic handling and storing of the food for her family in the home? Give your reasons in the answer. (L)

6. What precautions can be taken to ensure that meat and fish do not spread disease? What diseases can be caused by these foods? (L)

7. In providing and preparing food for the family what general rules should guide (a) the choice of food in all income groups, (b) the hygiene of its preparation? Give reasons for these rules. (L)

8. What diseases can be transmitted by an unclean milk supply? Describe the precaution which should be taken to ensure that it is safe for the consumer. (L)

9. Describe two experiments which prove the existence of microscopic living things. What would you deduce from these experiments concerning the importance of hygienic personal habits? (S)

10. What measures can an individual take to lessen the danger of food poisoning? (S)

11. The food we eat can spread disease. Explain why this is so, and show how (a) the local authorities and (b) the individual can prevent such spread. (RSA)

12. Explain how bacteria make people ill and how they cause food to go bad. What precautions can the individual take to prevent these things happening to himself and his food? (RSA)

13. What is hygiene, and what do you understand by 'an unhygienic condition'? How can such a condition be maintained in (a) the kitchen, (b) the living room, of a family which includes several small children? Give reasons for your answer. (RSA)

14. Give an account of the undesirable practices you have yourself observed in food shops, markets, restaurants and canteens. Point out the risks to the community that result from these practices. (J)

Summary of 29

1. Owing to crops of different kinds being grown in different parts of the world the *storage*, *preservation* and *transport* of food is important. Handling of food must be *hygienic*.

2. Foods may be preserved by *salting*, *smoking*, *pickling*, *bottling*, *dehydrating*, *canning* and *refrigeration*.

3. Food may be made more appetising and more easily digested by cooking. *Roasting*, *frying*, *boiling*, *stewing*, *steaming* and *grilling* are ways of cooking food.

4. Some *vitamins* are destroyed by heat so it is necessary to include raw *vegetables* and *fruit* in the diet.

5. Unhygienic handling of food may frequently be seen in shops and restaurants. Hot water, soap and towels must be provided wherever food is handled. Food should be covered to protect it from flies.

30. Housing: lighting, heating and ventilation

General Requirements for Housing

The basic requirement which a house must provide is adequate shelter from unfavourable weather. Early paintings show that this has always been so, for they often depict primitive Man at the entrance to his cave. Caves also gave him protection from wild beasts and other men. As human beings became more civilised the function of the 'house' became more and more important as protection from the elements. Man has shown considerable powers of adaptation in the building of his home in different parts of the world, the structure, site and size of the dwelling varying according to climate, season and place. In any one part of the world Man is restricted, to some extent, by the type of building materials available—the Eskimo (Plate 23), for example, has little else to use but snow and ice. Along the banks of the Amazon, houses must be raised upon stilts to lift them above the marshy ground, and to hold the inhabitants out of the reach of crocodiles and other dangerous beasts. In hot countries the only requirement for a home is adequate shelter from the heat of the sun and a certain degree of privacy.

In Britain the weather is so variable from season to season that a house must be constructed so that it prevents dampness rising from the ground, and snow, rain and wind

from entering. It must also have adequate window space to allow sufficient light to enter without too much heat escaping from the rooms. The walls of houses and flats must be durable, strong, heat-insulating and, as far as possible, sound-proof. Frequently the outer walls of houses are double structures being made of two layers of bricks with a cavity between them. These *cavity walls*, as they are called, help to prevent heat-loss and the entry of moisture. Fig. 30.1 shows the construction of a wall with a damp-proof course. The roof must, of course, be weather proof and as it usually has a considerable surface area it is best heat-insulated from the rest of the house by some material such as fibre glass or wood chips laid between the joists of the loft.

Rooms within the house should be well lit, ventilated and free from damp. The size and the number of rooms depends on the size of the family. Generally speaking a room 10 square metres in area is considered a minimum size for two people to live in. Unfortunately many families are condemned to live in slums, in very crowded conditions, owing to the housing shortage and to the rapid increase in the population which has occurred since many houses, flats and estates were built. Plate 93 shows a mother trying to bring up five children in a very crowded

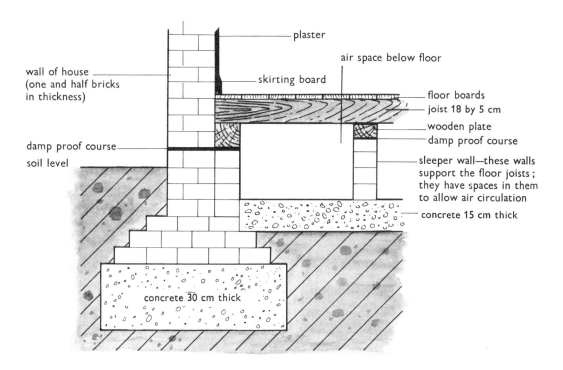

FIG. 30.1. The construction of a wall and damp-proof course.

space. Notice the boy in bed at the back of the room—a room which serves as a general living room as well as a bedroom.

Ideally a house should have in addition to the living rooms and bedrooms a bathroom supplied with hot and cold water. A W.C. pan must be available either in the bathroom or in a separate room. The house should be adequately heated and artificial light must be supplied. In the kitchen a sink, supplied with hot and cold water, must be present as well as cooking and storage facilities.

Outside the house there must be room to store fuel, and sheds for accommodating bicycles and tools are always useful. Space for dustbins is essential. Even today there are many houses and flats where these things

PLATE 93. Overcrowded living conditions.

PLATE 94. Poor housing conditions.

PLATE 95. A block of modern flats.

are not available. Plate 94 shows very poor housing conditions. One can see the lack of facilities at a glance and can imagine the difficulties experienced by elderly people living at the top of the block in obtaining fuel from the coal bunkers in the yard. Fortunately such housing conditions are disappearing and many old buildings have been pulled down and replaced by blocks of modern flats such as those shown in Plate 95. The Town Planning authorities are responsible for building new houses and flats on estates with sufficient space between buildings to ensure adequate light, air and open space without using too much land. Fig. 30.2 shows how land may be more economically used for housing by building upwards rather than spreading a building over a large area. This allows more space for air to circulate round adjacent blocks and more space for children to play on.

Slum clearance is a long and arduous task which started between the two World Wars and which is still continuing. The rapid increase of population makes this work very difficult.

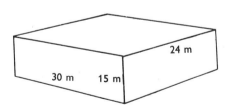

a. Area of ground occupied by building is 720 m².

340

Ventilation (Figs. 30.3, 30.4 and 30.5)

A well-ventilated room contains air which is fresh, at a comfortable temperature and constantly renewed. The air which enters a room may vary in its freshness depending on how close the windows are to other buildings —especially industrial buildings which frequently produce smoke or fumes. The presence of people in a room decreases the oxygen content of the air and increases the humidity because of the processes of respiration and perspiration which are going on continuously and the air gradually becomes over-heated and stagnant. Respiration of persons present also increases the carbon dioxide content of the air. The result of remaining for some time in a badly ventilated room is that headaches may develop and a general lassitude will be felt. You will have noticed that in a stuffy room people begin to yawn one after another; this is due not to tiredness but to lack of oxygen, the yawning being an unconscious effort to get more oxygen into the lungs.

It was mentioned in Chapter 26 that some infectious diseases are spread from one place or person to another by the bacteria and viruses being carried in the air. These airborne diseases are more likely to spread from one person to another in a confined and overcrowded room, especially if it is badly ventilated. Tuberculosis is a disease which thrives in overcrowded conditions as we saw in Chapter 26.

Resistance to infection of all types is lowered by living in overcrowded and unhygienic conditions.

Considerable care must be exercised in the design of large buildings such as offices, factories and schools to ensure that every room is adequately ventilated. During and immediately after the Industrial Revolution

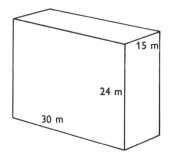

b. Area of ground occupied by building is 450 m².

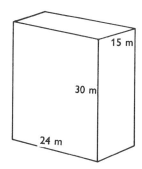

c. Area of ground occupied by building is 360 m². This is only half the area occupied by the building in figure a. The other half is available for grass and gardens.

FIG. 30.2. Diagram to show how ground space may be saved by building high. All three buildings have the same volume.

341

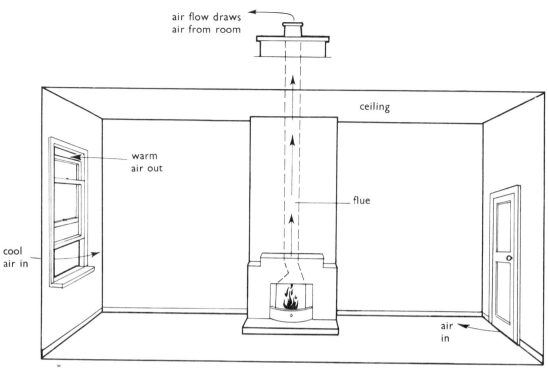

ceiling

warm
air out

flue

cool
air in

air
in

a. Showing how open fire helps to ventilate room

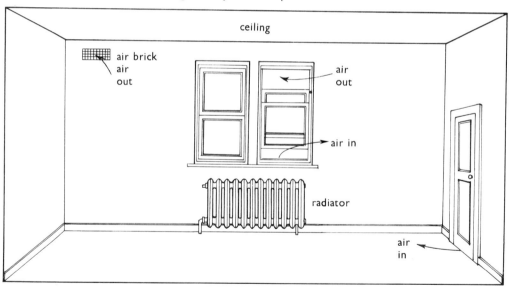

ceiling

air brick
air
out

air
out

air in

radiator

air
in

b. Central Heating. Thermostat controls room temperature. Central heating sets up air currents but air flow is slower than with open fire heating

FIG. 30.3. How heating a room helps to ventilate it.

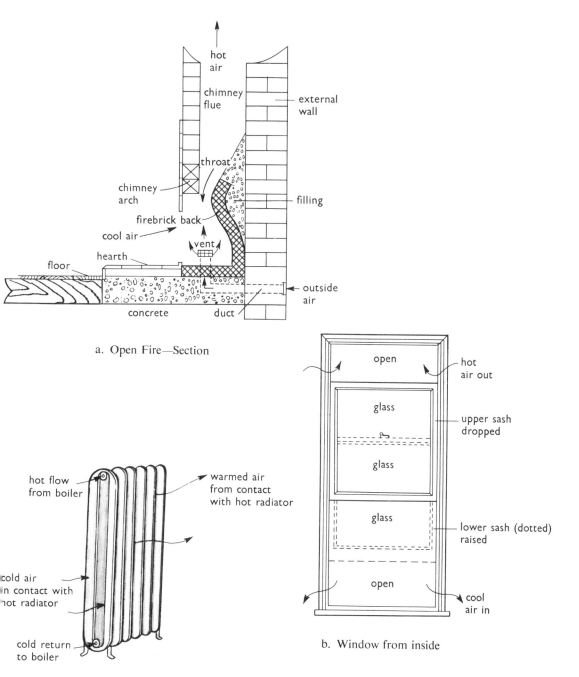

a. Open Fire—Section

b. Window from inside

c. Cast-iron hot-water radiator in six sections

FIG. 30.4. Heating and ventilating.

343

little or no attention was paid to the health of the factory workers but during this century various Factory and Building Acts have been passed to ensure that buildings are designed with a view to maintaining the health of all who work or live in them. Today every building whether it is for work, for living in, or for recreation must comply with strict regulations concerning the safety and health of the people who use them. Minimum requirements are laid down for window and floor space per person accommodated.

The problem of ventilation is to exchange the stale, used air of the rooms in which we live for fresh air from the atmosphere. Normally this atmospheric air is washed by the rain and bacteria in it are to some extent killed by the ultra-violet rays of the sun. Rooms may be ventilated either by some natural means or by artificial means. Hot air always rises and its place is taken by cooler air which enters at windows, doors and ventilators. Air which is near fires or radiators will be constantly rising and drawing in fresh air from outside. For this reason air inlets should be lower than air outlets. When a house is built special ventilation bricks are built into the walls high up near the ceiling. Other ventilators allow air to flow underneath the floorboards of the house: this discourages the growth of fungi such as dry and wet rot. A constant stream of hot air rises up the chimney when an open fire is burning beneath it and for this reason a room heated in this way will be automatically ventilated at the same time. Central heating does not have this desirable effect, for radiators are not equipped with chimneys and therefore it is especially important in centrally heated rooms to have other adequate means of ventilation. Various devices fixed in the walls, windows or roof make use of this natural ventilation by allowing the hot, stale air to escape and cooler air to be constantly drawn into the room. In large buildings a whole planned system of ventilation is worked out by the architect.

Electric fans or pumps are sometimes used to force fresh air through buildings where natural ventilation is insufficient. In private houses electrically driven extractor fans are frequently used in bathrooms and kitchens to remove steam and cooking smells. In many large modern buildings air-conditioning is such that it not only draws in fresh air but also filters, warms and humidifies it. The air which enters a room either by natural or artificial means should be free from any foul fumes and should ventilate the rooms without causing draughts.

Lighting

We have to consider both natural and artificial light in this section. Natural light enters the rooms through the windows and, ideally, windows should occupy one-third of the total outside-wall area. Sunlight which enters through an open window has, as well as the bacterial effects mentioned earlier, a health-giving effect on the skin. Adequate lighting safeguards against eyestrain, and is important for the mental outlook of the occupants. Ultra-violet light cannot travel through glass and for this reason the windows of hospital wards are very large in some cases, and can be completely removed in suitable weather to allow fresh air and sunlight to exert their maximum benefits and for the same reason it is important to have open windows as frequently as possible in private houses.

Where there is little natural light available in a room it is important to decorate with light colours, for these will reflect whatever light there is, and will increase the general cheerfulness of the room. This is of particular

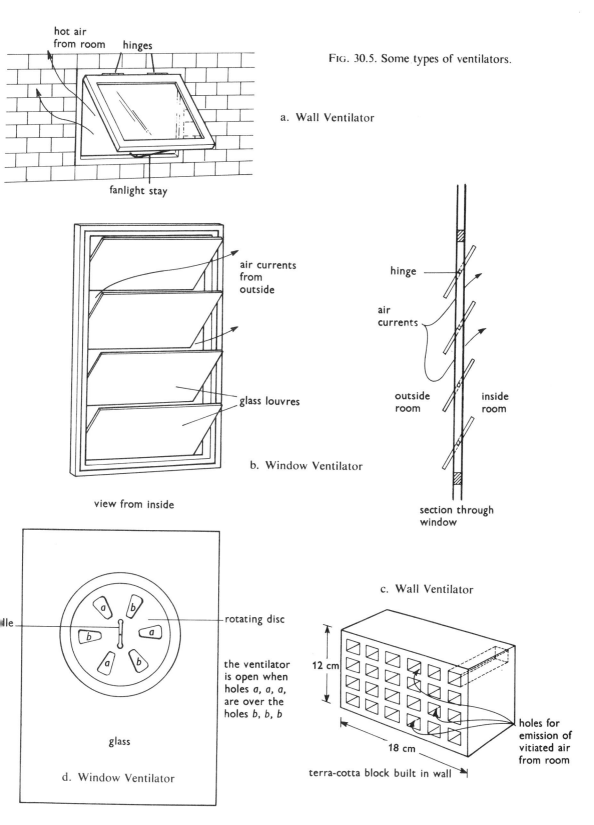

hot air from room   hinges

fanlight stay

a. Wall Ventilator

Fig. 30.5. Some types of ventilators.

air currents from outside

glass louvres

view from inside

b. Window Ventilator

hinge

air currents

outside room   inside room

section through window

c. Wall Ventilator

rotating disc

the ventilator is open when holes a, a, a, are over the holes b, b, b

glass

d. Window Ventilator

12 cm

18 cm

terra-cotta block built in wall

holes for emission of vitiated air from room

importance in hospitals, schools and factories. South-facing windows give a room a warm and sunny aspect. In a classroom the light from the windows should enter from the left-hand side of the pupils in order that their work should not be shadowed by their right shoulder and hand.

When natural light is insufficient it must be supplemented by artificial light and here, of course, the main modern method is the use of electricity. Filament electric lamps may provide either direct or diffuse light. Fluorescent lighting gives a strong light and casts no shadows and is therefore used often in kitchens, workshops and factories. A light which is either glaring or dull has a bad effect on the eyes and it is most important that a good light is provided over work benches and tables. In the home it is considered desirable to have in living rooms one central light with smaller lamps for reading, sewing, etc., although, if too strong, local patches of light may cause eyestrain. Lighting on stairs and steps should be adequate if accidents are to be avoided. Electricity is the preferable method of lighting and has almost entirely superseded gas and oil lighting.

Gas lighting is still used where it has not been replaced by electricity. Its disadvantages are that it contaminates the air with the products of the combustion of the coal-gas. One gas burner produces as much carbon dioxide as the respiration of four people. Candles have low lighting power, also have harmful combustion products and are used today mostly for the effect of their light rather than for its efficiency.

Paraffin oil is still used in oil lamps in some country areas where electricity or gas are not available. The burning of the wick gives off an unpleasant smell and oxygen is used up from the surrounding air.

Heating

The aim of heating homes is to maintain a comfortable and healthy temperature. Today we try to obtain a background temperature of $7-10°C$ throughout the house with living rooms at a temperature of $16-18°C$. Bedrooms should be kept at a somewhat lower temperature, perhaps about $13°C$. Fuel bills may be greatly reduced by our preventing heat from escaping through walls, roof and windows. This may be achieved by building with special insulating bricks, by lagging the loft and by use of double-glazing on the windows.

In addition to keeping rooms warm heat must be provided to supply sufficient hot water. The main methods of heating are the use of solid fuel, gas (natural or manufactured), electricity or oil.

Modern open fires produce a great heat in proportion to the amount of fuel needed and are therefore economical. Some are designed to burn continuously, some can be modified to supply hot air to the rest of the house and, with a back-boiler, open fires may be used to heat the water supply. Solid fuel may be in the form of coal, coke or smokeless fuels. In many areas in big towns and cities a smokeless fuel must be used by law in order to reduce atmospheric pollution.

Electricity is an expensive but clean method of heating. Individual heating units can be of the convector or radiant type. Some radiators can now be heated by electricity, the elements being contained in concrete or in oil. These can be thermostatically controlled. One good but expensive method of heating with electricity is having the elements below the floor of the rooms, or they may be set into the walls or ceiling. Electricity can also heat the domestic hot water supply.

Gas fires heat the room by radiation of heat from the hot clay pipes and also by convection of the heated air. The room should always be well ventilated when gas heating is used.

Portable paraffin heaters are used for heating rooms but there is great danger in carrying these heaters about when they are alight and through careless use they have caused much loss of life and damage. They must be used in well-ventilated rooms only as they quickly use the oxygen present.

Central heating is becoming increasingly common and is now installed in many homes and offices. It can be either full central heating for the whole house or partial central heating for certain rooms only. It can either provide a background temperature which can be supplemented by gas or electricity or maintain a high temperature over the whole house. Central heating may be installed to use oil, gas, electricity or solid fuel. Whatever the method employed most central-heating systems can be controlled thermostatically. The disadvantages of central heating are that it sometimes causes a lack of adequate ventilation and hot pipes may discolour walls and ceilings.

Heat for cooking is provided by gas, electricity or solid fuel.

By ensuring that houses and flats are well-spaced, soundly constructed, well-lit and ventilated, and adequately heated, we can provide the living conditions for a healthy nation.

QUESTIONS ON CHAPTER 30

1. What are the symptoms of discomfort experienced in a crowded, ill-ventilated room, and how do you account for them? Explain how adequate ventilation prevents their occurrence. (C)

2. What are the main reasons for condemning a house as unfit for human habitation? When rehousing families what steps should be taken when building the new house to see that it will be satisfactory? (O)

3. State *five* methods of heating a room in a house. Give a list of advantages and disadvantages for each method. Which method do you consider to be the healthiest? (W)

4. From the point of view of health, what are the most important factors to be considered when designing a house? (W)

5. What factors contribute to a 'stuffy atmosphere'? Discuss critically one method of heating and ventilating (a) a kitchen, (b) a classroom, (c) a living room. (S)

7. A well-built school is one which has adequate heating, lighting and ventilation. Explain briefly the method you consider the most suitable for each of these services and state the harm which may result to the health of the children in the school if these services are not satisfactorily provided. (RSA)

8. What gases are present in normal, clean air and what impurities are to be found in the air of a busy town? How can these impurities affect the health of the people in the town and how can each individual person help to reduce both the amount of these impurities and the harm that they cause? (RSA)

9. Explain how the composition and physical conditions of the air in a building may affect the health and comfort of people living and working there. (J)

10. What are the ways in which the body produces and loses heat and maintains, in health, a uniform body temperature? What guidance does this information give in formulating the principles underlying the heating and lighting of buildings? (J)

347

Summary of 30

1. Houses must provide adequate shelter against bad weather. They must also provide privacy.

2. Houses are built to include, besides living rooms and bedrooms, a bathroom, with hot and cold water, and a toilet. Heating and lighting and a means of disposal of waste are important.

3. Rooms should be well ventilated if the occupants are to be healthy. Stale air may contain microbes and may lack oxygen and be saturated with water vapour. Overcrowding assists the spread of disease.

4. It is important to have adequate light—either natural or artificial—or the eyesight may be impaired.

5. Temperatures between 16 and 18°C are the best for living rooms: bedrooms should be at a somewhat lower temperature.

31. Water Supplies

The Need for Water

The provision of a reliable supply of drinking water is one of the corner-stones of civilised society and there has been an increasing need for water supplies through the ages especially in towns and cities. In the days when most communities were small rural villages it was relatively easy to keep the population supplied with sufficient water but with the growth of large towns and cities, especially during and following the Industrial Revolution, the problem became increasingly difficult. The fact that most of the rain falls over the hills and mountains, whereas most of the population lives in the low-lying parts of the country, only serves to accentuate the problem. The water must be carried from the hilly country districts to the towns. This is not an entirely new problem, for the Romans built *aqueducts* to convey water to their cities. The *size* of the problem is new, however, for the tremendous increase in the population of this and other countries during the last 150 years has meant that a greatly increased water supply has become necessary. For example, the population of London was less than one million in 1801 when the first national census was taken but by 1851 it had already risen to over two and a quarter million; and today, when the figure is probably nearly nine million, the problem of water supplies is indeed great. It is no mean triumph of engineering that all Londoners are now supplied with as much clean, fresh water as they require and that, in addition, the great industries of the metropolis have their needs adequately met.

It is interesting to note the vast quantities of water required to produce certain common industrial products: a megagramme of paper requires for its manufacture 200 cubic metre: a megagramme of bleached cotton some 300 cubic metre and a megagramme of lactose about 1000 cubic metre.

Not only must a supply of water be obtained but it must be of adequate *purity*, especially if it is to form the source of drinking water for the population. Water forms a means of transport of bacteria and if these are pathogenic there is obvious danger. The chief diseases likely to be carried by water are dysentry, cholera and typhoid fever. These diseases are caused by organisms present in human excreta, so that an obvious source of infection of the water supply is from a broken sewer. Such a situation is rare but this has not always been the case, for as late as the nineteenth century lavatories were allowed to drain direct into the river (Plate 3) and one water company at Chelsea had its intake pipe in the Thames only a few yards from the outlet pipe of a large sewer! It is not surprising that in 1831 there was a terrible outbreak of cholera in London. Some 50,000 persons died as a result of this epidemic and the resulting outcry led to the passing, later in the nineteenth century, of

Public Health Acts which regulated the discharge of excreta and the intake of water.

Before considering further the purification of water we must study first the sources from which water is obtained.

The Water Cycle

Fig. 31.1 shows how water circulates in nature. All water which is used by mankind for personal and industrial purposes falls in the first place from clouds either as rain, hail or snow. Some of this precipitation will drain into rivers, lakes, etc., some will percolate through the soil and form an underground source of water and some will evaporate from the soil and pass upwards as water vapour to form cloud. The amount of rain varies in different parts of the country but is, broadly speaking, heavier in the west than in the east and greater over high ground

than over the lower areas. The amount falling also varies from year to year and from season to season. Plate 96 shows the Manchester reservoir during the drought of 1956, a year when farmers throughout the country were worried by the lack of water to provide for their stock. The level of many reservoirs fell alarmingly and emergency measures with regard to water supplies were enforced in some towns and cities. Normally there is more than sufficient water 'in stock' and the actual annual rainfall is probably several times that which this country requires.

Sources of Water

The water which falls as rain may either remain on the surface of the ground or it may sink into it, depending upon the type of soil. If the soil is impervious, as in the case of clay soils, water will not freely soak into

FIG. 31.1. THE WATER CYCLE.

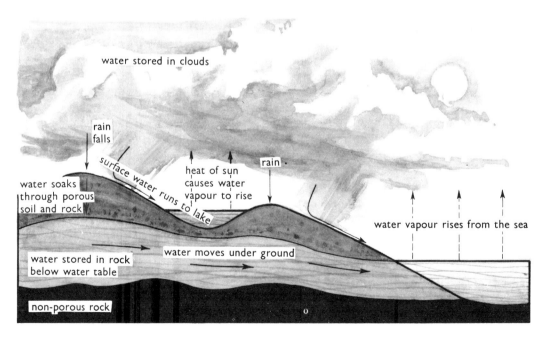

water stored in clouds

rain falls

surface water runs to lake

heat of sun causes water vapour to rise

rain

water soaks through porous soil and rock

water vapour rises from the sea

water stored in rock below water table

water moves under ground

non-porous rock

it but will stay on the surface forming ponds, lakes and rivers. In such areas the source of supply for the population will be *overground*. In cases where the rain falls on porous rocks such as chalk and limestone it rapidly sinks below ground until it strikes an impervious layer some way below the surface. This allows large supplies of water to accumulate *below ground* and these may be tapped for Man's use. Fig. 31.2 shows how water falling on the porous chalk of the North Downs and Chiltern Hills forms a supply for London, either by emerging as springs or by being drawn from wells. The fountains in Trafalgar Square, for example, are fed by water drawn from the chalk lying below the London Clay and at one time the force of the water was sufficiently strong to enable the fountains to play without the aid of pumps. Now, however, continual drawing of the supply from the chalk has lowered the level to such an extent that pumps must be used. It will be seen from the figure that rain falling on the porous chalk can sink in only so far: it then is held by the impervious clay and thus forms a huge underground reservoir or *artesian basin*. Rain falling on the impervious London

FIG. 31.2. LONDON'S WATER SUPPLY.

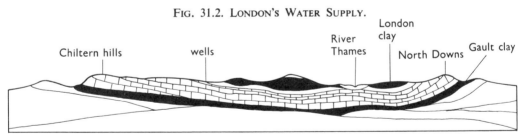

a. A Section through the London Basin. Rain falling on the chalk hills drains through to the impervious clay and may be tapped from wells

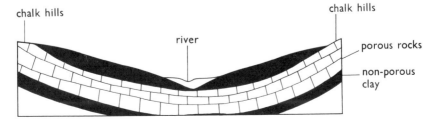

b. Diagram to show how rain falling on chalk forms an underground reservoir of water

clay itself drains into the Thames or its tributaries such as the Lea and the Wandle which, together with a considerable number of artificial lakes or reservoirs, form the main London water supply. The first of the reservoirs was built by the Metropolitan Water Board at Stoke Newington in 1834 and since that time over fifty more have been constructed in the London area. The largest of these is the Queen Mary reservoir at Littleton in Middlesex which has an area of more than 3 square kilometres.

Other areas of the country which are near porous rocks also obtain some or all of their water supply from underground. Bournemouth is one such area.

Most of the large towns and cities depend on lakes and reservoirs for their water— London has been mentioned; Manchester depends on Thirlmere Lake; and Birmingham obtains its supply from the reservoirs of the beautiful Elan Valley in Wales. Plate 97 shows the reservoir near Blackburn. This plate also shows the use made of *dams* in enlarging natural lakes or in creating artificial ones.

In parts of the world where rainfall is low, other methods of producing water suitable for drinking have to be employed. Several methods of obtaining drinking water from *sea water* have been tried with varying degrees of success, a limiting factor here being the expense involved, although as the result of research in the United States the cost of desalinated water has been reduced from five dollars per five cubic metre to half a dollar for the same amount over the last ten years. Over one hundred desalination plants are now in operation in various parts of the world producing between them over 120,000 cubic metre of drinking water a day. Few of these plants are in Europe and only one is in the United Kingdom, for, as has already been mentioned, the European rainfall far exceeds requirements.

Another way in which water may be con-

PLATE 97. The Blackburn reservoir.

served i ɔy the treatment of waste water from industry and from sewage. Water which is polluted must be purified carefully, especially if it is to be used for drinking. Objectionable substances which must be removed include micro-organisms, organic matter, dissolved gases, dissolved mineral salts, metals, oils, fats, greases and radioactive matter. It is obvious that as industries increase in any country the amount of waste water they produce also increases so that the importance of saving some of it for re-use becomes greater.

Purification of Water

Whatever the source of water it must be carefully purified before it can be safely released for public use. In addition it should be free from colour, taste and odour. Purification takes several forms. In the first place a certain amount of 'natural' purification occurs in large reservoirs and in lakes, for sand and other solids settle under the influence of gravity, provided the water is not moving quickly. In addition the bacteria and protozoa present in the water break up organic matter. Water plants use carbon dioxide present in the water and give oxygen to it and natural sunlight helps to destroy harmful bacteria. If the source of water is not from lake or reservoir it may be necessary to pass it to man-made sedimentation basins where it remains for some time to allow the larger particles to settle. The water is next passed through sand filters which may be of two types—*slow filter-beds* and *pressure filters*. The structure of a filter-bed is shown in Fig. 31.3. A gelatinous film composed of *algae* and micro-organisms forms in the upper few inches of the sand and this removes harmful bacteria. The layers of sand and

FIG. 31.3. The structure of a filter-bed.

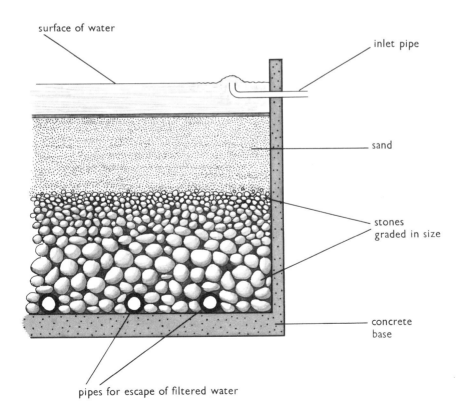

surface of water

inlet pipe

sand

stones graded in size

concrete base

pipes for escape of filtered water

gravel provide mechanical filtration. After some time the layer of algae slows up the filtration process and the filter-bed has to be taken out of action while the surface of the sand is removed and a new layer applied. A few days must be allowed for the correct amount of algae to form before the water from the filter can be considered sufficiently pure. Pressure filters (concrete tanks through which the water is passed under pressure through the sand) are closed. Such tanks are cleaned by the forcing of compressed air and clean water up through the layers of sand.

After the processes of sedimentation and filtration the water is *chlorinated*, that is, chlorine at the rate of about 1 part per million, is passed into the water to kill any remaining harmful bacteria and to oxidise any remaining organic matter. The purified water is lastly passed to service reservoirs which are frequently in the form of water towers. These are closed to exclude the light in order to prevent the growth of algae.

PLATE 98. Power pumps in a modern water works.

354

32. Refuse Disposal

Dry Refuse

Not only does each home in the country produce a large amount of waste material which must be removed but also an ever-increasing amount of waste is produced, during the manufacture of all types of articles, by factories both large and small. In the home the chief waste materials are removed either in the sewers or by men employed by local councils. Factories make every effort to use, in the making of one product, waste materials formed during the manufacture of another. Much waste collected by Local Authorities is salvaged and sold to factories. The chief waste substances of value are: bones—for making fertilisers; paper; metals such as iron and steel and empty tins; rags and bottles. Where these substances are awaiting collection from the home strong galvanised bins should be used for their storage. These should be raised from the ground to prevent their becoming rusted and they must also have tightly fitting lids to keep flies from gaining entry. The collecting vehicles should be closed to prevent dust and dirt from blowing out.

Once the refuse has been collected it is sorted in order to salvage any valuable materials—for example an electro-magnet may be used to separate the scrap metal—and then the remainder is either burnt or placed on a tip. Large incinerators are used by some local authorities for this purpose.

If incinerators are not available tips may be used. All kinds of dry refuse may be placed by lorries on the tip but if there is much organic matter present each layer of refuse should be covered by a thick layer of earth. One drawback to the use of tips is that they provide an excellent habitat for rats to live and breed in.

Sewage Disposal

It is obvious from what we learned in the chapters on disease that the collection and disposal of sewage, especially from large towns, is a very important aspect of public hygiene. Until the middle of the last century sewage was allowed to pass directly into rivers but now, of course, it must be carried in enclosed pipes to specially designed sewage works where it is treated to render it harmless.

The materials carried in the sewers are excreta and waste water from houses, rainwater from streets and waste from factories. Sometimes the rainwater is carried in pipes separate from those carrying sewage; especially is this so in large towns where a great deal of water may suddenly accumulate on the streets during a storm.

The water in the sewage pipes will ultimately enter the sea, rivers or lakes but before it does so it must be rendered harmless. This responsibility falls on the local councils who are required to make the water safe. They

355

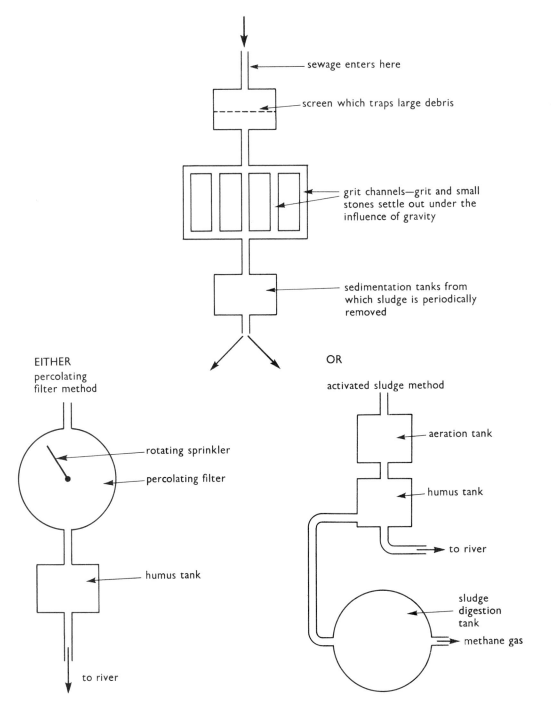

sewage enters here

screen which traps large debris

grit channels—grit and small stones settle out under the influence of gravity

sedimentation tanks from which sludge is periodically removed

EITHER
percolating filter method

OR
activated sludge method

rotating sprinkler

percolating filter

aeration tank

humus tank

to river

humus tank

sludge digestion tank

methane gas

to river

FIG. 32.1. Sewage plant. The three preliminary stages are shown at the top of the page. Below them are shown the percolating filter method on the left and the activated sludge method on the right.

356

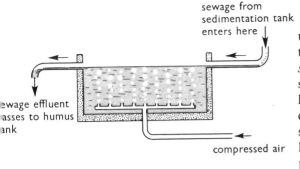

sewage from
sedimentation tank
enters here

sewage effluent
passes to humus
tank

compressed air

Section through aeration tank

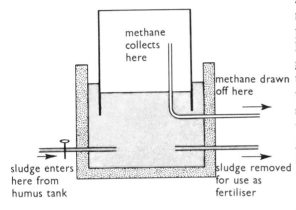

methane
collects
here

methane drawn
off here

sludge enters
here from
humus tank

sludge removed
for use as
fertiliser

Section through sludge digestion tank

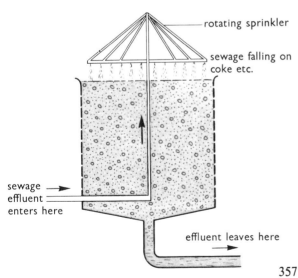

rotating sprinkler

sewage falling on
coke etc.

sewage
effluent
enters here

effluent leaves here

Section through percolating filter

usually employ one of two methods, either the *percolating filter method* or the *activated sludge method*. Both these methods of sewage treatment depend on the activity of live micro-organisms for their success. These creatures break down the organic matter into simple chemical compounds and also help to kill pathogenic bacteria. Both methods are preceded by similar preliminary treatment which consists of three processes. First the sewage is *screened* by passing it through large metal grids which trap all the large pieces of paper, rags, pieces of wood, etc., which may have found their way into the sewer. The grids are cleaned by mechanical rakes and the material which has been collected from them is burned or buried. Secondly the sewage passes on into narrow open channels through which it moves slowly in order that grit and stones washed from the roads may settle. Lastly, the sewage passes into sedimentation tanks (Fig. 32.1), where much of the solid waste settles to the bottom. This sediment is called *sludge* and its disposal will be considered later.

The liquid, which is called effluent and which is still very dangerous as it contains much organic matter, passes on for further treatment before being allowed to pass into rivers, etc. This treatment consists of one or other of the two methods already mentioned.

The percolating filter method employs circular tanks built of concrete, each tank being some six feet high and being filled with coke and clinker. This central core of coke ensures that there is a plentiful supply of air throughout the tank for use by the millions of bacteria which break down the sewage. One such tank is shown in Plate 99. The steel pipe seen above the clinker rotates slowly and pours effluent on to the clinker. As the effluent trickles slowly through the clinker its organic content is broken down by the bacteria which are present in countless millions as a thin gelatinous film on the surface of the clinker. Some of the dead bacteria, worms and algae which are always present in the filter get washed out and must not be allowed to enter rivers; so before the effluent is discharged it passes through a humus tank which gives the solids time to settle. The effluent passes to the rivers but it is, of course, tested at regular intervals for purity.

In the activated sludge method the effluent is passed into *aeration tanks* which have compressed air forced through them (Plate 100).

This provides a fine supply of oxygen for the bacteria. After some six hours the effluent is passed to a settling tank (Plate 101) where sludge settles out. It is this sludge, full of active bacteria, which gives its name— activated sludge—to the method.

Some of this activated sludge is pumped back to the aeration tanks to mix with the fresh sewage coming in thus providing a plentiful supply of bacteria. The remaining sludge is pumped out of the tanks and disposed of. In both methods of sewage disposal a large amount of sludge is left after the

PLATE 99. A percolating filter in a sewage works.

PLATE 100. Aeration tanks in a sewage works. Sludge digestion tanks in background.

PLATE 101. A settling tank.

effluent has been discharged. Much of this sludge is, by weight, water and this must be removed either by spreading the sludge over a large area of land, or by heating it for a few hours. The dehydrated sludge is sold as manure and the process of drying itself produces methane—a gas which can be used for driving machinery.

Questions on Chapters 31 and 32

1. Give an account of a visit that you yourself have made to any public or private undertaking that has a bearing on the health of the community, drawing attention to those aspects of the work that impressed you most. (C)

2. What are the methods of disposing of kitchen waste? How may careless disposal encourage the spread of disease? What precautions should any housewife take? (O)

3. How can sewage be safely disposed of in the absence of a piped water supply? What dangers are avoided by satisfactory methods of disposal? (L)

4. What can contaminate drinking water? How can water in small quantities be made safe for drinking? What are the disadvantages of hard water in the home? (L)

5. Suggest, with reasons, the best methods of disposing of household refuse by (a) the householder, (b) a large Local Authority. (S)

6. If you were in charge of a school camp what rules would you lay down for (i) obtaining drinking water, (ii) storing, preparing and cooking food, so that the risk of infection from these sources was reduced to a minimum? (S)

7. How does a body obtain water and maintain a water balance? Describe, in outline only, how a town may obtain a supply of pure water. (S)

8. List the sources of our water supply. What impurities may be found in water and what is the source of these impurities? Describe a method of purification of river water to make it safe as a supply for drinking purposes. (W)

9. Give an account of the precautions which must be taken by the occupants and by the Public Health Authorities to ensure the hygienic disposal of sewage from a town house. (W)

10. From what *two* sources may water be obtained to supply a large town? List the impurities that are likely to be present in each source and explain briefly how the impurities you mention are removed at the water-works. (RSA)

11. Fresh air and sunlight, chlorine and the zoogloea layer (layer of one-celled organisms) all play their part in the destruction of harmful bacteria. Describe carefully the use which is made of each of the above factors in the purification of water at the water-works. Describe the structure of a primary filter-bed, state the impurities which are removed by it, and explain how it differs from a secondary filter-bed. (RSA)

12. Explain the harm caused by the fly and *two* other house pests. Describe the steps taken by Local Authorities to ensure that household refuse does not form a breeding place, and explain how the householder can help to get rid of flies and the other *two* pests you mention. (RSA)

13. Why must river water be purified before it is used for drinking purposes? Explain fully how the living impurities are removed at the water-works, giving a diagram of any filter-bed you mention. (RSA)

14. What are the chief types of refuse requiring removal from homes and schools? Describe and comment upon methods of removal and disposal in any urban area you know. (J)

Summary of 31 and 32

1. A supply of *pure water* for drinking has been a necessity for many centuries. The problem of supply has increased in difficulty with the rapid growth of large towns during the last two centuries.

2. Water falls in the form of *rain* and *snow*, flows into *rivers* or *lakes*, sinks into the *soil* or *evaporates*. Thus there is an *overground* supply from lakes and rivers and an *underground* supply from rocks soaked with water. *Dams* are constructed to make artificial lakes or reservoirs.

3. Modern science has placed the water of the oceans at Man's disposal but *desalinating* plant is expensive. Water used in industry may be purified and re-used.

4. Water is purified by *slow filter-beds* or by *pressure* filters.

5. *Dry refuse* is collected by Local Authorities and buried or burnt. Some may go as salvage.

6. Sewage disposal is the responsibility of the Local Authorities who employ either the *percolating filter* method or the *activated sludge* method. Both methods depend on the action of bacteria in breaking down organic matter to harmless substances.

33. The Individual and the Community

Introduction

People live together in larger or smaller communities or societies—family groups, villages, towns, counties, etc. Each person has some influence on others in the community, and some responsibility towards them. In return the community accepts some responsibility towards the individuals comprising it, and provides them with such Public Services as sewage works, water supplies, police stations and hospitals. In this country we are particularly well supplied with such Services, as we shall see in the section which follows.

Responsibilities of the Community

The responsibility of the community to the individual has slowly developed over the last 120 years or so, starting perhaps with the First Coal Mines Regulation Act of 1842 which forbade the employment of women and children underground, and continuing until we have the Welfare State as we know it today. We have seen in earlier chapters how the Industrial Revolution led to the growth of slums which in turn, owing to overcrowding and the lack of sanitary facilities, provided perfect conditions for the spread of disease and misery. It is owing to a growing sense of responsibility in the population at large, led by the great reformers of the last

150 years, that social advance has been possible, until today we have reached a stage when few go without the bare necessities of life, and most have at least a little to spend on luxuries.

The result of better living and working conditions has been to improve the general health of the nation and this has meant that people can be more effective at work. Owners and managers of factories now realise that people work better, and have a greater output, if they are healthy and happy; and many large business concerns nowadays provide their workers with clubs and playing fields. Some factories even enlist the services of a chaplain to look after the spiritual welfare of their employees.

The recent nature of these developments is brought home to us when we learn that the first Public Health Act was not passed until 1875. It was concerned with dividing the country into urban and rural districts and county boroughs each with a Council concerned with sanitation. From the beginning of this century onwards there have been a considerable number of Acts passed by Parliament aimed at improving the nation's health. These Acts have dealt with maternity and child welfare, food safety and education. It was not until 1870 that education for children from five to fourteen years of age became compulsory.

In 1946 the National Health Act was passed and this attempted to link the work of several Ministries such as those of Education, Health, Housing and Local Government. The Ministry of Social Security provides the means by which everyone between school-leaving and pensionable age can gain benefits during maternity, sickness and retirement. All these Public Social Services and benefits cost a great deal and the money comes from rates, taxes and insurance contributions.

The Ministry of Health is headed by a Minister who is advised by a Chief Medical Officer and a Chief Nursing Officer. Each County Council or Borough has a Medical Officer who is assisted by a number of specialists including the School Medical Officer, the Children's Officer, Welfare Workers, Health Visitors and Midwives. The Medical Officer of Health is responsible for such matters as sanitation, housing conditions, control of infectious diseases, maternity and child services, vaccination and ambulance services. He is helped by a Public Health Inspector who deals in particular with sanitation.

The duty of a midwife is to attend an expectant mother before, during and after the birth of her baby. Her work is continued by the health visitor who visits the home at intervals. The mother has the services of the child clinic where she can obtain essential vitamins and other food preparations which supplement the normal diet and where she may receive free medical advice until her child is of school age. From then on the School Medical Officer is partly responsible for the health of the child. While at school the child will receive free milk and a meals service provides lunch at a low cost. The child at school will also have free dental and medical inspections. Medical inspections are held when the children are seven and eleven years of age and again when the child is due to leave school. Immunisations are given at the school. Special schools exist for the education of physically or mentally handicapped children and for those who are maladjusted. Once a person has left school he is himself responsible for his own health and must decide when he should see a doctor.

At one time factories were dirty, dark, overcrowded and unhygienic; and working hours were long. There was no holiday with pay. Factory Inspectors and Medical Inspectors now are appointed to take care of the health of all who work in the factory, making certain that the working conditions are both safe and hygienic. There should always be a trained first-aid worker in every factory. Care must be taken to see that the workshops are adequately lit and ventilated and that no overcrowding occurs. Water and food supplies at the works canteen must be regularly inspected. Of course water closets and washing facilities must be provided. Sanitary arrangements are of special importance where food is the factory's chief product —as, for example, in canning and bottling works. In such places the factory workers should wear clean white overalls and these must be regularly laundered.

Some diseases are associated with particular trades and industries e.g. *silicosis* of the lungs, in connection with stone quarry workers, and *pneumokoniosis* in colliery workers. In the first of these diseases fine particles of stone are the cause and, in the second, coal dust. In both the diseases the dust settles on the surface of the alveoli of the lungs preventing proper oxygen exchange. Nowadays people who work in factories where dangerous substances may be inhaled are provided with masks which filter the air they breathe. Modern dangers include the use of hair lacquers and paint sprays both of which may be inhaled and damage the lungs. In other industries the danger comes not from breathing substances but from their action on the skin of those who handle them. Eczema and warts, which may become malignant, are frequently caused by contact with certain chemicals. Coal tar is one example of a dangerous substance. In some cases the chemicals are in the body for a long time before their ill-effects become apparent: cancer of the bladder has, for example, been known to develop many years after the dangerous substances have been handled. The safety of workers is assisted by the use of barrier creams and rubber gloves. Lead and mercury are other substances which are dangerous to those who work with them continually, for they are absorbed slowly into the body and may lead to slow poisoning.

Agriculture is today one of Britain's major industries and precautions are taken to protect the health of the agriculture worker—by giving anti-tetanus injections, for example.

As the length of life of people in Britain is continually increasing the problem of keeping elderly folk occupied and happy becomes more acute. These people want to keep their independence and at the same time may need help to run their homes: it is for such that many of the voluntary organisations such as the Red Cross, the Scouts and the Guides are a great asset. The State must also play its part here by providing homes and pensions, but the State can never give the unselfish help so characteristic of voluntary workers (Plate 102).

Mentally handicapped people are today given special care in homes and hospitals by nurses and doctors who have trained with this type of work in mind. The modern attitude is to aim at curing the patient rather than just keeping him, and many advances have recently been made in this field; par-

ticularly hopeful are the recent discoveries of new drugs. Training in some useful occupation is given and as much of the treatment as possible is aimed at returning the patient to work as soon as possible.

One problem which is increasing today is that of broken marriages and divorce, and in order to prevent such tragedies occurring the National Marriage Guidance Council was formed and has set up Marriage Guidance Centres in most large towns. Here

PLATE 102. An example of a voluntary service —the British Red Cross Society.

364

sympathetic understanding and help may be obtained from experienced workers. Many homes have remained united and happy as a result of such work. Some churches, as well as the Marriage Guidance Council, give advice to engaged and married couples.

Responsibilities of the Individual

In Western society a family consists of the father, mother, their children and perhaps also some close relatives. This type of family is known as a 'nuclear' family in contrast to the 'extended' family which is more usual in Eastern countries where a bride enters the large tribal family of her husband.

In Britain the husband is normally the bread-winner while the work of the mother is to keep the home clean and to care for her husband and children with their individual needs. Husband and wife usually discuss all family matters together and decide issues such as the arrangement of the family budget, and the schooling of the children. The husband normally sees to financial transactions and the wife concerns herself with shopping, cooking and other household matters.

Sometimes both husband and wife go out to work for various reasons and the husband is then usually expected to take a share of some of the housework in the evenings. If the home is easy to run and the wife works part-time only she may be able to cope without assistance from her husband.

After marriage a young couple may live in a flat, maisonette or house which they may either rent or buy. Acquiring a home is a great problem because the increase in population is tending to outweigh the number of new houses built and very often a couple may, by choice or circumstance, find themselves living with in-laws and this may, or may not, be a satisfactory arrangement. Help in buying a home of one's own can be obtained from Building Societies who lend money for house purchase at a rate of interest, the capital sum borrowed being paid back over a long period—usually between twenty and thirty years.

Not so very long ago in this country marriages were often arranged by the parents of the couple concerned, more as a matter of convenience rather than of 'love', only the so-called lower classes marrying through a genuine affection for one another. The idea of marriage for convenience has almost died out and the feelings of the two people getting married are now regarded as the important factor. The success of a marriage depends on many factors but common interests— social background, religious convictions, political beliefs and so on—are generally recognised as important.

Today a father may be so occupied with his work that he sees his children only at weekends so that the burden of the upbringing of the children rests almost entirely on the mother. This may be one of many factors which lead to tension between members of the family and may even lead to separation or divorce. Many people are alarmed at the increasing divorce rate which has reached an unprecedented level particularly in the U.S.A. In Britain, too, the number of divorces has increased nearly tenfold since the beginning of the century. Because the family is the social unit in this country, a high divorce rate threatens the foundations of our national life. It is interesting to note that the divorce rate is highest amongst those who married very young. There is another high rate amongst those who have been married twenty years or over, and this may be because many couples stay together for the sake of their children, not taking divorce proceedings until the children are grown up.

One aspect of divorce, then, is its effect on the children of the divorced man and wife. Children from broken homes are deprived of a sense of security and lack parental training and discipline, and consequently many become delinquent: for example, nearly 95% of girls who give birth to illegitimate babies come from broken homes. Children from unhappy homes will be anxious to choose their life-partner very carefully and to make as certain as possible that they have sufficient in common with each other to make their marriage a success, and to avoid the mistakes their parents made.

The birth of a baby is usually an event of great joy and many parents like to mark the new arrival by some special social occasion. To some parents this may mean a christening or dedication service, of greater or lesser religious meaning, according to the faith of the parents. This may be almost the only time the new child enters a church unless his parents encourage him to do so as he grows older. Sometimes a child is left to make up his own mind with regard to church-going but he normally tends to follow the example set by his parents. Once the little child starts school he may receive some religious education, and indeed, must do so by law, but its value to him will depend almost entirely on the convictions and enthusiasm of the teacher.

The age at which a child starts school varies in this country. Some children begin by attending play-groups between the ages of two and two-and-a-half years. Later they may start at nursery school at the age of three or four. Full-time schooling is compulsory from five to sixteen years of age. Parents have some choice in the school to which they send their children but much depends on the schools available in a particular neighbourhood. A child's attitude to school depends on various factors but one of great importance is the way in which he is encouraged—or otherwise—by his parents. Some parents stress the importance of examinations too strongly while others take no interest: a happy and intelligent interest without being over-forceful is possibly best.

The duty of a school may be to see that children are prepared for life in mind, body and spirit, and to teach the importance of giving as well as receiving—in other words, to make certain that the pupils leave the school ready to play their part in the community. The school will try, in conjunction with the parents, to ensure that each pupil is aware, when the time comes for him to leave, of the various opportunities open to him to carry on part- or full-time education.

Leaving school and starting a job brings with it the pleasure and responsibility of earning and spending money. A wise parent will already have seen to it that his boy or girl has learnt to appreciate the value of money by the way in which he has given, or made his child earn, his pocket money.

The responsibility of the community towards elderly people was mentioned in the last section: now we must consider what individuals may do. Children who have been brought up to love and respect their grandparents will have already a sense of responsibility towards the elderly. If young people have been encouraged to consider others, as well as themselves, then the enthusiasm and energy of adolescence will be channelled into satisfying service to the community, and they will regard their parents, and other older people, as valuable friends rich in knowledge and experience of life, from whom they may seek advice and to whom they may give help.

Recent technological discoveries have led

to machines taking over more and more of the work so far done by men and women, and one consequence of this is a decrease in working hours and an increase in the leisure time available. For this reason it is becoming more and more important that people should be educated to occupy their free time usefully. People will have more time to develop their critical sense and to take an intelligent interest in the great issues of the day. They will form definite views on social, moral and world problems and thus will be part of the thinking public rather than cogs in the wheel. People now have more time to think of the problems connected with the purpose and meaning of our existence. This will be the case whether or not the person has any religious back-ground or belief, for an intelligent child will, from its earliest days, ask questions about life. No parent can give a child his own religious experience and neither can a teacher hope to impart it, no matter how sincerely he holds his own views. It is the person himself who with mind and spirit fully alert will accept or reject a faith and this will in turn influence the whole of the rest of his life.

There remains so much need in the world today that we can never lack opportunities to help, as is our constant duty, our neigh-bours and the community as a whole. Many voluntary societies exist where one can serve others thereby helping to relieve suffering of one kind or another.

34. Some World Health Problems

Introduction

In the last chapter we saw how there has occurred a gradual growth of the idea of responsibility, both in the individual and the community as a whole, in Britain. Developments in transport and communications during this century have led to people in this country—and in others too—becoming increasingly aware of the suffering due to ill-health and ignorance in other parts of the world. This awareness of suffering has stirred the conscience of many people who have become determined to do something to help. Help is offered either through bodies supported by governments—the World Health Organisation, for example—or through voluntary organisations such as 'Oxfam'. Help is given to the under-developed countries by those whose economic position is stronger.

The problems involved are concerned with maintaining health and with preventing disease, and they are difficult to solve owing to such factors as the uneven spread of resources, and the different state of education in the various parts of the world. One factor of ever-increasing importance is the rapid increase in world population which, unfortunately, outstrips the rate of increase of food production.

The Population 'Explosion'

Fig. 34.1 shows the increase in world population from the time of Christ to the present day and carries on to the year 2000 by giving an estimated number. You will notice that the population increased relatively slowly until about 1850 but that since that date it has trebled from 1,000 million to 3,000 million. Furthermore the population is expected to double within the next 25 or 30 years to a figure of 7,000 million.

World population is now increasing at the rate of 2% per annum. This may not sound much at first but in fact it means another 60 million mouths to feed each year. This poses a problem of considerable size especially when it is realised that the biggest population increase is in children in the new under-developed countries. In other words not only are the 'new mouths' too young to work but they occur in countries where the populations are already undernourished.

The causes of the population explosion are: first, the improvements in agriculture and transport which have made the support of larger populations possible; second, the improved medical services which have resulted in a decline in the death rate; and third, the present lack of large areas suitable for migration. It is worth noting that between 1846 and 1930 over 50 million Europeans emigrated to places such as the U.S.A. and Australia. The world is beginning to fill up.

Those who are too young or too old to work must be supported by the 'working'

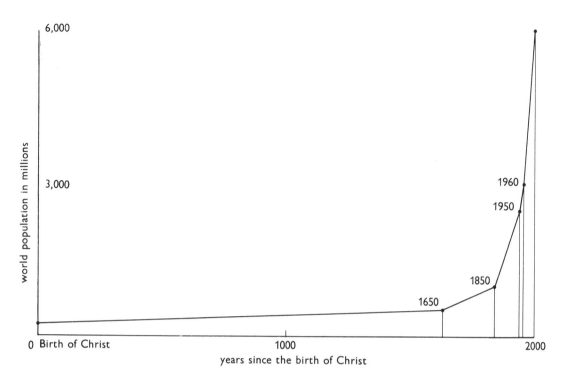

FIG. 34.1. INCREASE IN WORLD POPULATION.

population: unfortunately the working population is smallest in those countries where it is most needed:

	Population under 19	Working population 20–64	Non-workers over 65
Britain	29·0%	59·5%	11·5%
Peru	58·4%	42·2%	3·0%

In other words in a well-developed country like Britain only 40·5% of the population need to be supported whereas in an underdeveloped country such as Peru the figure is 61·4%. A large proportion of the world's population suffers from undernutrition or from malnutrition or from both.

Undernutrition and Malnutrition

These two terms are used to express two aspects of nutritional problems. *Undernutrition* refers to an insufficient calorie intake: a person does not eat a large enough *quantity* of food to give him the number of calories he needs. *Malnutrition* refers to the *quality* of the diet. The quantity of food consumed may be sufficient but the quality may be inferior: there may be too high a proportion of carbohydrate and a lack of protein, salts and vitamins. The importance of a balanced diet was discussed in Chapter 10.

A diet may be insufficient in both quantity and quality so that a person may be both undernourished and malnourished at the

369

same time. Correcting the balance of the diet of a malnourished person will lead to a quick improvement in his health and happiness.

As we learned in Chapter 10 a balanced diet depends on eating a variety of foods and while this is relatively easy in the West, and in all the better-developed countries, it is much more difficult in less-developed areas. Not only have the better-developed countries more food resources but the standard of education is higher and, generally speaking, mothers can understand why their children need a variety of foods. Ignorance and superstition both play a part in hindering the improvement of health in the under-developed countries for not only do the people not know what foods they should eat but in addition may be forbidden to eat certain foods. The eye disease known as *Trachoma* (Plate 103) is due to deficiency of Vitamin A. Yet in West Africa the disease is common in spite of the availability of foods containing the vitamin. Prevention of the disease is largely a matter of persuading the local people to eat the correct food. In parts of Tanzania women are not allowed to drink milk—a food which, as we have learnt, is of immense value. In other parts of Africa women fear infertility if they eat eggs.

It must not be thought, however, that overcoming ignorance and superstition would immediately set matters right, for many families in various parts of the world could not afford to buy sufficient food even if it were available. Feeding schemes are a temporary measure in cases of famine owing to sudden calamities—floods, droughts and so on. Plate 104 shows a Salvation Army mobile feeding unit in Korea.

It has been estimated that out of the total world population of 3,000 million some 300 to 500 million are undernourished—that is, they lack the necessary amount of food energy to lead a normal active life—and that up to one half suffer from malnutrition.

Table 17 gives a number of diseases which are due to malnutrition. In addition to these specific diseases it must be remembered that both undernutrition and malnutrition cause general weakness and make the sufferer less able to resist invasion by bacteria and viruses, less able to work both physically and mentally and less able to show initiative.

PLATE 103. A child, blind because of vitamin deficiency.

PLATE 104. A Salvation Army winter mobile feeding unit.

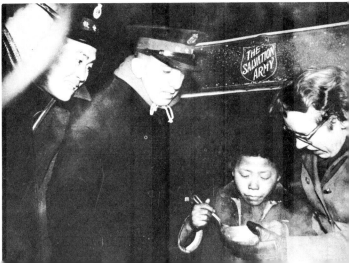

Disease	Cause	Notes
Kwashiorkor	Lack of protein in the diet	Common in Africa, particularly West Africa, and in South-East Asia. Prevalent in children age 1–5 years. FAO estimates every African has suffered from it at some time. Symptoms are lack of growth, swelling of arms, legs and body. Patches of skin peel off. Treat with high protein fluids.
Nutritional Marasmus	This means starvation—diet lacks food energy and proteins	Symptoms similar to those for Kwashiorkor but usually no swelling or rash. Children are very ill and have to be artificially fed. Hook-worms frequently present.
Beri-Beri	Lack of Vitamin B	This disease is found where polished rice is the main diet, that is in Asia and the Far East. Symptoms are nervous trouble and loss of memory, swellings and heart failure. Cure is by giving Vitamin B.
Goitre	Lack of Iodine	Swelling of neck indicates lack of iodine—cure is by adding iodine to cooking salt (see also Chapter 19).
Rickets and Osteomalacia	Lack of Vitamin D	Deformities of the bones due to upset calcium metabolism. Rickets is common in children fed mainly on carbohydrates. Osteomalacia is the adult form and occurs mainly in women kept indoors for much of their life.
Pellagra	Lack of Niacin	Found mostly in people whose staple diet is maize. Symptoms are varied and include diarrhoea, inflammation and scaly skin.
Trachoma	Lack of Vitamin A	Eye disease which may lead to blindness. Frequent in Africa and the East. Perhaps one-sixth of the world population is affected. Treatment is by improving diet to include such items as fish liver oil and red palm oil.

TABLE 17. SOME DISEASES DUE TO MALNUTRITION

World Resources and their Distribution

Only about 30% of the land surface of the world is suitable for the cultivation of crops, for much of it is covered with ice and snow, is too high or too dry, or has too little soil. About 450 million square kilometres are suitable for cultivation but the distribution of this land does not correspond with the distribution of the population. For example while Canada has half a square kilometre of land per head of population, only about 14,000 m² per head are cultivated. Great supplies of food could be grown on the land available but it is not needed in Canada: the need is, say, in the Far East or in Africa.

Fig. 34.2 shows the proportion of food energy obtained from different parts of the diet in different regions of the world. It is at once clear that the distribution of the all-important animal proteins is most irregular and that it is very much higher in the more fortunate areas such as North America and Europe than in areas such as the Far East and Africa.

The uneven production of food has led to some countries having more than enough to supply their own populations. The U.S.A. for example as early as 1950 had large supplies of surplus food which the Government of that country made available to voluntary organisations for distribution to countries whose need was great. The food given away in 1960 was worth some $1,500 million and included dried milk and eggs, and much wheat and rice.

Various methods of improving existing cultivated land and of making new areas

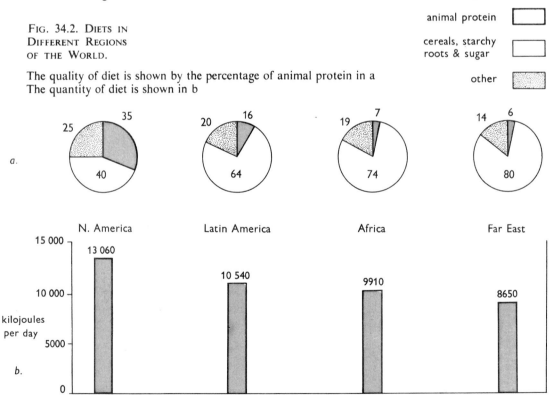

Fig. 34.2. Diets in Different Regions of the World.

The quality of diet is shown by the percentage of animal protein in a
The quantity of diet is shown in b

animal protein

cereals, starchy roots & sugar

other

372

available have been tried with success. Increased *irrigation* is one obvious method of increasing the area of the earth under cultivation—the production of fresh water from sea water has been mentioned in Chapter 31. Again the prevention of *soil erosion* by careful cultivation and planting of trees is a fruitful line of development in some areas and the improving of soils by use of *fertilisers* is another. In fact it has been estimated that the food production of most countries could be increased by 50% by better use of fertilisers and legumes. These last are plants which help to replace nitrates in the soil.

Technical advances in agriculture help to make soil cultivation easier and more profitable—new types of tractors, harvesters and so on. Again, the quality of food produced, as well as the yield, has been improved by careful *breeding experiments*. Much food loss due to the ravages of insects can now be prevented by the use of *insecticides*. Locusts alone can completely destroy a vast crop in a few hours and much research has gone into the swarming and migrating of these pests. One source of food as yet but little tapped is the *sea*. At present fish supply only about 10% of the total animal protein in the world's food supply and yet there is a vast reserve of fish which could swell the source of protein, especially in the southern hemisphere where most of the under-developed countries are found. Finally, advances are being made in the production of synthetic proteins which may help to meet the world's needs and in extracting proteins in the form of 'milk' from plant leaves.

Medical Service

The improvement in the science of medicine has already been mentioned as one factor in the increase of the world population. Much work has been carried out on disease and some of this was described in Chapters 25–27. However, the position of the under-developed countries is serious in its lack of doctors, nurses and other medical workers, and in hospitals. Some idea of the uneven distribution of doctors and of hospital beds may be gained from Table 18.

Organisations Concerned with World Health

There are many governmental and voluntary organisations concerned with improving world health. Three are mentioned here as of special interest.

1. The World Health Organisation (WHO) of the United Nations was formed in order that scientists might study, and doctors might cure, diseases in areas of the world where the need was great. There are now some 800 campaigns in progress in the six WHO regions—Africa, America, South-East Asia, Europe, the Eastern Mediterranean and the Western Pacific. WHO sponsors fights against yaws, malaria and smallpox and many other diseases, and studies such topics as water sanitation in India to combat cholera and new drug therapy in Japan in a fight against tuberculosis.

2. The Food and Agriculture Organisation (FAO). FAO, like WHO, is a specialised agency of the United Nations Organisation. Its work, which started soon after its formation in 1945, is to improve the living standards of member nations particularly with regard to nutrition. It also aims to increase the standard of production and distribution of all types of food, the term agriculture here including such products as fish, forestry products and animals.

3. OXFAM—the Oxford Committee for Famine Relief—started in a small way during the war in 1942, being registered as a war

Country	Number of People per Hospital Bed	Number of People per Doctor
United Kingdom	—	473
Western Europe	62	—
Nigeria	2,650	40,000
Somalia	620	23,000
Tunisia	400	7,800
Sudan	1,000	35,000
Iran	1,100	3,900
Yemen	3,800	156,000
United Arab Republic	480	2,600
Israel	150	410

TABLE 18. DISTRIBUTION OF DOCTORS AND HOSPITAL BEDS IN SOME COUNTRIES

charity for the relief of suffering which arose out of the war or any other cause in any part of the world. OXFAM is mentioned here as a voluntary organisation which arose from the concern of a small number of people in Oxford and stresses the fact that there is still a place in the world for voluntary organisations. The original purpose of OXFAM was to send relief to children in Greece who were suffering from starvation during the German occupation of their country. From this small beginning OXFAM has grown into a large organisation sending help to people in 90 countries. In the year 1963–1964 OXFAM sent abroad £2·2 million for the help of the more unfortunate parts of the world.

The organisation of OXFAM is such that it depends largely on voluntary workers who help by collecting clothing and articles for resale, and money. Many manufacturers of clothing, blankets, drugs and so on help by making contributions to the work while shipping lines offer cheap transport rates and, in emergencies, airlines have carried goods free. There are permanent Gift Shops in Oxford, Guildford, Cheltenham, Leeds and London. Pledged Gift subscribers give 5p or 12½p a month over a long period in order to ensure a steady income. In 1964 about half a million Pledged Gift subscribers gave some £338,568 gathered in by some 44,000 voluntary collectors. There is an OXFAM Education Department and through its work over a third of the schools in Britain have lent their support.

Some of the work carried out by OXFAM is given in Table 19.

Final Note on World Problems

It will have been readily seen by now that although the problems of health facing the world today appear to be immense there is no need for despair. Much remains to be done but much has already been achieved. One of the important aspects is that people are now aware of the problem and are beginning to assume responsibility. The difficulties are now seen more clearly; the researches of such organisations as WHO, FAO and OXFAM have shown how help is best given and large sums of money have already been spent in actual help. Not only is food, medicine, etc., given but an attempt to educate the peoples of the world into better ways of cultivation of the soil (Plate 105), sanitation and prevention of disease has been made. The greater the spread of medical knowledge and assistance, the greater becomes the expectation of life of a people and thus the world population must inevitably grow unless checked. Part of the work of health organisations in the future must be to provide instruction in family planning to prevent the work done to improve health from being offset by population increase.

PLATE 105. Teaching better methods of cultivation—Morocco 1957.

Country	Grant	Notes
Aden	£2,000	Royal Commonwealth Society for the Blind—Mobile Eye Clinic.
Algeria	£5,000	Salvation Army feeding programme.
	£3,100	Catholic Relief Services for milk distribution.
	£2,500	Friends Service Council and American Friends Service Committee for work with refugees.
Bechuanaland	£15,000	For digging water holes to obtain water for cattle. Each purchaser to repay his share of the cost in 5 years to finance similar projects.
Ceylon	£340	Service Civil International. To set up work camp to demonstrate improved techniques in cultivation.
India	£1,000	Duncan Hospital, Bihar. Feeding and drugs for destitute lepers.
Kenya	£11,000	Via Save the Children Fund, for Starehe Boys Centre, Nairobi. New classrooms.
Korea	£2,000	British Red Cross Society. Relief work following Typhoon Shirley in June.
Nepal	£17,850	Government of Nepal. To control Rinderpest disease in cattle by vaccination. Three-year project.
Yugoslavia	£5,000	Yugoslav Red Cross to assist with distribution of food to 30,000 children and mothers who are being cared for after the Skopje earthquake.

TABLE 19. A Few Examples of Grants Made by OXFAM

October 1962–September 1963

(Total Grant was £1,554,762)

Questions on Chapters 33 and 34

1. You are provided with a map of an area for development. Imagine that as a member of Health and Planning Committees you are interested in the development of this area for a town with a population of 20,000 people. Fill in your ideas for the positions of factories, residential areas, recreational sites, schools, clinics, shopping facilities, disposal arrangements and water supply. Give notes on these on a separate sheet. (C)

2. You have been asked to show a visitor from another country one aspect of the National Health Service. Describe a visit you would arrange and the comments and explanations you would give. (C)

3. If you were concerned with the planning of a 'new town' what would be the chief points you would consider and support in order to ensure a healthy life for its inhabitants? (C)

4. Assuming that you were responsible for planning a new town, describe with reasons the main points to be considered so that the health requirements of the population are met. (L)

5. What conditions are important for ensuring the health of workers in a factory? Some industrial work produces hazards to health. Describe the precautions taken against such hazards in a named industry known to you. (L)

6. Explain the main provisions of the 1937 Factories Act under the headings (a) employment of young children, (b) cleanliness and sanitation, (c) washing and amenities, (d) atmospheric pollution, (e) accidents and industrial diseases. Name *three* common industrial diseases. (O)

7. Write an account of the services that are available for the maintenance and improvement of the health of school children. (W)

8. *Either*, Give an account of an actual visit that you have made during your study of the Health Service and other Social Services (e.g. to a sewage works, water works, dairy, hospital, etc.). Discuss the value to the health of the community of the work you saw being done.

Or, Write an illustrated account of the life-history of the house fly. State two diseases which are commonly carried by this insect. What precautions could be taken to prevent the spread of these diseases? (W)

9. Discuss the measures which must be taken to maintain the health and safety of factory workers. (S)

10. Discuss the role of the following in the maintenance of the health and well-being of the community: Health Visitor, Public Health Inspector, Medical Officer of Health, Medical Social Worker. (S)

11. Give an account of the services provided for safeguarding the health of (a) schoolchildren, and (b) factory workers. (RSA)

12. Public Health Inspectors and Medical Officers of Health are all concerned with the prevention of disease. Explain, as clearly as possible, the nature of the duties carried out by each of these officials. (RSA)

13. Calling upon your own observations, discuss the value of the following parts of the National Health Service: (a) Infant Welfare Clinics, (b) Mass Radiography. (J)

THINKING POINTS ON 33 AND 34

1. Discuss in your class the relative responsibilities of the individual and the community. Why should the individual feel responsibility towards other people? How far should the state help in the support of the disabled and the aged?

2. Consider the responsibilities of factory owners and discuss together the changing attitude over the last fifty years. What precautions can easily be taken to avoid such diseases as silicosis and lead poisoning?

3. The population of the world is increasing at an ever-increasing rate. What steps should governments take to control the population explosion?

4. The distribution of food is most uneven throughout the world. Discuss together the ways in which help may be quickly given to the under-developed countries. What are the best long-term attitudes to these problems?

Miscellaneous Questions

1. Describe the origins and functions of the following: enzymes, vitamins, hormones, genes. Give two examples of each. (S)

2. Write a short account of each of the following: (a) haemoglobin, (b) sleep, (c) umbilical cord, (d) internal parasites in children. (W)

3. Choose *four* of the following, give a named example and show how their spread may be controlled: (a) a disease produced by bacteria; (b) a disease produced by a virus; (c) a disease produced by protozoa; (d) a disease produced by an intestinal worm; (e) a disease produced by a fungus. (L)

4. When proteins, starches and fats are eaten they are made soluble in the alimentary canal. Give the name of the soluble form of each of these foods, and say where and how each enters the blood stream. Explain further how each is used by the body and where its waste products are excreted. (RSA)

5. You must have heard older people talking about the improvement in the health of children today as compared with that in their own childhood. What are the chief scientific factors and social changes responsible for this improvement? (C)

6. Explain how *four* of the following could prove dangerous to health: (a) adulteration of milk, (b) broken sewage pipes, (c) house flies, (d) a smoky atmosphere, (e) lack 'of fresh fruit and vegetables in the diet. (L)

7. Answer both (a) and (b).
(a) Explain how the ear enables us to hear sounds.

(b) Explain how the skin helps our body to remain at the right temperature. (RSA)

8. What is a gland? Give two examples *each* of: (a) glands with ducts, (b) ductless glands. In each case state (i) the position of the gland, (ii) the names and functions of the substances produced. (S)

9. Write a concise account of the structure of human blood. What changes would you expect to find in its composition as it passes through: (a) the lungs, (b) the kidneys, (c) the liver? (W)

10. Of what use to the body are the following secretions: (a) sweat, (b) bile and (c) saliva? (L)

11. Write a short account of *two* of the following: (a) the pancreas, (b) the spinal cord, (c) joints. (RSA)

12. Write short accounts of: (a) lymph, (b) synovial fluid, (c) the mitral valve. (C)

13. Write a short account of each of the following: (a) arteries and veins, (b) liver and gall bladder, (c) the cerebrum. (RSA)

14. The delicate organs of the body need protection from injury. Describe the ways in which each of the following organs are protected: (a) the brain, (b) the heart, (c) the eye, (d) the kidney. (RSA)

15. Describe the source, action and importances of *five* of the following: thyroxine, carbon dioxide, amino-acids, antibodies, red blood cells, adrenalin, sperms, mucus. (S)

16. Write brief illustrated notes on any *four* of the following: (a) the comparison

between animals and plants, (b) mucous membranes, (c) incisor teeth, (d) endocrine organs, (e) ball and socket joints. (W)

17. What do you understand by: (a) enzymes, (b) hormones? Give *one* example of each, stating where it is produced and explaining its function. Describe *one* experiment which you have carried out to show the action of a named enzyme. (RSA)

18. Describe the structure and contents of the nose cavities. Explain the part played by the nose in preparing air for entry into the lungs, and the part played by the mouth in the process of digestion. Give the other functions of the nose and mouth. (Do *not* describe in great detail.) (RSA)

19. Describe in detail any experiments you have done to show: (a) the presence of 'germs' in the air, (b) the increase in the amount of carbon dioxide in expired air. (C)

20. Using your own experience and observation discuss the importance of *two* of the following: (a) an infant welfare clinic, (b) the schools meals service, (c) mass radiography. (C)

21. The following all help the body to fight against organisms which cause disease: (a) the skin, (b) antibodies, (c) lymph glands, (d) white corpuscles. Describe briefly the nature and position of each of these and the part that each plays in the fight against disease. (RSA)

22. Make a large, fully labelled diagram of the excretory and reproductive organs of a *named* male mammal. What are the functions of: (a) the prostate gland, (b) the tubules within the kidney, (c) the bladder? (W)

23. In what ways are the following particularly important for the maintenance of good health: (a) regular exercise, (b) adequate housing conditions, (c) inspection of food, (d) notification of infectious diseases? (W)

24. Write a careful account of each of the following: (a) immunity, (b) moulds which have a harmful effect on health and moulds which help to cure disease. (RSA)

25. Write brief notes on each of the following: (a) the interdependence of animals and plants, (b) the importance of internal respiration, (c) voluntary muscles. (W)

26. Why are the following a danger to health: (a) a dirty roller towel in a cloakroom, (b) a cracked cup, (c) an open dustbin, (d) a smell of gas, (e) frozen food which has thawed and then been refrozen? (S)

27. Answer both (a) and (b).
   (a) Name the cavities of the trunk and give a fully labelled diagram of a section through the cavity which lies just above the diaphragm. Your drawing should show the nature of the walls and of the organs in the cavity. (A detailed diagram of each organ is *not* required.)
   (b) A child can be said to inherit some of the characteristics of his parents. Explain what is meant by this statement, and give a brief account of the means by which such inheritance takes place.

28. Give a clear account of each of the following: (a) the autonomic nervous system, (b) the small intestine. (RSA)

29. Answer both (a) and (b).
   (a) Wool, cotton and nylon are all used for making underwear. Give a brief account of the nature of each of these materials and state the advantages and disadvantages of each when used for underwear.
   (b) List the ways in which disorders of the feet can be prevented and show how neglected feet can affect the general health of the person. (RSA)

30. Give a brief account of each of the

379

following: (a) the ovaries, (b) the testes, (c) the thyroid gland. (RSA)

31. The aorta, the small intestine and the trachea are all tubular. Show how the structure of each helps it to fulfil its particular use in the body. (C)

32. Answer *two* of the following.

(a) Explain briefly the advantages, to the individual, of having (i) electricity, instead of oil, in the house and (ii) piped water in the house, instead of a well in the garden.

(b) Describe either the aerated-sludge method *or* the percolating-filter method of purifying sewage, and explain what happens to the sludge and to the purified liquid.

(c) Describe the proper use of dustbins for the disposal of refuse. (RSA)

33. Write a short paragraph on each of the following: Mendelian dominance, a named hormone, the semi-circular canals. (C)

34. Write a short essay on each of the following health topics that are at present receiving much public attention: (a) air pollution, (b) dental health. (J)

Glossary

ABDUCTION: a movement away from the median plane of the body.

ABSORPTION: sucking up, imbibing or taking in.

ACCESSORY GLAND: a gland associated with, but not part of, another system, e.g. the liver, gall bladder and pancreas in relation to the alimentary canal.

ACCOMMODATION: the adjustment of the eye to vision at different distances.

ACETABULUM: the cavity in the pelvis which receives the head of the femur.

ACETYLCHOLINE: a substance produced at nerve endings to initiate muscular action.

ACROMEGALY: glandular condition due to overactivity of the pituitary gland in the adult.

ADDUCTION: a movement towards the median plane of the body.

ADENOIDS: masses of lymph tissue in the nasopharynx. They may become swollen to give the condition known as *adenoids*.

ADENOSINE DIPHOSPHATE: *see under Adenosine triphosphate*.

ADENOSINE TRIPHOSPHATE: a complex compound containing three high-energy phosphate groups. Usable cellular energy is liberated on hydrolysis by the removal of one of these phosphate groups, the A.T.P. being converted to adenosine diphosphate, A.D.P. The process can be reversed, A.T.P. being formed from A.D.P., in living cells.

ADIPOSE CELL: a cell whose special function is to store fat.

ADIPOSE TISSUE: a tissue composed of adipose cells. It is found, for example, below the skin and as packing tissue round the kidneys.

ADOLESCENCE: the period from boyhood or girlhood to the adult; from puberty to maturity.

ADRENAL GLAND: one of a pair of small ductless glands situated just superior to the kidneys.

ADRENALIN: a hormone secreted by the adrenal glands.

AGGLUTINATION: sticking or clumping together, e.g. red blood cells, bacteria or sperm.

AGGLUTININE: a chemical substance bringing about agglutination.

ALCOHOL: any one of a number of inflammable, volatile, colourless liquids. Generally the word refers to *ethyl* alcohol—one of the products of fermentation of carbohydrates.

ALCOHOLIC: a person who drinks alcohol to excess under a compulsion he cannot resist.

ALCOHOLICS ANONYMOUS: an association which seeks to help alcoholics break their drinking habits.

ALCOHOLISM: a morbid condition resulting from inordinate and persistent drinking of alcoholic beverages.

ALGAE: a large group of simple plants occurring in fresh and sea-water, and in moist land habitats. They include the seaweeds and diatoms.

ALIMENTARY CANAL: the digestive tract of animals, extending from mouth to anus, and including the oesophagus, stomach, small and large intestines.

ALLELES: a pair of genes which behave in the Mendelian way. Only one of the pair can be carried by a single gamete.

ALVEOLUS: tiny pockets on the surface of the air-sacs of the lungs, surrounded by blood capillaries.

AMINO-ACIDS: organic acids containing nitrogen. They are the units from which proteins are built.

AMNION: one of the membranes surrounding the embryo in the uterus.

AMPULLA: a hollow swelling, in particular the swellings at the ends of the semi-circular canals of the ear.

AMYLASE: an enzyme which hydrolyses starch to maltose.

ANAEMIA: a deficiency of red blood cells or of haemoglobin or of both.

ANATOMY: the study of the structure of the body, learned chiefly from dissection.

ANDROSTERONE: one of the male sex hormones secreted by the testes.

ANGULAR MOVEMENT OR CIRCUMDUCTION: one of the three types of movement possible at synovial joints: it includes flexion, extension, abduction and adduction.

ANIMAL STARCH: *see under Glycogen*.

ANTHRAX: a disease of cattle. The bacterium causing the disease was discovered by Robert Koch.

ANTIBIOTIC: a substance produced by a fungus which has the power of destroying micro-organisms. One antibiotic is produced by one fungus. Many are used in the treatment of infectious diseases and some can be produced synthetically. The most famous is penicillin.

ANTIBODY: a protein produced in an animal when an antigen is introduced into the blood. The antibody combines with the antigen rendering it harmless.

ANTIGEN: a substance capable of stimulating the

formation of an antibody. Various enzymes, proteins and toxins can act as antigens.

ANTI-PROTHROMBIN: *see under Heparin.*

ANTITOXIN: a type of antibody which neutralises the toxins produced by bacteria present in the body. One anti-toxin neutralises one particular toxin produced by one particular bacterium.

ANUS: the opening, guarded by a sphincter muscle, which occurs at the end of the gut and through which the faeces are expelled.

AORTA: the name given to the large blood vessel arising from the left ventricle of the heart through which oxygenated blood is pumped to the body.

APPENDICULAR SKELETON: that part of the skeleton of vertebrates which comprises the limb girdles and the limbs.

APPENDIX, VERMIFORM: a small blind sac terminating the caecum.

AQUEOUS HUMOUR: the watery fluid which fills the space between the cornea and the lens of the eye.

ARACHNOID MATER: one of three membranes surrounding the central nervous system. It lies between the dura mater and the pia mater.

ARTERY: a vessel which carries blood away from the heart.

ARTICULAR FACET: a part of the surface of a vertebra—excluding the centrum—upon which another vertebra can move.

ARTICULATION: the joining of bones in such a way that movement between them is possible.

ASCENDING AORTA: that part of the aorta which arises from the heart and passes in a superior direction to the arch of the aorta.

ASSIMILATION: the transformation of digested foods into an integral part of the animal as in the formation of protoplasm.

ASSOCIATION CENTRES: areas of the brain which correlate information gained from more than one sense organ to give a true picture of a situation.

ASTIGMATISM: an eye defect in which horizontal and vertical lines are not seen with equal clarity.

ATLAS VERTEBRA: the first neck vertebra upon which the head moves as when indicating 'yes'.

ATRIUM OR AURICLE: one of the upper chambers of the heart through which blood is transferred to the ventricle.

AUDITORY OR ACOUSTIC NERVE: the eighth cranial nerve. The auditory nerves transmit nerve impulses from the ear to the brain.

AURICLE: *see under Atrium.*

AUTONOMIC NERVOUS SYSTEM: part of the nervous system consisting of two · longitudinally running nerves, with ganglia at intervals along them, one on each side of the spinal column. The ganglia are linked by *rami communicantes* to the spinal nerves and hence to the spinal cord. The autonomic system serves those tissues and organs which are not under voluntary control such as the heart, blood vessels and alimentary canal.

AXIAL SKELETON: that part of the skeleton which forms the main axis of the body, namely the skull and the vertebral column. It is usual to consider the ribs and the sternum as part of the axial skeleton.

AXIS VERTEBRA: the second neck vertebra, upon which the atlas vertebra rests. It enables the head to move as when indicating 'no'.

BACILLUS: a rod-shaped bacterium.

BACTERIUM: one of numerous micro-organisms, generally classed as plants. They may be harmless, harmful or beneficial to human beings.

BACTERIOPHAGE: an ultra-microscopic organism which has the power to destroy bacteria.

BALL AND SOCKET JOINT: type of joint in which the rounded head of one bone fits into the hollow cup in another bone allowing considerable movement.

BASAL METABOLIC RATE, B.M.R.: the metabolic rate of a resting person.

B.C.G. VACCINATION (Bacillus Calmette-Guerin vaccination): a person who has no contact with tuberculosis—and who thus has no immunity to the disease—may be given B.C.G. vaccine to guard against infection.

BED-WETTING: *see under Enuresis.*

BICEPS MUSCLE: the main muscle at the front of the upper arm. It has its origin in the scapula and its insertion on the radius.

BICUSPID VALVE: the valve between the left atrium and the left ventricle of the heart.

BILE: a yellowish-green liquid secreted by the liver. Its function is to emulsify fats.

BILE DUCT: a small tube which carries bile from the liver to the duodenum.

BILE PIGMENTS: two waste products—*bilirubin* and *biliverdin*—found in the bile as a result of the breakdown of red blood cells.

BILE SALTS: sodium glycocholate and sodium taurocholate emulsify fats in the small intestine and assist in the absorption of fatty acids.

BILIRUBIN: *see under Bile pigments.*

BILIVERDIN: *see under Bile pigments.*

BIOLOGICAL CONTROL: the use of one organism to control the spread of another, e.g. myxomatosis to limit the spread of rabbits.

BLADDER: *see under Gall bladder or Urinary bladder.*

BLIND SPOT: a small area at the back of the eye which is insensitive to light. It is formed from the axons of neurones passing from the retina through the optic stalk.

BLOOD: a sticky fluid contained within vessels through which it circulates carrying food, oxygen and other substances to all parts of the body. It contains both red and white cells carried in a liquid plasma.

BLOOD CELLS: *see under Blood, Erythrocyte and Leucocyte.*

BLOOD PLATELETS: minute fragments of cytoplasm formed from the breakdown of certain cells found in bone marrow. They are very numerous—250,000–500,000—per cubic millimetre of blood. They play an important part in blood clotting.

BLOOD SYSTEM: a closed system of vessels—arteries, veins and capillaries—together with the heart through which blood flows.

BLOOD TRANSFUSION: the process of injecting blood taken from one person into the blood system of another person.

BOLUS: a lump of masticated food which is swallowed and which passes down the gullet to the stomach.

BOTULISM: poisoning caused by eating spoiled foods. The micro-organism responsible is *Clostridium botulinum* and its spores are resistant to heat so that cooking does not render contaminated food harmless.

BOWMAN'S CAPSULE: capsule found in great numbers in the cortex of the kidney. Each contains a plexus of blood capillaries from which urea is extracted.

BRAIN: the anterior end of the central nervous system which is greatly enlarged in mammals and in Man especially. It is contained within the protective cranium.

BREATHING: the taking in and passing out of air by the lungs.

BRONCHIOLE: the name given to the fine branches of each bronchus.

BRONCHUS: one of the two main branches of the windpipe.

BUCCAL CAVITY: the cavity of the mouth.

BULBOUS CORPUSCLES: receptors in the skin which are sensitive to cold.

CAECUM: part of the large intestine: it is relatively large in grass-eating animals.

CANCER: a malignant growth or tumour formed by the uncontrolled multiplication of cells which may spread throughout a tissue causing its degeneration.

CANINE TEETH: the four long, sharp, pointed teeth found one on each side of each jaw in most mammals and especially in flesh-eaters. Each canine tooth lies between an incisor tooth and a premolar tooth. They are absent in mice, rats and rabbits.

CAPILLARY: a minute blood vessel a complex of which unites an artery and a vein.

CARBOHYDRATE: any one of a group of substances containing carbon, hydrogen and oxygen in the proportion $C_x(H_2O)_y$ where x and y can be almost any number. The starches, sugars and cellulose are carbohydrates.

CARDIAC MUSCLE: muscle found in the heart. It can contract rhythmically throughout the life of an animal without stimulation by nerves.

CARDIAC SPHINCTER: a circular muscle guarding the opening of the oesophagus into the stomach.

CARPAL BONE: one of eight small bones comprising the wrist skeleton. They are arranged in two rows of four.

CARRIER: a person who carries disease-causing organisms in his body and discharges them and

who is, thus, a danger to other people. He may not necessarily show symptoms of the disease himself.

CAVITY WALLS: walls made of two layers of bricks with a space between them which insulates against heat-loss and against the entry of damp.

CELL: the unit of protoplasm, consisting of cytoplasm containing a nucleus.

CELL BODY: that part of a nerve cell which contains the nucleus, and from which various protoplasmic processes arise such as axons and dendrites.

CENTROMERE: that portion of a chromosome to which the spindle becomes attached during cell division.

CENTRUM: the body of a vertebra from which the neural arch arises.

CEREBELLUM: that part of the brain which, arising from the hind-brain in the embryo, lies behind and beneath the cerebral hemispheres.

CEREBRAL CORTEX: the outer layer of the cerebral hemispheres. It is composed of grey matter and its surface is greatly increased by convolutions.

CEREBROSPINAL FLUID: the fluid found bathing, and inside, the brain and spinal cord. It is similar in composition to blood plasma but lacks the ability to clot.

CEREBRUM: the largest part of the brain. It is formed by the two cerebral hemispheres.

CERVICAL VERTEBRA: any of the seven neck vertebra. The first is modified as the atlas and the second as the axis vertebra.

CERVIX: the neck, especially of the uterus.

CHLOROPHYLL: the green colouring pigment found in plants. It is essential for the manufacture of carbo-hydrates and occurs in specialised areas of cyto-plasm known as *chloroplasts*.

CHORDAE TENDINEAE: strands which connect the edges of the bicuspid and tricuspid valves of the heart to the walls of the ventricles.

CHOROID: the middle layer of the three layers forming the eyeball, lying between the sclerotic and the retina. It forms the iris and the ciliary body at the front of the eye. It is rich in blood vessels.

CHROMATID: one of a pair of strands constituting a *chromosome*.

CHROMOSOME: a structure in the nucleus upon which hereditary characters are passed from one genera-tion to another by means of genes. They contain nucleo-proteins which may stain darkly with certain dyes. The number of chromosomes, while being constant for any given species, varies in different species.

CHYME: the fluid passed from the stomach to the duodenum via the pyloric sphincter.

CILIARY BODY: a structure composed of muscles which affect the tension on the suspensory ligaments of the eye, thus bringing about changes in the thickness of the lens in order that the eye can focus on objects at different distances.

CLAVICLE: part of the pectoral girdle which connects the sternum to the shoulder blade. Commonly called the collar-bone.

CLEAVEAGE: the division of a zygote into smaller cells.

383

CLEFT PALATE: a condition in which the right and left sides of the palate fail to fuse together during development, leaving a gap between the two halves.

CLOT: scab formed at a wound by the precipitation of fibrinogen in which red blood cells become trapped. Clots may also occur in the blood vessels in certain diseases, e.g. coronary thrombosis.

COCCI: spherical bacteria; they may occur in chains.

COCCYX: the lower bone of the vertebral column formed by the fusion of several small vertebra.

COCHLEA: the spirally coiled tube found in the inner ear; it is the organ of hearing.

COLLAR-BONE: *see under Clavicle.*

COLLOID: a dispersion of large molecules or small particles of one substance in another. The particles never settle but remain in constant motion.

COLON: that part of the large intestine which extends from the caecum to the rectum.

COLOUR BLINDNESS: condition in which some colours cannot be appreciated.

COMPLEMENTAL AIR: that air which may be drawn into the lungs by making a special effort—it is about 1500 cc. in volume.

CONDITIONED REFLEX: a reflex action in which the natural stimulus has been replaced by a substitute stimulus. This is brought about by constant repetition of the natural and substitute stimuli occurring together until the substitute stimulus alone is sufficient to elicit the response.

CONDUCTION: one method of heat transfer. Heat passes along or through an object due to the increased movement of the molecules of the substance of which the object is made.

CONES: cells of the retina which are sensitive to light of different wave-lengths and which enable animals to detect colours.

CONJUNCTIVA: a transparent layer over the surface of the eye.

CONJUNCTIVITIS: inflammation of the conjunctiva.

CONTINUOUS VARIATION: a type of variation in which the differences appear to shade one into another and are not sharply marked from one another, e.g. variation in the height or weight of men.

CONVECTION: a method of heat transfer. Heat is carried from one place to another in a liquid or gas as when air heated by a convector heater rises upwards.

CORNEA: the transparent portion of the sclerotic at the front of the eyeball.

CORNIFIED LAYER: the outer layer of the skin composed of dead cells which are constantly being replaced by growth of the germinative layer beneath it.

CORPUS LUTEUM: structure formed from the Graafian follicle after ovulation. It produces the hormone progesterone.

CORTEX OF BRAIN: *see under Cerebral cortex.*

CORTEX OF KIDNEY: the outer layer of the kidney. It is composed largely of Malpighian bodies.

COSTAL CARTILAGES: cartilages which join the ribs to the sternum.

CRANIAL NERVES: those nerves which leave the brain and pass through the cranium. There are twelve pairs in the human being.

CRANIUM: that part of the skull which houses the brain.

CRETIN: a child abnormal because of lack of thyroxin.

CROSSING-OVER: the process which leads to an exchange of genetic material between chromosomes during meiosis. Chromatids from homologous chromosomes cross over each other at one or more points, each taking part of the other to itself.

CYSTIC DUCT: a small tube leading from the gall bladder to the bile duct.

CYTON: the cell body of a neurone.

CYTOPLASM: protoplasm excluding the nucleus.

DEAMINATION: the process by which amino-acids are broken down in the liver with the formation of urea.

DEFAECATION: removal of solid waste through the anus.

DEFICIENCY DISEASE: a disease arising through lack of one or more essential substances in the diet, in particular vitamins or salts.

DEHYDRATION: the process of extracting water as from egg or milk to produce a powder.

DELIRIUM TREMENS: a form of mental disturbance characterised by tremblings, delusions and distress, and frequently caused by excessive drinking of alcohol.

DENTAL FORMULA: a shorthand method of writing the number and position of the teeth of a mammal.

DENTINE: the chief substance of a tooth, lying below the enamel and surrounding the pulp cavity.

DEPOLARISATION: the abolition of the positive charge on the outer surface of a nerve fibre.

DERMIS: a layer of the skin lying beneath the epidermis and containing the roots of the hairs, sweat glands etc.

DESCENDING AORTA: that part of the aorta which continues from the arch of the aorta to the division into the common iliac arteries.

DIAPHRAGM: a more or less dome-shaped partition made of muscle which separates the thoracic from the abdominal cavity.

DIASTOLE: the period of relaxation of the whole heart between successive beats.

DIET: daily food, a regulated course of food and drink.

DIFFERENTIATION: process by which cells lose their ability to divide and take on a specialised function— usually accompanied by specialised structure.

DIFFUSION: process by which molecules of liquids and gases move freely and become evenly distributed throughout the vessel or space containing them. The passage of a gas across a membrane as when oxygen leaves a blood vessel to enter tissues.

DIFFUSION GRADIENT: the gradient which exists between two regions of different concentrations of a gas or liquid. Between the region of high and the region of low concentration there exist regions of gradually diminishing concentrations each of which 'shades' off into the next—there are no sharp changes. The liquid or gas flows from the region of high concentration to the region of low concentration.

DIGESTION: the breakdown of complex food substances into simple compounds by the action of enzymes.

DIGIT: a finger or toe.

DIHYBRID INHERITANCE: the inheritance of two pairs of contrasting characters.

DIPLOCOCCUS: spherical bacteria which are found in pairs.

DISACCHARIDES: a group of carbohydrates having the general formula $C_{12}H_{22}O_{11}$. Lactose, sucrose and maltose are examples.

DISCONTINUOUS VARIATION: variation in which marked changes appear between parents and offspring as when a litter of puppies are all black except for one which is, say, brown, there being no intermediate shades.

DISEASE: sickness or poor health owing to a variety of causes such as invasion of the body by harmful bacteria, lack of vitamins in the diet etc.

DOMINANT CHARACTER: a characteristic produced by a gene even in the presence of its allele.

DORSAL AORTA: a term used in zoology rather than in human anatomy to refer to the main blood vessel taking oxygenated blood from the left ventricle of the heart.

DROPLET INFECTION: the carrying of bacteria or viruses in drops of moisture, as when we sneeze or cough, and the consequent infection of another person.

DUCTLESS GLAND: a gland whose products are poured directly into the blood. One of the endocrine glands.

DUODENUM: the first part of the small intestine. It leads from the stomach to the jejunum.

DURA MATER: the outermost of the three membranes investing the brain and spinal cord.

EAR DRUM: *see under Tympanic membrane.*

EAR OSSICLES: three little bones—the malleus, incus and stapes—which convey vibrations of the ear drum across the middle ear.

EFFECTOR CELL: a cell which on being stimulated by a nerve impulse carries out some action. Usually they are muscle or gland cells which are stimulated to contract or to secrete respectively.

EGESTION: the removal of solid waste from the body.

EGG: the female gamete.

EMBRYO: the young organism developing from the zygote. It is housed within the mother. In human beings the term only applies for the first four weeks after which time it is termed the *foetus.*

EMPHYSEMA: a condition of shortness of breath due to bulbous condition of alveoli. Air may leak into the surrounding tissues.

ENAMEL: the hardest substance in the animal kingdom. It covers the crown of a tooth.

ENDEMIC DISEASE: a disease which is always present in a particular area of the world, e.g. yellow fever in some tropical areas.

ENDOCRINE GLAND: *see under Ductless gland.*

ENDOCRINE SYSTEM: the endocrine glands considered as a whole.

ENDOCRINOLOGY: the study of the endocrine system, its secretions, and its role in health and disease.

ENDOLYMPH: the fluid that fills the membranous labyrinth of the ear.

ENDOMETRIUM: the mucous membrane that lines the uterus.

ENDONEURIUM: sheath of delicate connective tissue which surrounds each nerve fibre.

ENERGY: capacity for doing work; power exerted. Various forms of energy are interconvertible, e.g. chemical, electrical, heat, atomic.

ENTEROCEPTOR: receptors which detect stimuli in the intestine and other internal organs.

ENTEROGASTRONE: a hormone which inhibits the production of gastric juice near the end of digestion.

ENTEROKINASE: a substance which converts trypsinogen to the active enzyme trypsin.

ENURESIS: inability to control the flow of urine, especially during sleep. Bed-wetting.

ENVIRONMENT: the surroundings of an organism. The environment is usually composed of many factors and frequently the term is used with reference to the internal factors of an organism also.

ENZYME: a complex organic substance, produced by living cells, which has the power to alter the rate of chemical reactions occuring in the organism. An organic catalyst.

EPIDEMIC DISEASE: a rapidly spreading disease which affects many people in a community at once.

EPIDERMIS: the outer layer of the skin.

EPIGLOTTIS: a cartilaginous flap which covers the opening of the windpipe during the act of swallowing.

EPINEURIUM: the sheath of connective tissue surrounding a nerve.

EPIPHYSIS: the extremity of a long bone, originally separated from it by cartilage but becoming progressively fused to it by ossification.

ERECTOR MUSCLE: a small muscle at the base of a hair follicle by the contraction of which the hair is moved.

ERYTHROCYTE: a red blood cell, containing the pigment *haemoglobin.*

EUSTACHIAN TUBE: a passage between the pharynx and the middle ear, which serves to equalise the pressure between the middle ear and the atmosphere.

EXCRETION: the removal of waste materials from the body which have been formed during metabolism.

EXOPHTHALMIC GOITRE: a condition caused by overactivity of the thyroid gland and characterised by enlargement of the gland and protrusion of the eyes.

EXOSKELETON: the skeleton covering the outside of the bodies of many animals such as insects, crabs and tortoises. In vertebrates the term is applied to nails, teeth, hooves etc.

EXPIRATION: to breathe out air from the lungs.

EXTENSION: to straighten out a joint.

EXTERNAL AUDITORY MEATUS: the passage from the exterior to the tympanic membrane of the ear.

EXTERNAL RESPIRATION: the physical process of obtaining oxygen from the air and of returning carbon dioxide to it (c.f. tissue respiration).

EXTEROCEPTOR: a peripheral sense organ or cell which responds to external stimuli.

FACTOR: that unit, present in a gamete, which causes a particular characteristic to develop in an organism. Factors occur in contrasting pairs, e.g. tallness and dwarfness in pea plants.

FAECES: the solid waste removed from the gut via the anus.

FALCIFORM LIGAMENT: a sickle-shaped ligament of the peritoneum attached to the liver.

FATIGUE: a condition of extreme tiredness brought on by prolonged exertion.

FATS: complex organic substances which are insoluble in water and which are composed of carbon, hydrogen and oxygen, the proportion of oxygen to hydrogen being low. One of the main groups of food substances.

FEMUR: the long bone of the thigh.

FENESTRA COCHLEA: a membrane-covered opening between the cochlea and the middle ear. Also known as the *fenestra rotunda* or round window.

FENESTRA OVALIS: an oval-shaped, membrane-covered opening between the middle and inner ears, in which the stapes rests.

FENESTRA ROTUNDA: *see under Fenestra cochlea.*

FERMENTATION: chemical changes in organic substances brought about by yeasts and bacteria by enzyme action. Usually applied to the alcoholic fermentation of sugars by the enzyme zymase, produced by yeast, and important commercially in the brewing and baking industries. Alcohol and carbon dioxide are produced during fermentation.

FERTILISATION: the fusion of two gametes to produce a zygote.

FERTILISERS: substances added to the soil to provide the elements essential to plant life.

FIBRIN: an insoluble protein which forms a network in clotting blood.

FIBRINOGEN: a complex protein of the blood plasma which is precipitated as fibrin when acted upon by the enzyme thrombin.

FIBULA: the outer of the two bones forming the skeleton of the lower leg.

FILIAL: pertaining to the generation following the parental generation. The first filial generation is designated F_1, the second as F_2, and so on.

FILUM TERMINALE: the lower thread-like end of the spinal cord.

FLAGELLUM: a whip-like protoplasmic thread found as an organelle for locomotion in some non-cellular organisms.

FLEXOR MUSCLE: a muscle whose contraction lessens the angle between two bones.

FLOATING RIB: one of two pairs which do not articulate at their lower end with costal cartilages.

FOLLICLE STIMULATING HORMONE, F.S.H.: hormone secreted by the anterior lobe of the pituitary gland in mammals, which stimulates the growth of Graafian follicles and the production of oestrogen.

FONTANELLE: a gap in the skeleton covering the brain in the baby.

FOREBRAIN: the anterior of the three regions of the embryonic brain. It gives rise to the cerebral hemispheres.

FOVEA CENTRALIS: shallow pit in the retina of the eye. It is the area of greatest acuity of vision.

FRUCTOSE: fruit sugar, one of the hexose sugars widely distributed in plants.

GALL BLADDER: a sac for storing bile between meals. Its walls are contractile so that bile can be poured on to food when it is present in the intestine.

GAMETE: a sex cell, either an egg or a spermatozoon.

GANGLION: a small, solid, swelling on a nerve containing cell bodies of neurones.

GASTRIC GLANDS: glands in the stomach which secrete gastric juice.

GASTRIC LIPASE: an enzyme found in the stomach whose function is to break down fats.

GASTROCNEMIUS MUSCLE: one of the muscles of the calf of the leg which gives force when walking, running etc.

GENE: the unit of inheritance, a particular piece of a chromosome responsible for the inheritance of a characteristic or characteristics.

GENE COMPLEX: the total gene complement of an organism.

GERM: word commonly used to refer to any microorganism causing infection, e.g. bacteria and viruses.

GERMINAL EPITHELIUM: the epithelium lining the seminiferous tubules of the testes (and covering the ovary) from which the gametes arise.

GERMINATIVE LAYER: the lowermost layer of the epidermis from which new cells arise.

GIANTISM: glandular condition due to over-activity of the pituitary gland in the child.

GLENOID CAVITY: cup-like hollow on each side of the pectoral girdle into which the head of the humerus fits forming the shoulder joint.

GLIDING JOINT: two flat surfaces slide against one another, e.g. the joint between the articular processes of two vertebrae.

GLOMERULUS: loose knot of capillaries in each Bowman's Capsule in the kidney.

GLOTTIS: the opening of the trachea into the pharynx.

GLUCOSE: a widely distributed hexose sugar found in plants and animals. Splitting of glucose is a major source of energy for metabolism.

GLUTEAL MUSCLE: general name for a number of muscles of the buttock.

GLYCINE: the simplest amino-acid—CH_2NH_2COOH.

GLYCOGEN: animal starch. A soluble polysaccharide built up of many glucose molecules. It is the form in which carbohydrate is stored in the muscles and liver.

GONAD: a reproductive organ—the ovary in the female and the testis in the male.

GRAAFIAN FOLLICLE: fluid-filled vesicle in the ovary containing an egg attached to its walls by cells which surround the egg. Mature follicle extrudes the egg into the body cavity, the follicle then becoming the *corpus luteum*.

GRANULOCYTE: a type of white blood cell containing a lobed (polymorphic) nucleus and granules in the cytoplasm.

GREY MATTER: tissue of the central nervous system containing many cell-bodies of neurones and synapses. It occurs as an inner layer surrounding the central canal but as an outer layer of the cerebral hemispheres and cerebellum. The co-ordinating work of the central nervous system is done by the grey matter.

GROWTH: the manufacture of new protoplasm by protoplasm already in existence accompanied by an increase in size and weight.

GULLET: *see under Oesophagus*.

GUT: *see under Alimentary canal*.

HABIT: an action which by repetition has become more or less spontaneous. There are both good and bad habits.

HAEMOGLOBIN: the respiratory pigment found in red blood cells. It contains iron and is closely related to chlorophyll. It is bright red when oxygenated and bluish red when deoxygenated.

HAEMOPHILIA: human disease, occuring in males only, in which blood clotting is defective. It is determined by a sex-linked recessive gene and is transmitted from mother to son.

HAIR FOLLICLE: a deep pit formed from the epidermis but sunk deeply into the dermis of the mammalian skin. It surrounds the root of the hair and the sebaceous gland opens into it.

HEALTH: condition of the body and mind where there is not only a lack of disease but a positive feeling of well-being and an efficient functioning of all the body systems.

HEART: the organ for pumping blood round the body. It is made largely of cardiac muscle.

HEPARIN: substance which prevents blood clotting by stopping the conversion of prothrombin to thrombin—hence it is also called *anti-prothrombin*.

HEPATIC PORTAL VEIN: a large vessel carrying blood containing food substances from the intestine to the liver.

HERMAPHRODITE: an animal or plant producing both male and female gametes.

HETEROZYGOTE: an organism in which two different 'factors' for a particular character are present on a pair of homologous chromosomes.

HEXOSE SUGARS: sugars with six carbon atoms, e.g. glucose and fructose.

HIND-BRAIN: the most posterior portion of the embryonic brain from which the cerebellum and medulla develop.

HINGE-JOINT: a joint formed between two bones, the convex surface of one bone fitting into the concave surface of the other bone in such a way that movement is possible in one plane only, e.g. the elbow joint.

HOMOZYGOTE: an organism in which two similar 'factors' for a particular character are present on a pair of homologous chromosomes.

HORMONES: organic substances which act as chemical messengers being carried from one part of the body to another in the blood. They are produced in ductless glands.

HYDROLYSIS: the chemical decomposition of a substance by water, the water itself also being decomposed. In animals hydrolysis is brought about with the aid of enzymes, e.g. the hydrolysis of cane sugar to glucose and fructose.

HYGIENE: the branch of medical science concerned with the preservation of good health and good sanitation.

HYPERMETROPIA: long-sightedness.

HUMERUS: the bone of the upper arm.

ILEUM: the part of the small intestine which precedes the large intestine. It is the part concerned chiefly with absorption of digested foods through villi.

ILIUM: that part of the pelvic girdle which is fused to the sacrum.

IMMUNITY: ability of an animal or plant to resist infection.

INCISOR TEETH: chisel-shaped teeth at the front of the mouth of mammals. In Man there are two pairs of incisors in both upper and lower jaws, i.e. eight incisors in the whole mouth.

INCUS: the middle bone of the three ear ossicles.

INFANTILISM: condition in which a child may be a dwarf owing to underactivity of the pituitary gland. A delayed development of the bones is accompanied by retarded sexual development.

INFECTIOUS DISEASE: a disease which can be passed from one person to another.

INFERIOR VENA CAVA: the main vein returning blood to the heart from the posterior part of the body.

INGESTION: the taking in of food.

INNER EAR: the membranous labyrinth; that part of the ear which lies within the auditory capsule and which is the sense organ of sound and balance.

INOCULATION: the introduction of disease organisms into Man as a means of securing immunity by inducing a mild form of the disease.

INSECTICIDE: chemical used for killing insect pests.

INSERTION: the end of a muscle, attached to a bone which moves when contraction occurs—compare with *origin* of a muscle.

INSPIRATION: taking air into the lungs.

INSULIN: a hormone which controls the amount of glucose in the blood.

INTERCOSTAL MUSCLES: muscles which help to move the ribs, thus changing the volume of the thorax, during breathing.

ISCHIUM: one of the bones comprising the pelvic girdle.

ISLETS OF LANGERHANS: groups of cells found in the pancreas which secrete insulin.

JEJUNUM: that part of the small intestine which succeeds the duodenum and precedes the ileum.

JOINT CAPSULE: a tough, ligamentous capsule surrounding the joint between two bones.

KIDNEY: the organ of excretion and water control in Man. It also helps maintain a correct salt balance in the blood.

KIDNEY TUBULE: also called *uriniferous tubule*; a narrow coiled tube of the kidney leading from the Bowman's Capsule to the pelvis and hence to the ureter. There are thousands in each kidney.

LACRIMAL DUCT: a duct draining excess secretion of the eye into the nasal cavities.

LACRIMAL GLAND: a gland lying in the outer corner of each orbit and opening beneath the eyelid by several ducts. Its secretions help wash the eyeball where it is exposed. Also called the *tear gland*.

LACTIC ACID: organic acid formed during the contraction of muscle. It is formed as a product of the splitting up of glucose with a resulting release of energy. Accumulation gives muscle fatigue.

LACTIFEROUS DUCT: small ducts which convey milk to *lactiferous sinuses* in the mammary glands.

LACTOSE: milk sugar.

LAMELLATED CORPUSCLE: a receptor in the skin which detects pressure.

LARGE INTESTINE: that part of the gut stretching from the ileum to the anus and comprising the caecum, appendix, colon and rectum. It is about five feet long in Man.

LARYNX: the upper part of the trachea where it opens into the pharynx. Contains the vocal cords in Man. The Adam's apple.

LATENT PERIOD: the time between the application of a stimulus to, and the response in, a muscle.

LEUCOCYTE: a white blood cell.

LIGAMENT: strong band of elastic tissue binding two bones together at a joint.

LIMB GIRDLE: a structure of bone by means of which the limbs are joined to the body. The pectoral girdle consists of the scapula, coracoid and clavicle, while the pelvic girdle consists of the ilium, ischium and pubis.

LIPASE: an enzyme for splitting fats into fatty acids and glycerol.

LIVER: the largest organ of the body and one with many functions including the storage of glycogen, deamination and bile production. It lies in the abdominal cavity beneath the diaphragm.

LOOP OF HENLE: a loop in the kidney tubules where water is reabsorbed to adjust the osmotic pressure of the blood.

LUMBAR VERTEBRAE: vertebrae lying between the thoracic and sacral vertebrae, each composed of a very strong centrum and neural arch. They are five in number.

LUMEN: a cavity; a space within a tube, duct or cell.

LUNG: an organ for effecting gaseous exchange between an animal and the air.

LUTEINISING HORMONE, L.H.: a hormone secreted by the pituitary gland which causes the extrusion of the ovum from the Graafian follicle.

LUTEOTROPIC HORMONE, L.T.H.: a hormone secreted by the pituitary gland which causes the corpus luteum to secrete progesterone.

LYMPH: fluid collected by lymph vessels from intercellular spaces. It is very like blood plasma in composition but has no red cells.

LYMPHATIC SYSTEM: system of small vessels which permeate most tissues and which collects tissue fluid. The small vessels join to form larger ones which finally join the venous system near the heart.

LYMPH NODE: sometimes incorrectly called lymph gland; structure which produces lymphocytes (a white blood cell) and which removes foreign bodies from the lymph.

LYSIS: the splitting of a bacterial cell wall which has become filled with newly formed virus particles.

MALLEUS: the outermost of the three ear ossicles.

MALNUTRITION: term referring to the *quality* of the diet and implying a lack of some essential substances. (*Compare with undernutrition.*)

MALPIGHIAN BODY: structure found in large numbers in the kidney and consisting of a Bowman's Capsule and its glomerulus.

MALTASE: an enzyme which splits a molecule of maltose into two molecules of glucose.

MALTOSE: a disaccharide sugar which occurs naturally in germinating seeds and as a result of the breakdown of starch during digestion.

MAMMARY GLAND: gland specialised for the production of milk. Milk production is partly controlled by lactogenic hormone from the pituitary.

MANTOUX TEST: a susceptibility test to show whether or not a person has been in contact with tuberculosis.

MANUBRIUM: that part of the breast bone with which the clavicles articulate.

MARROW: a soft vascular tissue found in the central cavities of bones.

MEDULLA: central region of an organ, e.g. kidney.

MEDULLA OBLONGATA: the most posterior part of the brain merging into the spinal cord. The centre for control of breathing and heart-beat.

MEIOSIS OR REDUCTION DIVISION: a type of cell division in which the number of chromosomes is halved. The process results in haploid gametes: the diploid condition is restored when two gametes fuse at fertilisation.

MEMBRANOUS LABYRINTH: *see under Inner ear.*

MENINGES: the membranes covering the central nervous system.

MENSTRUAL CYCLE AND MENSTRUATION: rhythmical changes occurring in the female reproductive system, controlled by ovarian hormones, in which the wall of the uterus is prepared for implantation of the fertilised egg. If fertilisation does not occur the inner layer of the uterus is in part shed at menstruation.

METABOLIC RATE: the rate at which metabolism is proceeding. The Basal Metabolic Rate, B.M.R., is expressed as the output of Calories per square metre of body surface per hour and is measured when a person is resting.

METABOLISM: the sum total of the chemical changes occurring in an organism—both building up and breaking down processes are included, the former being termed anabolic, and the latter catabolic, processes.

METACARPAL: bone in the palm of the hand articulating with the wrist bones and the phalanges. There are five metacarpals in each hand.

METATARSAL: a bone articulating with the ankle bones at one end and with the phalanges at the other. There are five in each foot.

MICROBES: any microscopic organism which is harmful.

MID-BRAIN: middle of the three areas of the embryonic brain. It becomes particularly concerned with sight and hearing.

MIDDLE EAR: the cavity between the ear-drum and the auditory capsule. It is crossed by the ear ossicles and communicates with the mouth by the Eustachian tube.

MILK: liquid produced by mammary glands for feeding new-born mammals. Rich in all essential food substances for early growth.

MILK DENTITION: the first set of teeth, preceding the permanent dentition.

MITOCHONDRIA: minute bodies occuring in large numbers in cytoplasm. They are made of protein and fat and contain many enzymes.

MITOSIS: the normal method of cell division. The term strictly applies to the division of the nucleus.

MITRAL VALVE: the valve between the left atrium and the left ventricle of the heart. Also called the *bicuspid* valve.

MOLAR TEETH: the teeth which are concerned with crushing food and which have no predecessors in the milk teeth.

MONOHYBRID INHERITANCE: the inheritance of one pair of contrasting characters.

MONOSACCHARIDE SUGARS: the simplest sugars, e.g. glucose.

MOTOR AREAS: those areas of the brain which send impulses to initiate activity.

MOTOR END PLATE: the termination of a motor nerve-fibre on a muscle fibre and through which its nerve impulses stimulate the muscle fibre.

MUCIN: a protein which, in solution, forms mucus.

MUCOUS COAT: innermost lining of the gut, its structure and folding varies in different parts.

MUCOUS MEMBRANE: the general name for a moist epithelium, e.g. the lining of the gut, nasal passages and urethra.

MUCUS: slimy solution of mucin.

MUSCLE: a tissue composed of cells in which the power of contraction is highly developed.

MUSCULAR COAT: the second layer of the gut wall, lying beneath the serous coat, and consisting of outer longitudinal muscles and inner circular muscles.

MUTATION: term used in genetics to indicate a sudden change in the structure of a chromosome, of importance because such changes may be passed from one generation to the next. The term may also be used to refer to a sudden change in a single gene. Deleterious mutations result from atomic fall-out.

MYELIN: a fatty substance making a sheath round some nerve fibres.

MYOPIA: short-sightedness.

NASAL MUCOSA: the mucous membrane of the nose.

NASAL PASSAGE: the passage through the nose through which air passes during breathing.

NASO-PHARYNX: the anterior part of the pharynx, lying at the back of the nose.

NERVE: a bundle of nerve fibres, connective tissue and blood vessels in a common sheath of connective tissue.

NERVOUS SYSTEM: a system which co-ordinates the activities of an animal, and which keeps it aware of changes in its surroundings by means of messages conveyed rapidly from one part to another.

NEURAL ARCH: an arch of bone above the centrum of each vertebra. The spinal cord runs below the neural arch and above the centrum.

NEURAL SPINE: a median dorsal projection above the neural arch forming a place for muscle attachment.

NEURILEMMA: outer covering of some nerve fibres.

NEURONE: a nerve cell. Its function is to carry nerve impulses.

NICOTINE: a poisonous, colourless, oily liquid ,with an acrid taste, contained in the leaves of tobacco.

NICTITATING MEMBRANE: a third eyelid present in birds.

NITROGENOUS WASTE: waste materials resulting from the breakdown of nitrogen-containing substances such as proteins and amino-acids.

NOTIFIABLE DISEASE: a disease which, under the Public Health Act of 1936, must be notified by family doctors to the Medical Officer, e.g. measles, whooping cough, smallpox, diphtheria.

NUCLEOLUS: small body, containing nucleo-protein,

inside a nucleus. Visible during the resting phase of a cell, they disappear during mitosis.

NUCLEO-PROTEINS: compounds of nucleic acid and protein.

NUCLEUS: a structure, which contains the chromosomes, present in nearly every cell.

ODONTOID PEG: bony projection on the axis vertebra which fits above the centrum and below the transverse ligament of the atlas vertebra. It enables the head to move as when indicating 'no'.

OESOPHAGUS: part of alimentary canal leading from the pharynx to the stomach.

OLFACTORY MUCOUS MEMBRANE: the moist lining of the nose.

OOCYTE: a cell in the ovary which undergoes meiosis to form an ovum or egg.

OPTIC CHIASMA: structure formed beneath the forebrain by nerve fibres of the right optic nerve crossing to the left side of the brain and vice versa.

OPTIC NERVE: the second cranial nerve; it links the eye with the brain.

OPTIC STALK: a stalk-like structure through which the optic nerve passes from the back of the eye to the brain.

ORBIT: bony hollow in the skull in which the eye fits.

ORGAN: part of an animal which forms a functional unit; it is usually compact in nature and composed of several tissues, e.g. kidney, heart, eye, testis.

ORIGIN OF MUSCLE: the end of a muscle which does not move when contraction occurs. Compare with *insertion* of muscle.

ORO-PHARYNX: that part of the pharynx which lies between the gullet and the naso-pharynx.

OSMOSIS: the movement of water across a semi-permeable membrane, from a region of high concentration to a region of low concentration of an osmotic substance.

OUTER EAR: the flap of skin and cartilage (pinna) together with the short tube leading from the outside to the ear drum.

OVAL CORPUSCLE: receptors in the skin whose nerve endings are enclosed in oval-shaped capsules; they are sensitive to touch and to warmth.

OVARY: the female gonad; it produces ova and hormones.

OVIDUCAL FUNNEL: a funnel-shaped structure at the end of the oviduct, where it opens into the body cavity, and through which the ova enter the oviduct after their extrusion from the ovary.

OVIDUCT: a tube carrying ova from the body cavity to the uterus. It is in the oviduct that fertilisation takes place.

OXYGEN DEBT: the excess oxygen used after an organism has been respiring with inadequate oxygen, e.g. after strenuous muscular work oxygen consumption remains above normal until the debt has been repaid.

OXYHAEMOGLOBIN: haemoglobin combined with oxygen. The compound is unstable in regions of low oxygen concentration and hence it yields up its oxygen in places where it is needed.

PALATE: the roof of the mouth separating the nasal from the food passage. There is an anterior hard, and a posterior soft, palate.

PANCREAS: a diffuse organ occurring in the mesentery near the duodenum and producing *pancreatic juice*, containing enzymes, which is discharged through the *pancreatic duct* into the duodenum. The pancreas also contains the islets of Langerhans which secrete insulin into the blood.

PARASITE: an organism living on or in another living organism (the host) and gaining its nutriment from it. It usually causes some harm to the host.

PARASYMPATHETIC SYSTEM: part of the autonomic nervous system which frequently has an antagonistic effect to the other part of the autonomic system, namely the sympathetic system.

PARATHYROID: endocrine gland occurring on either side of the thyroid gland. Its secretions are concerned with calcium metabolism.

PARENTAL GENERATION: the generation which produces the first filial generation.

PAROTID GLAND: one of the salivary glands. There is one parotid gland on each side of the head in front of the ear and below the zygomatic arch.

PASTEURISATION: partial sterilisation of milk by heating it to a temperature sufficiently high to kill bacteria but not their spores.

PATHOGEN: a parasite which causes disease.

PECTORAL GIRDLE: that limb girdle which joins the fore-limbs to the body. It never fuses with the backbone.

PELVIC GIRDLE: that limb girdle which joins the legs to the body. It is rigidly fused to the backbone. The *pelvis*.

PENICILLIUM: a mould from which the antibiotic *penicillin* is produced.

PENIS: organ used to pass urine from the male body and to introduce sperm into the female.

PEPSIN: a stomach enzyme which splits proteins to peptides in acid solution.

PEPTIDASE: an enzyme which splits peptides.

PEPTIDE: compound formed from two or more amino-acids. Peptides are formed during digestion of proteins.

PEPTONE: a compound more complex than peptides but less complex than proteins from which they are formed during digestion.

PERICARDIAL CAVITY: the cavity in which the heart lies. It contains *pericardial fluid*.

PERICARDIUM: the membrane forming the wall of the pericardial cavity.

PERILYMPH: fluid filling the space in which the membranous labyrinth of the ear lies.

PERINEURIUM: connective tissue investing a number of bundles of nerve fibres in a nerve.

PERIOSTEUM: the layer of connective tissue which tightly invests bones and to which muscles and tendons are attached.

PERIPHERAL NERVES: all the nervous system except the central nervous system. Peripheral nerves run from the central nervous system to the receptor cells and organs and to effectors.

PERISTALSIS: the waves of contraction which pass along the gut moving the contents along.

PERMANENT TEETH: the second set of teeth. They succeed the milk dentition, and include molar teeth which are not represented in the milk dentition.

PHAGOCYTES: cells which engulf bacteria by flowing round them—a process called *phagocytosis*. They form an important defence mechanism in human beings.

PHARYNX: region of the alimentary canal lying between the buccal cavity and the oesophagus.

PHOTOSYNTHESIS: the manufacture of carbohydrates by green plants from carbon dioxide and water, using energy from the sun and chlorophyll as a catalyst.

PHYSIOLOGY: the study of the processes which go on in living organisms.

PIA MATER: delicate membrane immediately covering the central nervous system.

PINNA: flap of skin and cartilage at the end of the tube leading from the middle ear to the exterior.

PITUITARY GLAND: one of the most important endocrine glands. It is situated beneath the brain and within the skull. Many hormones are secreted from the pituitary which is divided into both anterior and posterior lobes.

PLACENTA: composite structure formed from both maternal and embryonic tissue and present only in true mammals. It attaches the embryo to the mother and forms the means by which the embryo is nourished.

PLANT STARCH: a white, insoluble, tasteless powder. It is a polysaccharide and is stored in the form of granules by plants.

PLASMA: the fluid content of blood in which the blood cells float.

POLIOMYELITIS: an acute disease caused by a virus resulting in the paralysis of various muscles.

POLYSACCHARIDE: a carbohydrate formed by the combination of many monosaccharide molecules, e.g. starch, cellulose.

PONS: part of the brain in which tracts of nerve fibres from the cerebral cortex connect with tracts to the cerebral hemisphere of the opposite side. It is also the site of origin of several cranial nerves.

PORTAL SYSTEM: vascular system in which blood from one organ passes through another organ on its way to the heart, e.g. blood from the intestine passes through the liver before returning to the heart.

PREMOLARS: the cheek teeth which are preceded by the milk teeth (*compare Molars*).

PRESBYOPIA: hardening of the lens of the eye, usually in old age, with a consequent loss in the power of accommodation.

PROGESTERONE: a hormone secreted by the corpus luteum of the ovary. It helps prepare the reproductive organs for pregnancy and in maintaining pregnancy.

PROPRIOCEPTORS: sensory endings which sense tension in muscles and tendons.

PROSTATE GLAND: a gland of the male reproductive system which contributes to the production of semen.

PROTEASE: an enzyme taking part in the breakdown of proteins.

PROTEIN: highly complex organic compound composed of numerous amino-acids. Each protein molecule is made of hundreds or even thousands of amino-acid molecules joined together by peptide links. Proteins are a very important constituent of protoplasm and form a high percentage of its dry weight. They are the main 'body-building' food substances.

PROTHROMBIN: a protein from which thrombin is formed during blood-clotting.

PROTOPLASM: the living substance of organisms. The nucleus and cytoplasm of a cell.

PSITTACOSIS: an acute infectious disease of parrots caused by a virus. It can be transmitted to Man leading to an illness not unlike severe influenza.

PTYALIN: an enzyme secreted by the salivary glands which changes starch to maltose.

PUBIS: part of the hip girdle.

PULMONARY ARTERIES: vessels which take blood from the heart to the lungs. They are the only arteries to contain deoxygenated blood.

PULMONARY CIRCULATION: the blood circulation to and from the lungs.

PULMONARY VEINS: vessels which take blood from the lungs to the heart. They are the only veins to contain oxygenated blood.

PULP CAVITY: a cavity in the tooth which opens to the tissues in which the tooth is embedded by a narrow channel. It contains blood vessels and nerves.

PUPIL: the opening of the iris of the eye through which light reaches the retina.

PUS: thick yellow fluid exuded from inflamed tissues which have become putrid.

PYLORIC SPHINCTER: a muscle at the junction of the stomach and the duodenum, which shuts the stomach off from the duodenum during digestion.

QUADRICEPS MUSCLE: general name for a group of muscles which cover the front of the thigh and which help to extend the knee joint.

RADIOACTIVE ISOTOPES: varieties of an element which emit certain rays or particles. Such isotopes are used extensively as 'labels' in biological research. For example, radioactive iodine introduced into the body quickly collects in the thyroid gland where its presence can be detected by a Geiger-counter.

RADIUS: one of the two bones of the lower arm. It articulates with the hand on the side on which the thumb is located.

RAMI-COMMUNICANTES: nerves which link the ganglion

of the autonomic nervous system with the spinal nerves.

RECEPTOR: a sense organ or sense cell which detects what goes on outside or inside an organism. There are different receptors, each sensitive to a more or less specific stimulus, e.g. light, touch, temperature.

RECESSIVE CHARACTER: the converse of dominant, a recessive character does not show in the organism in the presence of its allele.

RECTUM: the last part of the intestine opening to the exterior at the anus.

RED BLOOD CELL: *see Erythrocyte.*

RED CORPUSCLE: an erythrocyte.

REDUCTION DIVISION: *see Meiosis.*

REFLEX ACTION: a simple form of reaction to a stimulus, not under the control of the will (it is more or less automatic); a certain kind of stimulus always leading to a more specific response. The action takes place by means of a nervous route known as a *reflex arc.*

REFRACTORY PERIOD: the short period of recovery following a nerve impulse before a fibre can transmit another impulse.

RENAL ARTERY: a large artery taking blood to the kidney.

RENAL VEIN: a large vein taking blood from the kidney.

RENNIN: an enzyme secreted in the stomach, particularly of young mammals, which clots milk by converting soluble caseinogen into insoluble casein.

REPLICATION: the method of multiplication of viruses; the production of exact copies of molecules of a complex type.

RESIDUAL AIR: that volume of air which cannot be removed from the lungs even by a special effort. It is about 1000 ml. in volume.

RESPIRATION: the process by which organisms gain energy. *External respiration* refers to the taking in of air, and pumping it out again, by the lungs, and to the obtaining of oxygen from the air and to the giving off of carbon dioxide. *Internal* or *tissue respiration* refers to the chemical reactions, going on in the protoplasm, which release energy.

RESPIRATORY PIGMENT: *see Haemoglobin.*

RESPIRATORY SUBSTRATE: the compound with which oxygen combines during respiration.

RETINA: the light-sensitive layer of the eye. It contains receptor cells known as rods and cones.

RIB: long bone of the thorax, rich in red bone marrow, which typically articulates with the backbone at one end and joins the sternum, by means of costal cartilage, at the other. In Man there are twelve pairs of ribs: seven pairs of *true ribs* joining the sternum directly and five pairs of *false ribs*, of which three pairs join the sternum indirectly, while two pairs—the *floating ribs*—do not join the sternum at all.

RICKETS: a malformation of bones owing to a lack of calcium or vitamin D or of both.

RODS: receptor cells of the retina which are particularly sensitive to dim light.

SACCULUS: part of the vestibule of the inner ear from which the cochlea arises.

SACRAL VERTEBRAE: five vertebrae lying between the lumbar and coccygeal vertebrae. They are fused together to form the sacrum.

SACRUM: the structure formed by the fusion of the five sacral vertebrae.

SALIVA: fluid, containing ptyalin, secreted from the salivary glands as a reflex action resulting from the presence of food in the mouth.

SALIVARY GLANDS: three pairs of glands of which the function is the secretion of saliva.

SCAB: a protective clot of blood formed over a small cut or wound.

SCAPULA: the shoulder blade.

SCIATIC NERVE: a large nerve of the leg formed by the joining together of several spinal nerves at the sciatic or sacral plexus.

SCLEROTIC: the outermost of the three layers of the eyeball. It is tough and protective and can be seen at the front as the white of the eye.

SCROTUM: sac holding the testes in the male.

SCURVY: a deficiency disease caused by a lack of vitamin C.

SEBACEOUS GLAND: a gland found in the skin of mammals in association with each hair follicle into which it opens.

SECRETIN: a hormone secreted by the wall of the duodenum and jejunum under the stimulus of the acid contents arriving from the stomach. Its function is to stimulate the secretion of pancreatic juice and bile.

SELFING: the process of cross-pollinating flowers over several generations to obtain a *pure-strain.*

SEMI-CIRCULAR CANALS: three tubes projecting from and joined at both ends to the inner ear. There is one tube in each plane, one horizontal and two at right angles to each other in the vertical plane. They are concerned with balance.

SEMINAL FLUID: liquid in which sperm are contained in the male.

SEMINAL VESICLE: organ in which sperm are stored in the male.

SEMINIFEROUS TUBULES: coiled tubes in the testes made of germinal epithelium and in which sperm are produced.

SENSE ORGAN: *see Receptor.*

SEPTUM: a partition.

SEROUS COAT: the outermost layer of the gut wall.

SERUM: fluid obtained from clotted blood or clotted plasma. It is plasma without its clotting constituents.

SEX CELLS: *see Gamete.*

SEX CHROMOSOME: chromosome responsible for determining the sex of an organism.

SKELETAL MUSCLE: also known as *voluntary* or *striped* muscle. Muscle which serves the bones. It undergoes rapid contraction when suitably stimulated. Consists of long cells with many nuclei and striations at right angles to the long axis of the muscle.

SMALL INTESTINE: that part of the alimentary canal formed by the duodenum, jejunum and ileum.

SMOOTH MUSCLE: also called *plain* or *involuntary* muscle; consists of long, spindle-shaped fibres without cross-striations. Undergoes slow contraction. Is controlled by the autonomic nervous system.

SOIL EROSION: the wearing away of large areas of land by the weather—sun, rain etc. Often helped by poor cultivation by man.

SPERM: male sex cell, *see Gamete.*

SPERMATIC CORD: a cord composed of connective tissue and blood vessels serving the testes in the male.

SPERMATOZOON: a sperm.

SPINAL CORD: the central nervous system excluding the brain, from which it arises at the medulla oblongata.

SPINAL NERVE: a nerve arising from the spinal cord by dorsal and ventral roots. There is one on each side of each segment.

SPLEEN: organ for removing red blood cells at the end of their life and for storing fresh red blood cells. Produces lymphocytes.

STAPES: the innermost of the three ear ossicles.

STAPHLOCOCCUS: bacterium which causes boils and makes wounds go septic.

STEREOSCOPIC VISION: vision obtained because each eye registers a picture slightly different from the other since each sees an object from a slightly different angle. A three-dimensional picture is obtained which gives ability to judge distances.

STERNUM: the breast-bone, to which most of the ribs are attached.

STRIATED MUSCLE: *see Skeletal muscle.*

SUBLINGUAL GLAND: salivary glands lying beneath the tongue, one on each side.

SUBMANDIBULAR GLAND: a salivary gland posterior to the sublingual gland and beneath the mandible.

SUB-MUCOUS COAT: one of the four layers of the gut, lies between the mucous coat and the muscular coat and is composed largely of connective tissue and blood vessels.

SUCCUS ENTERICUS: the digestive juice secreted by the small intestine.

SUCROSE: cane sugar. One of the disaccharides.

SUPERIOR VENA CAVA: a main vein returning blood to the heart from the head and arms.

SUPPLEMENTAL AIR: that air which it is possible to breathe out by a special effort. About 1500 ml.

SUSPENSORY LIGAMENT: ligament which suspends the lens in the eye.

SUTURE: junction between bones of the skull. Also a term used in surgery.

SWEAT: dilute solution of salt and other substances secreted from the skin.

SWEAT GLAND: glands in the skin which secrete sweat, its purpose being to cool the animal. Under control of the autonomic nervous system.

SYMPATHETIC SYSTEM: part of the autonomic nervous system which frequently has an antagonistic effect on the other part of the autonomic system, namely the parasympathetic system.

SYNAPSE: place where distinct nerve cells touch each other. There is no continuity between the cells. A nerve impulse passes from one cell to another at the synapse by chemical transmission.

SYNOVIAL JOINT: type of joint surrounded by a *synovial capsule*, containing *synovial fluid* secreted by a *synovial membrane.*

SYSTOLE: the phase of heart beat, as opposed to diastole, in which the heart is contracting. Sometimes it is considered to be of two parts—auricular systole and ventricular systole.

TARSAL BONES: bones of the ankle, articulating at one end with the metatarsals and at the other with the tibia and fibula.

TARSAL GLANDS: glands on the eyelids which secrete a fluid to prevent the lids sticking together.

TASTE PAPILLAE: projections on the upper surface of the tongue containing *taste buds.*

TECTORIAL MEMBRANE: membrane of the organ of Corti in which protoplasmic projections of hair cells are embedded.

TENDON: a non-elastic tissue joining a muscle to a bone.

TESTES: the male reproductive gonads.

THORACIC CAGE: structure made up of the ribs, the sternum and the thoracic vertebrae.

THORAX: one of the main divisions of the body composed of the thoracic cage, the intercostal muscles and the diaphragm. It contains the heart and lungs.

THROMBIN: an enzyme which converts fibrinogen to fibrin during blood clotting.

THROMBOKINASE: substance liberated from wounded tissues which activates the formation of thrombin from prothrombin.

THYMUS: organ at the base of the neck which reaches its maximum size at puberty and thereafter slowly decreases. Possibly an endocrine organ.

THYROID: endocrine gland in the neck region. It secretes thyroxin.

THYROXIN: a hormone secreted by the thyroid gland. Iodine is essential to its formation. Lack of the hormone results in cretinism.

TIBIA: one of the two long bones of the lower leg.

TIBIALIS ANTERIOR: a muscle which has its origin on the tibia and its insertion on the first metatarsal. It helps balance when standing.

TIDAL AIR: that air which flows in and out of the lungs during normal quiet breathing. Its volume is about 500 ml.

TISSUE: an aggregation of similar cells, e.g. muscle tissue, nerve tissue.

TISSUE FLUID: liquid bathing cells and tissues through which substances diffuse. Food substances and oxygen thus arrive at the cells and waste products are removed from them. Tissue fluid leaves the capillaries and is collected in the lymph system.

TISSUE RESPIRATION: see Respiration.

TONSILS: patches of lymph tissue at the sides of the pharynx.

TOXIN: a poison. Usually the word toxin is confined to the poisons produced by bacteria.

TRACE ELEMENTS: elements which are only required in minute quantities by organisms.

TRACHEA: the windpipe. It stretches from the pharynx to the bronchi through the neck. Its lumen is kept open by incomplete rings of cartilage.

TRACHOMA: an infectious virus disease of the eye. Also due to lack of vitamin A.

TRANSVERSE LIGAMENT: ligament passing transversely across the spinal canal of the atlas vertebra. The odontoid peg of the axis vertebra fits below it.

TRANSVERSE PROCESS: lateral projections, one on each side, of the vertebrae.

TRICEPS MUSCLE: the only muscle at the back of the upper arm. It has one origin on the scapula and two on the humerus, while its insertion is on the olecranon process of the ulna. It extends the lower arm.

TRICUSPID VALVE: valve between the right atrium and right ventricle of the heart. It consists of three membranous flaps.

TRISTEARIN: a fat-like substance, $C_{57}H_{110}O_6$.

TRYPSIN: an enzyme which converts protein to amino-acids.

TRYPSINOGEN: an inactive fore-runner of trypsin.

TUNICA ALBUGINEA: the outer fibrous covering of the testis.

TURBINATE BONES: scroll-like bones in the nose.

TYMPANIC MEMBRANE: the ear drum.

ULNA: bone of the lower arm on the side opposite the thumb.

ULTRA-VIOLET LIGHT: electromagnetic waves, similar to those of light, but of smaller wave-length than those causing violet colour. Radiation from the sun is rich in ultra-violet light.

UMBILICAL CORD: stalk joining embryo to the placenta. Contains the umbilical artery and vein.

UNIVERSAL DONOR: persons of blood Group O. Their blood may be mixed with that of any other Group during blood transfusions.

UNIVERSAL RECIPIENTS: persons of blood Group AB. They can receive blood from persons of any other Group.

UREA: a nitrogen-containing compound, $CO(NH_2)_2$, readily soluble in water. It is the chief nitrogenous waste substance, formed during deamination by the liver and excreted by the kidney.

URETER: tube connecting each kidney with the urinary bladder.

URINARY BLADDER: sac for storing urine.

URINE: the solution of urea in water, together with certain salts, which is stored in the urinary bladder and excreted via the urethra.

UTERUS: part of the female reproductive system. It lies between the oviducts and the vagina and forms a protective organ in which the embryo develops.

UTRICULUS: part of the inner ear.

UVULA: the inner end of the soft palate.

VACCINATION: the act of inoculating with a vaccine especially as a preventive measure against smallpox.

VACUOLE: a fluid-filled space within a cell.

VASCULAR SYSTEM: the blood system and the lymph system.

VAS DEFERENS: tube which carries sperm from the testes to the urethra.

VECTOR: organism, usually an insect, which carries a parasite from one host to another.

VEIN: any blood vessel taking blood towards the heart.

VENEREAL DISEASE: general name for a number of diseases contracted through the reproductive system during sexual intercourse.

VENTRICLE: lower chamber of the heart. They are two in number and pump blood from the heart.

VERTEBRAE: bones forming the vertebral column or backbone.

VILLUS: Intestinal: finger-like projections present in enormous numbers in the small intestine for absorbing food substances.
Chorionic: projections of embryonic membranes into the placenta.

VIRUS: a disease-causing agent which is on the borderline between living and non-living. Cannot reproduce outside host tissues and can only be seen with the electron microscope.

VITAL CAPACITY: total volume of air which can be exchanged by the lungs.

VITAMIN: organic substances which are essential for health. Lack of certain vitamins in the diet leads to deficiency diseases.

VITREOUS HUMOUR: a jelly-like substance which fills the space behind the lens in the eye.

WHITE BLOOD CELL: cells found in the blood which contain a nucleus and which are capable of ingesting invading bacteria. They form an important part of the defence system of the body.

WHITE MATTER: a tissue of the central nervous system made largely of nerve fibres. It lies outside the grey matter in the spinal cord but within it in the brain.

WOMB: see Uterus.

YELLOW SPOT: the most sensitive area of the retina.

ZYGOTE: cell resulting from the fusion of two gametes.

Index

396

399

Acknowledgements

We should like to thank the following for photographs: The Cleveland Health Museum, Ohio, Plate 1; Smith Kline and French Laboratories, Plate 2; The Bermondsey Public Library, Plate 3; The Geological Survey and Museum, Plate 4; Radio Times Picture Library, Plates 12, 13, 14, 15, 24, 58, 71, 87, 89, 93, 95, 96, 97; The Chester Beatty Research Institute, Plates 8, 9, 31, 70; Zoological Society of London, Plates 16, 18, 19; The National Portrait Gallery, Plates 17, 20, 21, 38, 43, 69; The Wellcome Historical Museum, Plates 22, 49, 56, 60, 64, 76, 78, 79; T. Gerrard Ltd., Plates 27, 30, 65, 77, 83; King's College Hospital, Plate 29; The Royal College of Surgeons, Plates 32, 33, 34, 35, 40, 41, 42, 44, 47, 48, 54, 55, 59, 61, 62, 63, 66, 67, 68, 74; The Royal College of Physicians, Plates 72, 73, 75; Shell International Petroleum Co. Ltd., Plates 80, 81, 82, 84, 85, 86; The Ministry of Agriculture, Fisheries and Food with the permission of the Controller of Her Majesty's Stationery Office, Plates 88, 90, 91, 92; The Stockholm City Health Board, Plate 98; Ames Crosta Mills Ltd., Plates 99, 100, 101; The British Red Cross, Plate 102; The Oxford Committee for Famine Relief, Plates 103, 104, 105. We are also indebted to OXFAM for permission to use some of the data given in Chapter 34. In a few cases we have been unable to trace the original source of photographs, and we apologise to any whose rights have been thus overlooked.

The following University Boards gave permission to reproduce questions from past papers: University of Cambridge Local Examinations Syndicate (C); Southern Universities' Joint Board for School Examinations (S); Oxford Delegacy of Local Examinations (O); University of London Schools Examination Council (L); Welsh Joint Education Committee (W); the Joint Matriculation Board (J) and the Examinations Department of the Royal Society of Arts (RSA).

400